Kim
Murphy
340 3rd Street
Cloquet, Minn.
55720

area code 218

TREASURY OF LITERATURE READERS—BANNER EDITION

ENCHANTED ISLES

Selected and Edited by

LELAND B. JACOBS

Professor of Education

Teachers College, Columbia University

ELEANOR M. JOHNSON

Editor-in-Chief

My Weekly Reader

and

JO JASPER TURNER

Editor of Books for Children

Formerly Elementary School Teacher, Principal, and Supervisor

CHARLES E. MERRILL BOOKS, INC.

Columbus, Ohio

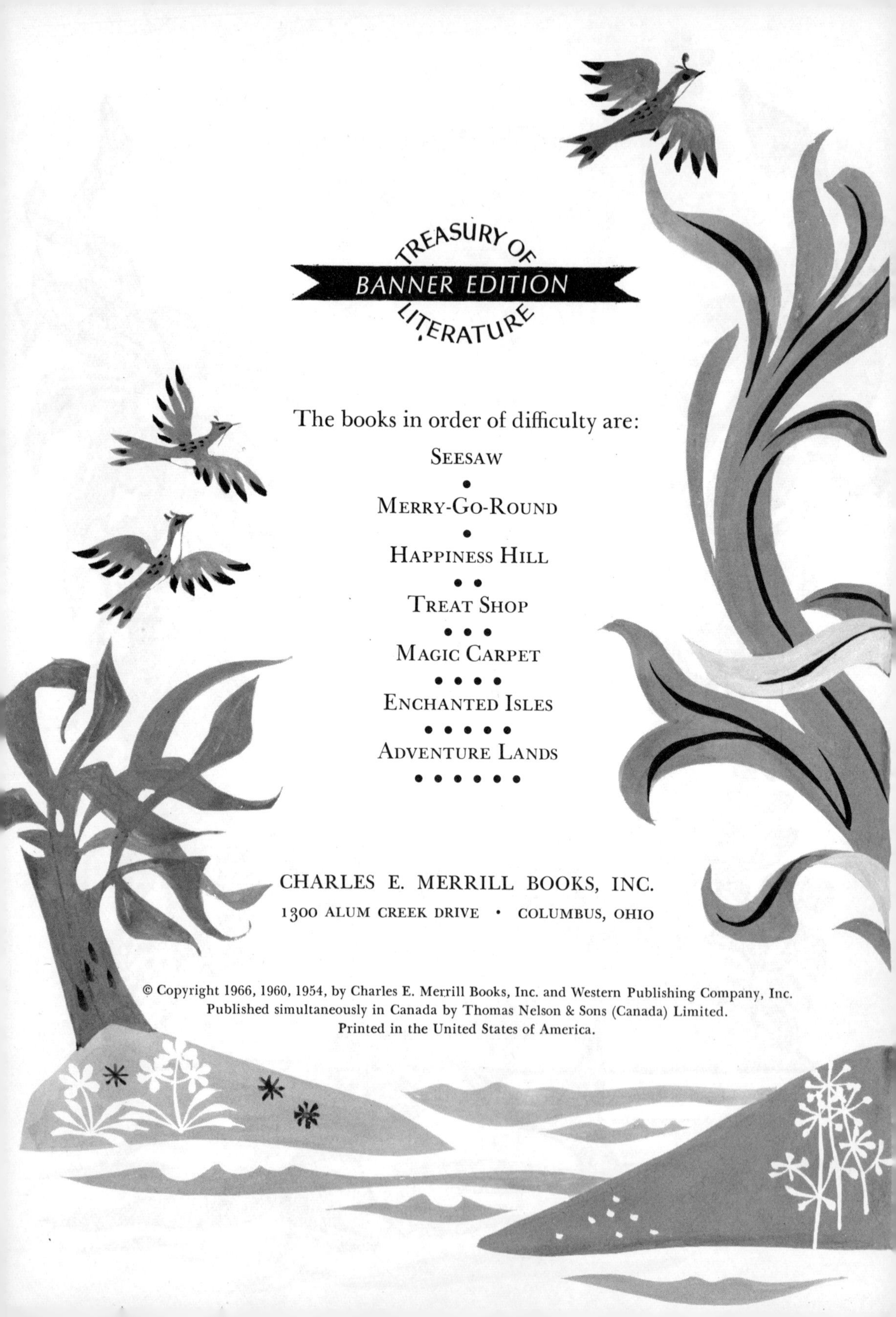

The books in order of difficulty are:

SEESAW
•
MERRY-GO-ROUND
•
HAPPINESS HILL
• •
TREAT SHOP
• • •
MAGIC CARPET
• • • •
ENCHANTED ISLES
• • • • •
ADVENTURE LANDS
• • • • • • •

CHARLES E. MERRILL BOOKS, INC.
1300 ALUM CREEK DRIVE · COLUMBUS, OHIO

Published simultaneously in Canada by Thomas Nelson & Sons (Canada) Limited.
Printed in the United States of America.

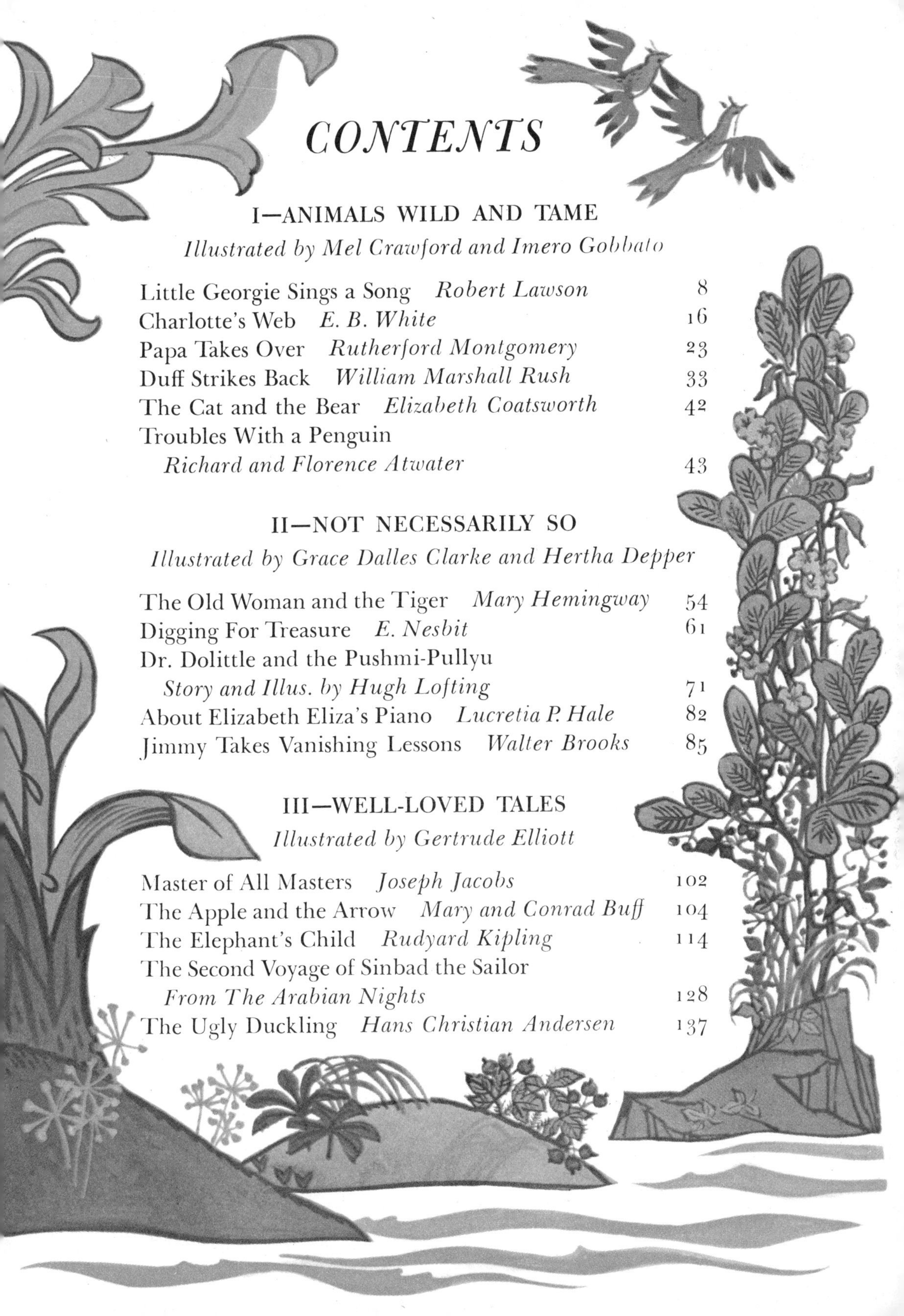

CONTENTS

I—ANIMALS WILD AND TAME

Illustrated by Mel Crawford and Imero Gobbato

II—NOT NECESSARILY SO

Illustrated by Grace Dalles Clarke and Hertha Depper

III—WELL-LOVED TALES

Illustrated by Gertrude Elliott

IV—OTHER LANDS AND OTHER FACES

Illustrated by Kurt Wiese and Gerald McCann

V—GO WEST, YOUNG MAN

Illustrated by Robert Magnusen and Gerald McCann

VI—WHISTLING DOWN THE STREET

Illustrated by Decie Merwin and Bernice Myers

VII—REAL PEOPLE

Illustrated by Robert Magnusen and Hamilton Greene

Animals Wild and Tame

Be gentle and kind
To the Auk and the Hind;
Be good to the gallant Gnu:
For animals all—
Both tremendous and small—
Have feelings, exactly like you.

—Dorothy Hall

Little Georgie Sings a Song

Robert Lawson

New folks were coming to the old house on Rabbit Hill! All the animals were very excited. The right folks would mean a good garden, good days to come.

Little Georgie, one of the big rabbit tribe, was sent by his family to get Uncle Analdas, who lived several miles away. They all thought Uncle Analdas would enjoy watching things happen at the Hill.

It was barely daylight when Little Georgie started his journey. In spite of her worrying, Mother had managed to put up a small but nourishing lunch. This, along with a letter to Uncle Analdas, was packed in a little knapsack and slung over his shoulder.

Father went along as far as the Twin Bridges. As they stepped briskly down the Hill, the whole valley was a lake of mist on which rounded treetops swam like floating islands. From old orchards rose a mounting chorus as the birds greeted the new day.

The houses were all asleep. Even the dogs of the Fat-Man-at-the-Crossroads were quiet, but the Little Animals were up and about. They met the Gray Fox returning from a night up Weston way. He looked footsore and sleepy, and a few chicken feathers still clung to his ruff. The Red Buck trotted daintily across the Black Road to wish them good luck and good morning. But Father, for once, had no time for long social conversation. This was Business, and no rabbit in the county knew his business any better than Father—few as well.

"Now, Son," he said firmly, "your Mother is in a very nervous state. You are not to add to her worries by taking unnecessary risks or by carelessness. No dawdling and no foolishness. Keep close to the road, but well off it. Watch your bridges and your crossings. What do you do when you come to a bridge?"

"I hide well," answered Georgie, "and wait a good long time. I look all around for dogs. I look up the road for cars and down the road for cars. When everything's clear I run across—fast. I hide again and look around to be sure I've not been seen. Then I go on. The same thing for crossings."

"Good," said Father. "Now recite your dogs."

Little Georgie closed his eyes and dutifully recited: "Fat-Man-at-the-Crossroads — two Mongrels. Good Hill Road—Dalmatian. House on Long Hill—Collie, noisy, no wind. Norfield Church corner—Police Dog, stupid, no nose. On the High Ridge, red farmhouse—Bulldog and

Setter, both fat, don't bother. Farmhouse with the big barns – Old Hound, very dangerous –" and so on he recited every dog on the route, clear up to Danbury way.

"Excellent," said Father. "Now, do you remember your checks and doublings?" Little Georgie closed his eyes again and rattled off, quite fast, "Sharp right and double left, double left and double right, dead stop and back flip, right jump, left jump, false trip and briar dive."

"Splendid," said Father. "Now attend carefully. Size up your dog; don't waste speed on a plodder–you may need it later. If he's a rusher, check, double, and freeze. Your freeze, by the way, is still rather bad. You have a tendency to flick your left ear; you must watch that. The High Ridge is very open country, so keep in the shadow of the stone walls. Porkey has lots of relatives along there and if you are pressed hard, any of them will gladly take you in. After a chase, hide up and take at least ten minutes' rest. And if you have to *really* run, tighten that knapsack strap, lace back your ears, and *run!*

"Get along with you now, and mind—no foolishness. We shall expect you and Uncle Analdas by tomorrow evening at the latest."

It was gray and misty as Little Georgie crossed Good Hill Road. The Dalmatian still slept. So, apparently, did the Collie up the road, for all was quiet as he plodded up Long Hill. People were beginning to stir as he approached Norfield Church corner. Little plumes of blue smoke were rising from kitchen chimneys, and the air was pleasant with the smell of frying bacon.

As he expected, the Police Dog rushed him there. Loping along with tantalizing slowness until they were almost on an old fallen apple tree buried in briars, he executed a dead stop, a right jump, and a freeze. The bellowing brute overran him, and plunged headlong into the thorny tangle. His howls were sweet music to Little Georgie as he hopped sedately along toward the High Ridge. He wished Father had been there to note that during the freeze his left ear hadn't flickered once.

The sun was well up when he emerged on the High Ridge. On the porch of the Red Farmhouse, the fat Bulldog and the Setter slept soundly, soaking up its warmth. On any other occasion, Little Georgie would have been tempted to wake them, but he kept dutifully on his way.

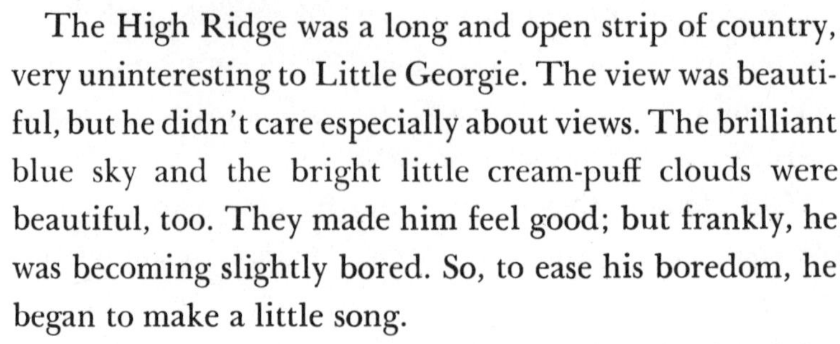

The High Ridge was a long and open strip of country, very uninteresting to Little Georgie. The view was beautiful, but he didn't care especially about views. The brilliant blue sky and the bright little cream-puff clouds were beautiful, too. They made him feel good; but frankly, he was becoming slightly bored. So, to ease his boredom, he began to make a little song.

The words had been rattling around in his head for some days now. The music was there, too, but he couldn't quite get them fitted together. So he hummed and he sang and he whistled. He tried the words this way and that way, he stopped and started and changed the notes around. Finally, he got the first line of the song so that it suited him.

The Leap at Deadman's Brook

It must have been his song that made Little Georgie careless and almost led to his undoing. He scarcely noticed that he had passed the house with the big barns. And he was just starting to sing his first line for the forty-seventh time when there came the roaring rush of the Old Hound right on his heels.

Instinctively, Little Georgie made several wild springs that carried him temporarily out of harm's way. He paused a fraction of a second to tighten the knapsack strap, and then set off at a good steady pace. "Don't waste speed on a plodder" was Father's rule. He tried a few checks and doubles and circlings, although he knew they were pretty useless. The great fields were too bare, and the Old Hound knew all the tricks. Georgie looked for woodchuck burrows, but there were none in sight. "Well, I guess I'll have to run it out," said Little Georgie.

He pulled the knapsack strap tighter, laced back his ears, and *ran*. And *how* he ran!

The warm sun had loosened his muscles, the air was invigorating, Little Georgie's leaps grew longer and longer. Never had he felt so young and strong. His legs were like coiled springs of steel. He was hardly conscious of any effort, only of his hind feet pounding the ground. Each time they hit, those wonderful springs shot him through the air. Why, this was almost like flying!

He glanced back at the Old Hound, far behind now, but still coming along at his plodding gallop. He was old and must be tiring. Why didn't the old fellow give up and go home?

And then, as Georgie shot over the brow of a slight rise, he suddenly knew. *He had forgotten Deadman's Brook!* There it lay before him, broad and deep, curving out in a great silvery loop. Whether he turned to right or left, the loop of the creek hemmed him in and the Old

Hound could easily cut him off. There was nothing for it but to jump!

This sickening realization had not reduced Little Georgie's speed; now he redoubled it. The wind whistled through his laced-back ears. Still he kept his head. He picked a spot where the bank was high and firm. He spaced his jumps so they would come out exactly right.

The take-off was perfect. He put every ounce of leg muscle into that final kick and sailed out into space. Below him, he could see the cream-puff clouds mirrored in the dark water. He could see the pebbles on the bottom and

the silver flash of frightened minnows. Then, with a breath-taking thump he landed, turned seven somersaults, and came up sitting in a clump of soft grass.

He froze, motionless except for heaving sides, and watched the Old Hound come thundering down the slope, slide to a stop, and take his way slowly homeward.

Little Georgie did not need to remember Father's rule for a ten-minute rest after a good run. He was blown and he knew it, but he did remember his lunch. So he unstrapped the little knapsack and combined lunch and rest. As his wind came back and his lunch went down, his spirits came up.

Father would be angry, and rightly, for Georgie had made two very stupid mistakes. He had let himself be surprised, and he had run right into a dangerous trap. But that leap! Never had any rabbit jumped Deadman's Brook, not even Father. Georgie marked the exact spot and calculated the width of the stream there—at least eighteen feet! And with his rising spirits, the words and the notes of his song suddenly tumbled into place.

Little Georgie lay back in the warm grass and sang his song—

New Folks coming, Oh my!
New Folks coming, Oh my!
New Folks coming, Oh my!
Oh my! Oh my!

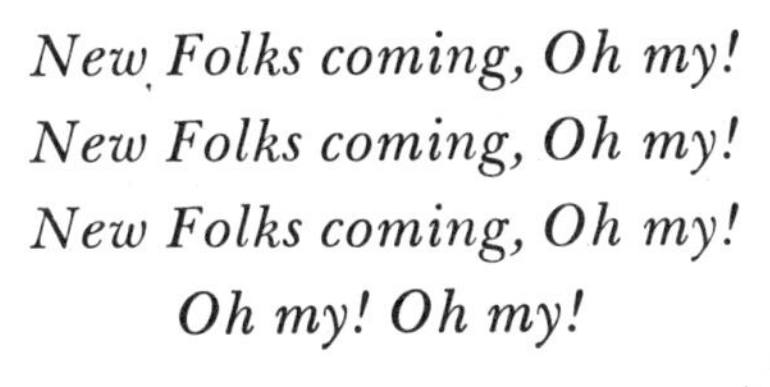

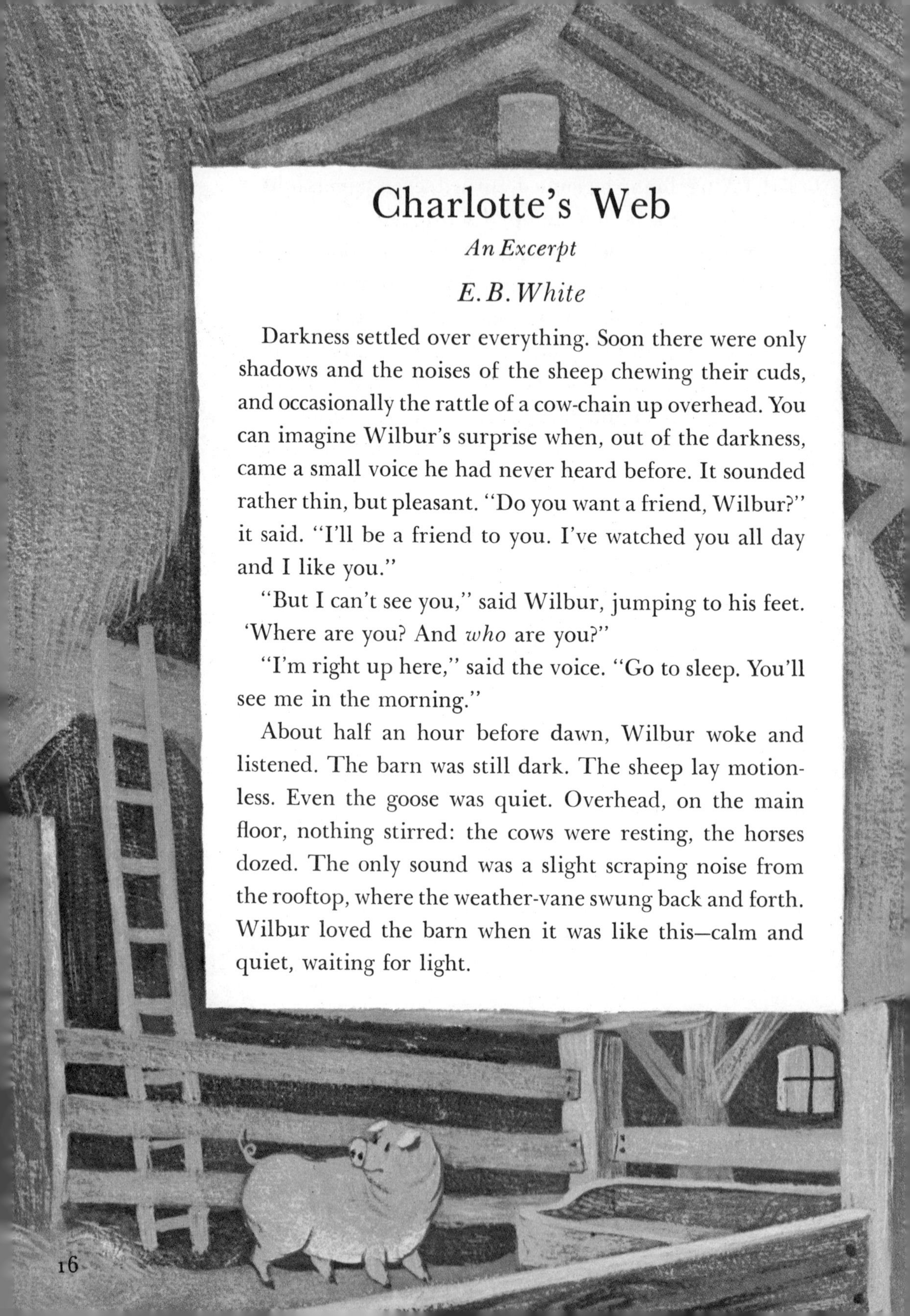

Charlotte's Web

An Excerpt

E. B. White

Darkness settled over everything. Soon there were only shadows and the noises of the sheep chewing their cuds, and occasionally the rattle of a cow-chain up overhead. You can imagine Wilbur's surprise when, out of the darkness, came a small voice he had never heard before. It sounded rather thin, but pleasant. "Do you want a friend, Wilbur?" it said. "I'll be a friend to you. I've watched you all day and I like you."

"But I can't see you," said Wilbur, jumping to his feet. 'Where are you? And *who* are you?"

"I'm right up here," said the voice. "Go to sleep. You'll see me in the morning."

About half an hour before dawn, Wilbur woke and listened. The barn was still dark. The sheep lay motionless. Even the goose was quiet. Overhead, on the main floor, nothing stirred: the cows were resting, the horses dozed. The only sound was a slight scraping noise from the rooftop, where the weather-vane swung back and forth. Wilbur loved the barn when it was like this—calm and quiet, waiting for light.

"Day is almost here," he thought.

Through a small window, a faint gleam appeared. One by one the stars went out. Wilbur could see the goose a few feet away. She sat with head tucked under a wing. Then he could see the sheep and the lambs. The sky lightened.

"Oh, beautiful day, it is here at last! Today I shall find my friend."

Wilbur looked everywhere. He searched his pen thoroughly. He examined the window ledge, stared up at the ceiling. But he saw nothing new. Finally he decided he would have to speak up. He hated to break the lovely stillness of dawn by using his voice, but he couldn't think of any other way to locate the mysterious new friend, who was nowhere to be seen. So Wilbur cleared his throat.

"Attention, please!" he said in a loud, firm voice. "Will the party who addressed me at bedtime last night kindly make himself or herself known by giving an appropriate sign or signal!"

Wilbur paused and listened. All the other animals lifted their heads and stared at him. Wilbur blushed. But he was determined to get in touch with his unknown friend.

"Attention, please!" he said. "I will repeat the message. Will the party who addressed me at bedtime last night kindly speak up. Please tell me where you are, if you are my friend!"

The sheep looked at each other in disgust.

"Stop your nonsense, Wilbur!" said the oldest sheep, If you have a new friend here, you are probably disturbing his rest; and the quickest way to spoil a friendship is to wake somebody up in the morning before he is ready. How can you be sure your friend is an early riser?"

"I beg everyone's pardon," whispered Wilbur. "I didn't mean to be objectionable."

He lay down meekly in the manure, facing the door. He did not know it, but his friend was very near. And the old sheep was right—the friend was still asleep.

Soon Lurvy appeared with slops for breakfast. Wilbur rushed out, ate everything in a hurry, and licked the trough. The sheep moved off down the lane, the gander waddled along behind them, pulling grass. And then, just as Wilbur was settling down for his morning nap, he heard again the thin voice that had addressed him the night before.

"Salutations!" said the voice.

Wilbur jumped to his feet. "Salu-*what?*" he cried.

"Salutations!" repeated the voice.

"What are *they,* and where are *you?*" screamed Wilbur. "Please, *please,* tell me where you are. And what are salutations?"

"Salutations are greetings," said the voice. "When I say 'salutations,' it's just my fancy way of saying hello or good morning. Actually, it's a silly expression, and I am surprised that I use it at all. As for my whereabouts, that's easy. Look up here in the corner of the doorway! Here I am. Look, I'm waving.' "

At last Wilbur saw the creature that had spoken to him in such a kindly way. Stretched across the upper part of the doorway was a big spiderweb, and hanging from the top of the web, head down, was a large grey spider. She was about the size of a gumdrop. She had eight legs, and she was waving one of them at Wilbur in friendly greeting. "See me now?" she asked.

"Oh, yes indeed," said Wilbur. "Yes indeed! How are you? Good morning! Salutations! Very pleased to meet you. What is your name, please? May I have your name?"

"My name," said the spider, "is Charlotte."

"Charlotte what?" asked Wilbur, eagerly.

"Charlotte A. Cavatica. But just call me Charlotte."

"I think you're beautiful," said Wilbur.

"Well, I am pretty," replied Charlotte. "There's no denying that. Almost all spiders are rather nice-looking. I'm not as flashy as some, but I'll do. I wish I could see you, Wilbur, as clearly as you can see me."

"Why can't you?" asked the pig. "I'm right here."

"Yes, but I'm near-sighted," replied Charlotte. "I've always been dreadfully near-sighted. It's good in some ways, not so good in others. Watch me wrap up this fly.

A fly that had been crawling along Wilbur's trough had flown up and blundered into the lower part of Charlotte's web and was tangled in the sticky threads. The fly was beating its wings furiously, trying to break loose and free itself.

"First," said Charlotte, "I dive at him." She plunged headfirst toward the fly. As she dropped, a tiny silken thread unwound from her rear end.

"Next, I wrap him up." She grabbed the fly, threw a few jets of silk around it, and rolled over and over, wrapping it so that it couldn't move. Wilbur watched in horror. He could hardly believe what he was seeing, and although he detested flies, he was sorry for this one.

"There!" said Charlotte. "Now I knock him out, so he'll be more comfortable." She bit the fly. "He can't feel a thing now," she remarked. "He'll make a perfect breakfast for me."

"You mean you *eat* flies?" gasped Wilbur.

"Certainly. Flies, bugs, grasshoppers, choice beetles, moths, butterflies, tasty cockroaches, gnats, midges, daddy longlegs, centipedes, mosquitoes, crickets—anything that is careless enough to get caught in my web. I have to live, don't I?"

"Why, yes, of course," said Wilbur. "Do they taste good?"

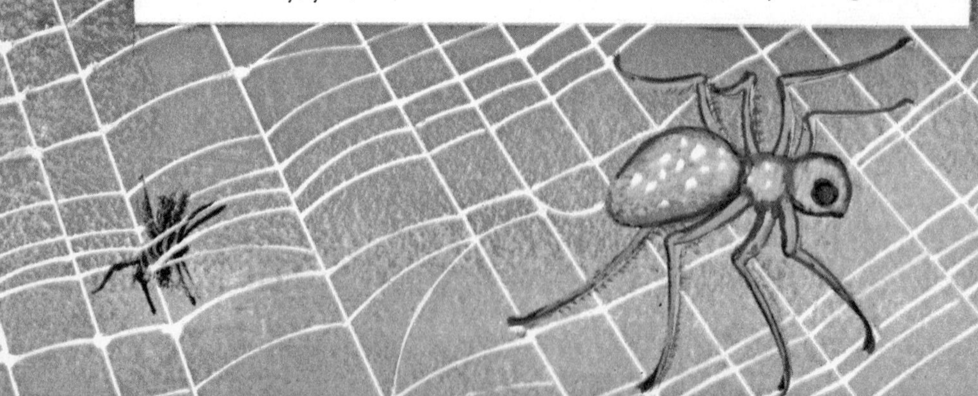

"Delicious. Of course, I don't really eat them. I drink them—drink their blood. I love blood," said Charlotte, and her pleasant, thin voice grew even thinner and more pleasant.

"Don't say that!" groaned Wilbur. "Please don't say things like that!"

"Why not? It's true, and I have to say what is true. I am not entirely happy about my diet of flies and bugs, but it's the way I'm made. A spider has to pick up a living somehow or other, and I happen to be a trapper. I just naturally build a web and trap flies and other insects. My mother was a trapper before me. Her mother was a trapper before her. All our family have been trappers. Way back for thousands and thousands of years we spiders have been laying for flies and bugs."

"It's a miserable inheritance," said Wilbur, gloomily. He was sad because his new friend was so bloodthirsty.

"Yes, it is," agreed Charlotte. "But I can't help it. I don't know how the first spider in the early days of the world happened to think up this fancy idea of spinning a web, but she did, and it was clever of her, too. And since then, all of us spiders have had to work the same trick. It's not a bad pitch, on the whole."

"It's cruel," replied Wilbur, who did not intend to be argued out of his position.

"Well, *you* can't talk," said Charlotte. "*You* have your meals brought down to you in a pail. Nobody feeds me.

I have to get my own living. I live by my wits. I have to be sharp and clever, lest I go hungry. I have to think things out, catch what I can, take what comes. And it just so happens, my friend, that what comes is flies and insects and bugs. And *further*more," said Charlotte, shaking one of her legs, "do you realize that if I didn't catch bugs and eat them, bugs would increase and multiply and get so numerous that they'd destroy the earth, wipe out everything?"

"Really?" said Wilbur. "I wouldn't want *that* to happen. Perhaps your web is a good thing after all."

Charlotte stood quietly over the fly, preparing to eat it. Wilbur lay down and closed his eyes. He was tired from his wakeful night and from the excitement of meeting someone for the first time. A breeze brought him the smell of clover—the sweet-smelling world beyond his fence. "Well," he thought, "I've got a new friend, all right. But what a gamble friendship is! Charlotte is fierce, brutal, scheming, bloodthirsty—everything I don't like. How can I learn to like her, even though she is pretty and, of course, clever?"

Wilbur was merely suffering doubts and fears that often go with finding a new friend. In good time he was to discover that he was mistaken about Charlotte. Underneath her rather bold and cruel exterior, she had a kind heart, and she was to prove loyal and true to the very end.

Papa Takes Over

Rutherford Montgomery

Jerome Kildee, a retired stone-carver, lived in the California hills in a house built against a giant redwood tree. With Jerome lived two raccoons—Old Grouch and his wife Charmine—and their babies, and Mama and Papa Skunk and their family.

Then Charmine was killed by Strong Heart, Donald Cabot's dog. Emma Lou, who lived near-by, hated Donald and his dog as much as she liked Jerome; and she was determined to revenge Charmine's death. Jerome had begun to carve a headstone for Charmine.

Jerome opened his eyes and sat up. Sunshine was coming in through the big window. Old Grouch was sitting by the window in the sun.

Jerome sighed deeply. As he expected, the young raccoons had not returned. He felt sad. The place would be pretty quiet with only Old Grouch around.

"Just a couple of old bachelors," he said.

Old Grouch grumbled an answer. He was hungry and wanted his breakfast.

Jerome laced his boots. Then he washed his face. Old Grouch marched around the room grumbling and scolding. Jerome fried a strip of bacon and an egg for himself, and a strip of bacon and an egg for Old Grouch. As he ate, he studied the figure he was chiseling out of the cream-colored stone.

He hurriedly finished breakfast and washed up the dishes. Then he set to work upon the figure again. He worked steadily into the afternoon. He was now adding the fine touches, a chip off there, a sliver here. He had caught the coy look Mrs. Grouch always lifted to him. He worked awhile on the lower lip. Then he got up and stepped back. Yes, there was the little lady peeping over the edge of her box at him.

Old Grouch came wandering across the meadow. His face wore a discouraged frown instead of the scowl which was usually there. He had searched far for his wife, but had failed to find any of her tracks except very cold ones. He marched into the cabin and began demanding lunch. Jerome gave him some canned meat, and then made himself a sandwich.

Jerome got the sheet of paper Emma Lou had written the inscription on. He was busily figuring a layout for the wording when a shadow darkened the doorway. He looked up and saw Donald Roger Cabot standing there.

Donald Roger stepped into the cabin. In spite of an

attempt to appear bored, he showed quite a little interest as he looked around.

"You ought not to come here," Jerome said.

"I came up to pay you for the raccoon my dog killed," Donald said stiffly. He reached into his hip pocket and pulled out a billfold.

Jerome looked quickly toward the door. Donald Roger smiled coldly. "I tied Strong Heart to a tree down the hill," he said.

Jerome's cheeks began to flush. The boy's manner and his offer to pay for the death of Mrs. Grouch stirred anger in him. "You can't pay for a thing like that," Jerome said sharply. "And you better go before Emma Lou shows up."

Donald shrugged his shoulders. He looked around the cabin. "Nice fireplace," he said.

Jerome stirred impatiently. Donald was looking at the figure on the table. He bent forward. "Not bad at all," he said. Then he added, "It's good."

In spite of his worry and dislike, Jerome was pleased. "It's not finished yet," he said.

"A raccoon looking over a wall watching you," Donald said. "What is it for?"

"It's a headstone," Jerome said.

Donald turned and looked at Jerome. Then he turned back to the figure. "I'll get some red stone and you can do a dog's head for me. I'd like to have it for my room."

"I'm not doing any work for anybody," Jerome said.

"You're doing this for that redhead, aren't you?" Donald asked.

"It goes on a grave," Jerome said.

Donald looked at Jerome again. The man was as odd as his house.

Jerome was looking through the window. Suddenly his mouth closed into a tight line. Emma Lou was coming across the meadow. "There she comes now," Jerome said.

Donald turned and glanced out through the window. His air of bored laziness left him. "Golly," he said. "I can't let her catch me here."

"No way for you to get out." Jerome stepped to the door. Perhaps he could get Emma Lou away from the house long enough for Donald to escape.

"Hello!" Emma Lou greeted him. "Did you get it finished?" She was looking down at the rock chips scattered on the doorstone.

"Not yet," Jerome said, without moving out of the doorway. "Thought you might take a look in the woods. The young raccoons went off and haven't come back." As he spoke, Jerome stepped out on the doorstone and looked

down the slope. He expected Emma Lou to follow him.

"Soon as I have a peek at the lovely lady." She stepped past him quickly.

Jerome jumped, but he could not stop her. So he followed her into the house. Looking over her shoulder, he was relieved to see that Donald had vanished. He did not have to make more than one guess as to where he was. Jerome was certain Donald was under the bed.

Emma Lou drew in her breath as she looked upon the figure. She clasped her hands. "Oh! Oh! It's beautiful! Why, she's smiling up at us!"

Jerome beamed proudly. Emma Lou moved about, looking at the statue from different angles. "I'll bet no raccoon ever had such a fine headstone," she said.

"Lucky I had a nice piece of stone left," Jerome said. Then he heard a noise under the bed. He glanced quickly at Emma Lou. She hadn't heard the noise.

Papa Enters the Scene

At that moment, Papa Skunk appeared at the door. He had heard Emma Lou's voice and had roused himself to see if she had brought anything for him. He walked over to her, waving his tail and churring a warm welcome. Emma Lou reached down and scratched his head. Papa looked up at her. She hadn't brought anything. He cocked his head and listened. He had heard a faint sound under the bed, and sounds from there meant mice. With a swish of his tail, he skipped across the floor and ducked under the bed.

Emma Lou laughed. "He'll be out in a minute with a mouse," she said. "He's a fast worker."

Jerome had an idea things were going to start happening.

"Say!" Emma Lou burst out suddenly. "I forgot all about the little raccoons. When did they leave?"

"They left last night right after supper. Haven't been back since," Jerome said. Out of the corners of his eyes,

Jerome was watching the blanket hanging over the edge of the bed. It was waving gently.

Emma Lou's lips tightened. "All the more reason for my bagging that Cabot dog."

"I don't think he'll bother up this way," Jerome said. He was beginning to squirm. His ears were strained for the sound of small feet stamping angrily. Unless young Cabot had iron nerves and sense enough to play dead, there would be an explosion.

At that moment, they heard a dog barking outside. The yelps and barks were rapidly coming closer. Emma Lou jumped to her feet. "That dog!" she shouted.

A black form darted across the floor. Papa had heard the dog and was on his way to defend his family. Jerome caught Emma Lou's arm. "Wait," he said.

Emma Lou struggled to get away from him. She could see Strong Heart through the doorway. He was bounding up the path. Then she saw Papa marching down the path to meet the dog.

Strong Heart was a society dog. The black and white animal walking toward him looked somewhat like a cat. In fact, he was certain it was a cat. It would turn and flee, but it had used poor judgment. It would never be able to get to a tree before he nabbed it.

Jerome pulled Emma Lou back a few feet. "Let Papa handle this," he said.

Emma Lou stopped pulling and started to grin. Papa had started stamping his feet and churring savagely. Then he did his handstand. Strong Heart let out a wild and eager yelp. This would be the easiest cat kill he had ever made. His mouth opened wide.

Papa's hind feet hit the path, and like a cowboy facing a badman, he fanned his gun and fired. Strong Heart's wild yelp changed to a stifled gurgle, which was followed by a wheezing gulp. He hit the path with all four feet planted and digging frantically. He lunged away toward the woods.

Emma Lou and Jerome dived out into the open as a wave of highly scented air rolled into the house. When they were in the clear, they stood and held their sides and laughed. Strong Heart had looked so foolish.

Finally Emma Lou said, "You'll have to move out for a while."

Jerome nodded. "If Papa could have taken him on down the hill a little way." Then he chuckled. He was thinking about Donald under the bed.

Emma Lou started off down the hill. "If I hurry, I may get that dog," she said.

Jerome didn't think she'd catch even a glimpse of Strong Heart. The dog had been traveling fast when he entered the woods. But he was glad Emma Lou was leaving for a little while.

Jerome turned toward his house. Donald burst forth, holding his nose. "Phooey!" he burst out. "Do you keep skunks too?"

"I have seven," Jerome told him, with a pleased grin.

"Seven?" Donald Roger looked startled. "I saw only one. The darned thing licked the end of my nose."

"Your dog trailed you here and tried to kill it." Jerome was still grinning. "I don't think your dog will ever bother another skunk."

"When he gets back from the dry cleaner's, he'll be locked up, I know that." Donald started away. "I don't smell so good myself."

Jerome walked to his house. There really wasn't any damage done. Papa was standing beside the doorstone, waiting. He beamed up at Jerome. Papa did not seem to have a bit of scent on himself. It was easy to see he was all puffed up over his victory.

After a while, Emma Lou came back.

"See him?" Jerome asked.

"No, he ran like a deer. I guess Papa did a better job than I could have done," Emma Lou said.

Duff Strikes Back

William Marshall Rush

When he was only a year old, Duff, the black bear, had wrecked the Doone cabin in search of food. Danny Doone and his uncle, Web Doone, had been hunting Duff ever since. Danny hunted Duff fairly, with a rifle. But Web Doone used an illegal set-gun—a shotgun that would go off if an animal touched a string tied to its trigger.

Insects had begun to be troublesome. Duff batted at the big horseflies that buzzed around his head. They even lighted on his nose and bored through the skin to suck his blood. Hitting at them with his paws rid Duff of the pests for a moment, but a fresh swarm came right back.

When evening came the horseflies left, but droves of small buffalo gnats crawled into his fur. The high, singing whine of mosquitoes added to his unhappiness.

He hunted a creek and crawled into a deep pool. That helped for a while. Flies, gnats, and mosquitoes did not like a wet bear. But as soon as his fur dried, they came down upon him with renewed strength. He loped off along a bear trail. But he could not outrun the pests.

The trail ended at some mineral springs in a big, grassy park. Duff caught sight of a pool of blackish mud in the middle of a clump of bushes. He splashed out to it, and sank down until only his eyes and nose were exposed. He brushed a muddy paw across his face so that even it would be covered with mud. When he crawled out, he let the mud stick to his coat until it dried, making an armor that neither mosquitoes nor horseflies could get through.

Duff climbed a tree and settled down for his first peaceful nap since warm weather came. Of course, the dried clay crumbled and brushed off as soon as he began his nightly travels. But insects did not bother so much at night. He went back to the wallow at the salt lick whenever they became troublesome in the daytime.

One very hot day, he had put off his mud bath longer than usual. Horseflies drove him in a fast lope toward the wallow. Fifty feet from the wallow, Duff lengthened his stride and galloped his best.

Suddenly, there was a deafening roar and the bitter smell of lightning. Red-hot pain burned his hip. He was thrown clear off his feet by the impact. He had run squarely into an almost invisible cord stretched across the bear trail, pulling the trigger of Web Doone's set-gun. If the bear had been traveling at his usual leisurely pace, the charge of buckshot would have hit him just behind the shoulder and killed him instantly.

As it was, he was still alive. He bawled loudly in pain and rage, tried to stagger to his feet, but fell again. Slowly, painfully, he got up and stood on three legs. He gave one more loud bawl. Then he shut his lips tightly together and without another sound crawled back along the bear trail, stopping to lie without moving for five, ten, fifteen minutes at a time to gather strength to go on. Within a mile, he came to a small creek. He lay for a while in its cooling water.

He was so weak he could hardly drag himself forward. At last, he crawled out of the creek and into a spruce swamp. He floundered out to where the mud was soft and lay there, while Web Doone hunted the forest looking for him. The blood trail was plain as far as the creek. There, the man lost all trace of the bear.

Web gave up. "Critter will die, anyway," he muttered. "No use for me to be wearing myself out looking for it."

For three days, Duff lay in the wallow—three days of absolute quiet. Mud stopped the flow of blood. It drew some of the soreness from his shattered hip. He needed something more, however, than mud and rest. He needed medicine.

On the evening of the third day, he eased himself out of the swamp, an inch at a time, and hobbled into the pine forest. Oregon grape was in bloom. Its roots were both blood purifier and tonic. Duff lay down to scratch them from the soil. He went on to a spring for a cooling drink. Anemones grew near by, and he dug some of the roots.

Duff lay for hours in the sun, ignoring flies and mosquitoes, while the herbs hastened his recovery. In a week, he could touch the foot of his hurt leg to the ground. In two weeks, he could bear some weight on it. It was stiff and very sore. But he would soon be able to travel the bear trails again.

The first day Duff was able to go along the trails for any

distance, he found Web Doone's camp. The horses were picketed in the meadow near the tent. Duff stole back into the forest to wait until darkness fell. Then, as silently as a mountain cat, he crept upwind toward the clearing.

Duff Watches His Chance

The man sat beside a campfire in front of his tent. Duff crept close. Web stared into the flames, not moving except when he got up to stretch his arms and add new fuel to the blaze.

Duff had no fear of fire. He had been near lightning fires in the forest, and he loved the smell of wood smoke. So he lay there, nose stretched out, watching the man who had tried to kill him.

Suddenly Web Doone moved uneasily, got up, and turned to peer into the darkness toward the bear. Duff did not move. His beady eyes did not shine in the light as the big ones of a cat would have done. Web stared for a moment, turned, and sat down. Duff eased forward until he was only thirty feet from the man. A swift rush, one blow of a front paw, the bear's powerful jaws could close on the man's neck—and Web Doone would never aim another set-gun. Duff opened his mouth and licked his chops with a red tongue. His great shoulders tightened.

One of the horses stamped restlessly. The other snorted as if displeased at some small sound, some drifting smell. Web peered toward them. These were signs that a good woodsman did not ignore. He stood up, picked up his rifle, and went off grumbling to see what was wrong with the animals.

Duff heard the sound of his boots on the soft ground. The bear could see him dimly as he walked through the darkness. He was gone for a long time. Duff did not move. When the man came back, he tossed the ends of his fire together. It blazed up brightly. He went inside his tent. Duff heard the rasp of canvas as tent flaps were tied shut. The man grunted as he pulled off his boots. Finally, there was the sound of heavy breathing. The man was asleep.

Duff stole back a hundred yards from camp. He could hear the horses greedily cropping grass. He had been afraid to attack Web Doone at the campfire. Web was too dangerous. But horses were different.

A foot at a time, the bear crept ahead, upwind, into a fresh breeze out of the southwest. Crunch—crunch—the horses did not sense that anything was wrong. Duff was only fifty feet away when one of them jerked up his head with a snort.

"Woof! Woof! Woof!" The bear exploded into sound and action at the same instant. He threw himself toward the horses, a thing of terror out of the quiet night. "Woof!"

The nearest horse reared, the picket pin pulled out, and the animal raced down the trail. The other horse's rope broke, and it was scarcely ten yards behind. Duff did not chase them far. There was no need. They would run for miles before they stopped. Duff limped off to a bear trail and vanished.

At daybreak, Web Doone bent over a plain track in the soft earth beside the creek. It was a bear track, but it was unlike an ordinary bear. On the right side, the hind footprint was ahead of the front footprint, as it should be, like that of a deer. On the left side, however, a lame hind leg shortened the stride a little. The hind footprint was squarely on top of the front one, more like the track of a wolf or coyote. The man would know that track, next time he saw it.

That afternoon, as Web went wearily after the runaways, fifteen miles from camp with halters over his arm, Duff came back to the tent. Once before, he had made a mess of men's belongings in a spirit of curiosity and play. This time, seeking revenge, he was more thorough. He ripped the white tent to ribbons with his sharp claws, banged the stove about until he had smashed it flat,

smashed the water pail by sitting on it, tramped on pots and pans, and chewed the saddles.

He ripped open packages of food, squashed cans, threw sacks of flour and sugar against the trees until the sacks burst. He scattered what oats were left among bushes along the creek. He even dragged Web Doone's blankets to the creek, wrinkling his nose in disgust at the strong man smell, and left them to float away.

He went back to see what was left, discovered a hunk of bacon and a kettle of dried stewed fruit, and ate his fill. Then he hobbled off into the forest, sure that nothing was left of that camp that could possibly be of use to any man.

And everywhere he left a plain track, the unmistakable track of a bear with a lame hind leg.

He traveled without stopping, day after day, away from the land where he had been so cruelly hurt. Fifty miles away, across the mountains, he came to a new land. Here were many black bears, a world of good food—and no men. Duff grew as fat as a cub and went into winter quarters, alone, under the roots of a giant spruce tree.

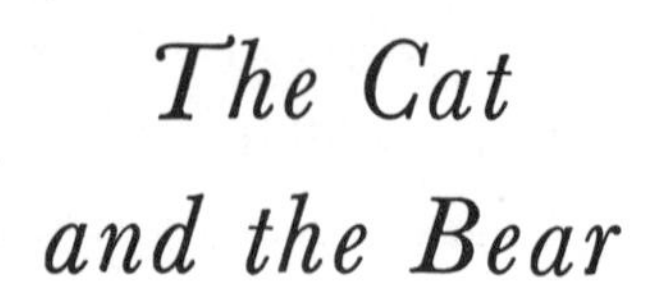

The Cat and the Bear

"Who are *you?*" asked the cat of the bear.
"I am a child of the wood,
I am strong with rain-shedding hair,
I hunt without fear for my food,
The others behold me and quail."
Said the cat, "You are lacking a tail."

"What can you *do?*" asked the cat.
"I can climb for the honey I crave.
In the fall when I'm merry and fat
I seek out a suitable cave
And sleep till I feel the spring light."
Said the cat, "Can you see in the night?"

Said the cat, "*I* sit by man's fire,
But I am much wilder than you.
I do the thing I desire
And do nothing I don't want to do.
I am small, but then, what is that?
My spirit is great," said the cat.

—Elizabeth Coatsworth

Troubles With a Penguin

Richard and Florence Atwater

When Admiral Drake sent Mr. Popper a real live penguin from the South Pole, the Poppers were rather pleased. They named their new pet Captain Cook, and decided that he should live in the refrigerator.

The day after the penguin's arrival was quite eventful at the Poppers'. First, there was the service man, and then the policeman, and then the trouble about the license.

Captain Cook was in the children's room, watching Janie and Bill put together a jigsaw puzzle. He was very good about not disturbing the pieces after Bill had spanked him for eating one. He did not hear the refrigerator service man come to the back door.

Mrs. Popper had gone marketing for canned shrimps for the penguin, so that Mr. Popper was alone in the kitchen to explain to the service man what he wanted done to the refrigerator. The service man put his tool bag down on the kitchen floor, looked at the refrigerator, and then at Mr. Popper, who, to tell the truth, had not shaved yet and was not very tidy.

"Mister," he said, "you don't need no ventilating holes in that there door."

"It's my icebox, and I want some holes bored in the door," said Mr. Popper.

They argued about it for quite a while. Mr. Popper knew that to get the service man to do what he wanted, all he had to do was to explain that he was going to keep a live penguin in the icebox, and that he wanted his pet to have plenty of fresh air. He felt a little stubborn about explaining, however. He didn't want to discuss Captain Cook with this unsympathetic service man, who was already staring at Mr. Popper as if he thought Mr. Popper was not quite right in his head.

"Come on. Do what I said," said Mr. Popper. "I'm paying you for it."

"With what?" asked the service man.

Mr. Popper gave him a five-dollar bill. It made him a little sad to think how many beans it would have bought for Mrs. Popper and the children.

The service man examined the bill carefully, as if he didn't trust Mr. Popper too much. But at last he put it

in his pocket, took a drill from his tool bag, and made five small holes in a neat pattern on the refrigerator door.

"Now," said Mr. Popper, "don't get up. Wait a minute. There is one more thing."

"Now what?" said the service man. "I suppose now you want me to take the door off its hinges to let in a little more air. Or do you want me to make a radio set out of your icebox?"

"Don't get funny," said Mr. Popper indignantly. "That is no way to talk. Believe it or not, I know what I'm doing I mean, having you do. I want you to fix a handle on the inside of that box so it can be opened from the inside."

"That," said the service man, "is a fine idea. You want an extra handle on the inside. Sure, sure." He picked up his tool bag.

"Aren't you going to do it?" asked Mr. Popper.

"Oh, sure, sure," said the service man, edging toward the back door.

Mr. Popper saw that for all his words of agreement, the service man had no intention of putting on an inside handle. "I thought you were a service man," he said.

"I am. That's the first sensible thing you've said."

'You're a fine kind of service man if you don't even know how to put an extra handle on the inside of an ice-box door."

"Oh, I don't, don't I? Don't think I don't know how. I've even got a spare handle in my tool bag, and plenty of screws."

Mr. Popper silently reached into his pocket and gave the service man his last five-dollar bill. He was pretty sure that Mrs. Popper would be annoyed at him for spending all that money. But it could not be helped.

"Mister," said the service man, "you win. I'll fix your extra handle. And while I am doing it, you sit down on that chair over there, where I can keep an eye on you."

"Fair enough," said Mr. Popper, sitting down.

The service man was still on the floor, putting in the final screws that held the new handle in place, when the penguin came out to the kitchen on his silent pink feet. Surprised at seeing a strange man sitting on the floor, Captain Cook quietly walked over and began to peck him curiously. But the service man was even more surprised.

"Ork," said the penguin. Or perhaps it was the service man. Mr. Popper was not sure just what had happened

when he picked up himself and his chair a moment later. There had been a shower of flying tools, a slamming of the door. And the service man was gone.

These sudden noises, of course, brought the children running. Mr. Popper showed them how the refrigerator was now all remodeled for the penguin. He showed Captain Cook, too, by shutting him inside it. The penguin at once noticed the shiny new inside handle and bit it with his usual curiosity. The door opened, and Captain Cook jumped out.

Mr. Popper promptly put Captain Cook back inside and shut the door again, to be sure that the penguin learned his lesson. Before long, Captain Cook became quite skillful at getting out. He was ready to be taught how to get inside when the door was shut. By the time the policeman came to the back door, Captain Cook was going in and out the refrigerator as easily as if he had lived in one all his life.

Captain Cook and the Law

The children were the first to notice the policeman.

"Look, Papa," said Bill. "There's a policeman at the back door. Is he going to arrest you?"

"Gook," said Captain Cook, walking with dignity to the door.

"Is this 432 Proudfoot Avenue?"

"It is," answered Mr. Popper.

"Well, I guess this is the place all right," said the

policeman. He pointed to Captain Cook. "Is that yours?"

"Yes, it is," said Mr. Popper, proudly.

"And what do you do for a living?" asked the policeman sternly.

"Papa is an artist," said Janie.

"I'm a house painter, a decorator," said Mr. Popper. "Won't you come in?"

"I won't," said the policeman, "unless I have to."

"Ha, ha!" said Bill. "The policeman is afraid of Captain Cook."

"Gaw!" said the penguin, opening his red beak wide, as if he wanted to laugh at the policeman.

"Can it talk?" asked the policeman. "What is it?"

"It's a penguin," said Janie. "We keep it for a pet."

"Well, if it's only a bird . . ." said the policeman, lifting his cap to scratch his head in a puzzled sort of way. "From the way that fellow with a tool bag yelled at me outside, I thought there was a lion loose in here."

"Mamma says Papa's hair looks like a lion's sometimes," said Bill.

"Keep still, Bill," said Janie. "The policeman doesn't care how Papa's hair looks."

The policeman now scratched his chin. "If it's only a bird, I suppose it will be O.K. if you keep it in a cage."

"We keep him in the icebox," said Bill.

"You can put it in the icebox, for all I care," said the policeman. "What kind of a bird did you say it was?"

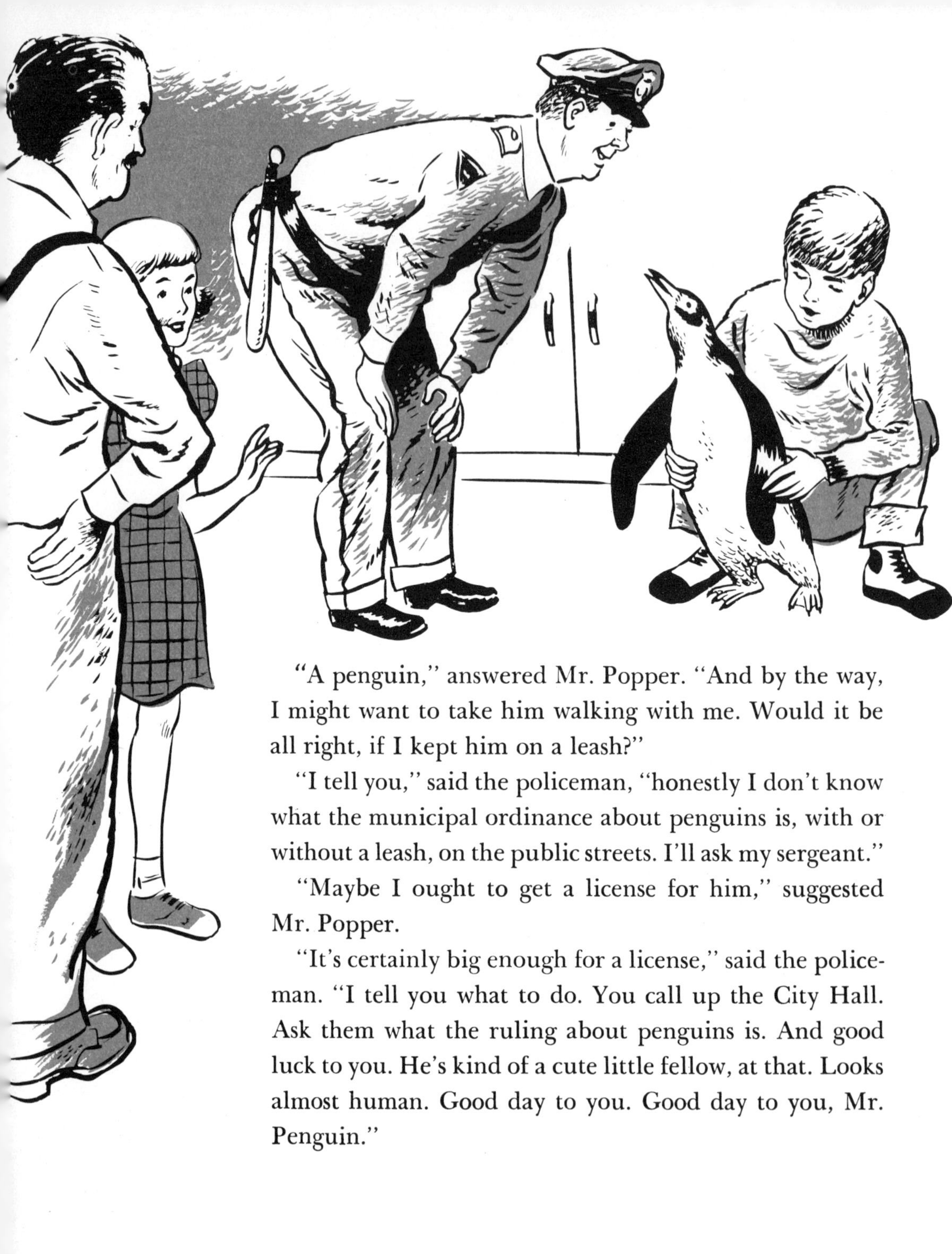

"A penguin," answered Mr. Popper. "And by the way, I might want to take him walking with me. Would it be all right, if I kept him on a leash?"

"I tell you," said the policeman, "honestly I don't know what the municipal ordinance about penguins is, with or without a leash, on the public streets. I'll ask my sergeant."

"Maybe I ought to get a license for him," suggested Mr. Popper.

"It's certainly big enough for a license," said the policeman. "I tell you what to do. You call up the City Hall. Ask them what the ruling about penguins is. And good luck to you. He's kind of a cute little fellow, at that. Looks almost human. Good day to you. Good day to you, Mr. Penguin."

When Mr. Popper telephoned the City Hall, he found it was not so easy to learn whether or not he must get a license for his strange pet. Every time he would explain, he would be told to wait a minute. Much later, a new voice would ask him what he wanted. This went on for considerable time. At last, a new voice seemed to take a little more interest in the case. Pleased with this friendly voice, Mr. Popper began again to tell about Captain Cook.

"Is he an army captain, a police captain, or a navy captain?"

"He is not," said Mr. Popper. "He's a penguin."

"Will you repeat that, please?" said the voice.

Mr. Popper repeated it. The voice suggested that perhaps he had better spell it.

"P-e-n-g-u-i-n," said Mr. Popper. "Penguin."

"Oh!" said the voice. "You mean that Captain Cook's first name is Benjamin?"

"Not Benjamin. Penguin. It's a bird," said Mr. Popper.

"Do you mean," said the phone in his ear, "that Captain Cook wishes a license to shoot birds? I am sorry. The bird-hunting season does not open until November. And please try to speak a little more distinctly, Mr.—Topper, did you say your name is?"

"My name is Popper, not Topper," shouted Mr. Popper.

"Yes, Mr. Potter. Now I can hear you quite clearly."

"Then listen," roared Mr. Popper, now completely outraged. "If you folks at the City Hall don't even know what penguins are, I guess you haven't any rule saying they

have to be licensed. I will do without a license for Captain Cook."

"Just a minute, Mr. Popwell. Our own Mr. Treadbottom of the Bureau of Navigation of Lakes, Rivers, Ponds, and Streams has just come in. I will let you speak to him personally. Perhaps he knows this Benjamin Cook of yours."

In a moment, a new voice was speaking to Mr. Popper.

"Good morning. This is the Automobile License Bureau. Did you have this same car last year, and if so, what was the license number?" Mr. Popper had been switched over to the County Building.

He decided to hang up.

Not Necessarily So

Is there gold at the foot of the rainbow?
Not necessarily so—
And yet there are riches in rainbows,
As every wise man should know.

Laughter and wonder and beauty
And even wisdom may glow
Through many a quaint old story
Not necessarily so.

—Dorothy Hall

The Old Woman and the Tiger

Retold by Mary Hemingway

In the village of Gwai-lin-di, between the curve of the Yellow River and the Great Wall of China, there lived a poor old widow woman. Every day, her only son went up into the mountains behind the village and gathered faggots and brought them home to his mother. She would exchange some of the faggots with her neighbors for a few handfuls of millet to cook in the pot. So from day to day they just got by.

But one day, while her son was up in the mountains gathering faggots, an enormous tiger leaped out of the bushes and ate him up. Some other boys from the village who were gathering faggots near by ran back to the village and knocked on the door of his mother's house. "Old woman, old woman, a terrible tiger has eaten up your son!"

The old woman was very indignant. Now that she had no son to gather faggots for her, how could she get along from day to day? She would have no millet to cook in

the pot, and no faggots to burn under it. So she determined to see that justice was done.

Seizing her stick in her hand, she hobbled straight to the headman of the village. She shook her stick under his nose and cried angrily, "A tiger from the mountains has eaten up my only son. Now how can I get along from day to day? There will be no millet to cook in the pot, and no faggots to burn under it. I demand that you capture this tiger and punish him, so that justice may be done!"

But the headman of the village replied, "The tiger ate up your son in the mountains behind the village. I have no authority outside the village. There is nothing I can do about it. So, old woman, I would advise you to go quietly home."

But the old woman did not go quietly home. She took her stick in her hand, and she hobbled along the dusty road until she came to the city of Funjo. There she went to the house of the magistrate of the city. She shook her stick under the magistrate's nose and cried angrily, "A tiger from the mountains behind the village of Gwai-lin-di has eaten up my only son. Now how can I get along from day to day? There will be no millet to cook in the pot, and no faggots to burn under it. I demand that you capture this tiger and punish him, so that justice may be done!"

The magistrate of the city of Funjo replied, "The tiger ate up your son outside of the city limits of Funjo. I have no authority over him. There is nothing I can do about it. So, old woman, I would advise you to go quietly home."

But the old woman did not go quietly home. She took her stick in her hand, and she hobbled along the dusty road until she came to the capital of the province of Shansi.

There she went to the palace of the governor of the province. But the gates were shut. No one would let the old woman in. So she banged on the gates with her stick. She shouted and scolded so long and so loudly that finally the governor inside the palace heard the noise. He sent his servants running to find out what was making such a terrible racket. They returned with the little old woman.

She shook her stick under the governor's nose and cried angrily, "A tiger from the mountains outside the village of Gwai-lin-di has eaten up my only son. Now how can I get along from day to day? There will be no millet to cook in the pot, and no faggots to burn under it. I demand that

you capture this tiger and punish him, so that justice may be done!"

Now the governor of Shansi at that time was a kind and a just man. He replied, "Venerable old woman, this seems to me to be a very reasonable request. Certainly, if justice is to be maintained in my province, this tiger must be punished."

The Case of the Dutiful Tiger

So he sent a score of his best hunters into the mountains behind the village of Gwai-lin-di. They captured the tiger, and bound him heavily with ropes, and loaded him onto a cart. Then they dragged him to the Court of Justice. A great crowd of people followed behind to see the tiger brought to justice.

The governor was dressed in his finest purple silk robes. When the tiger had been brought before him, the governor stepped forward and said:

"Tiger, it has been proved by many witnesses that you ate up the only son of this poor old widow woman while he was in the mountains gathering faggots for his mother. Now she is left alone in the world to starve. The punishment for murder is death. Therefore, Tiger, I sentence you to be dragged to the East Gate of the city, there to have the head chopped from your shoulders with a sharp

ax. You have heard the sentence, Tiger. Have you anything to say?"

"Only this," replied the tiger. "I am sorry now that I ate this woman's son. If I had known that he was the only son of his mother, and she a poor widow, I would certainly never have done it. Nevertheless, I do not see that justice will be served by beheading me. It will not bring back the old woman's son. It will not leave her any better off than she was before. And of course *I* will not like it at all. I have a better suggestion. If you will spare my life, I myself will be a son to her, for as long as she shall live. Every day, I will bring faggots to her. Every day I will bring her deer, or a rabbit, or a fat pheasant for the pot. I will be indeed a dutiful son to her, a truly filial tiger."

"This suggestion sounds to me like a very reasonable one," said the governor. "However, the old woman must agree to it. Venerable old woman, if this tiger will promise to be a dutiful son to you, for as long as you shall live, will you consent to adopt him?"

"He looks to me like a very honest tiger," replied the old woman. "If he will swear by the souls of his ancestors that he will do all that he has promised, I shall be content to adopt him for my son."

"Do you swear by the souls of your ancestors to do all that you have promised, and to be a good and dutiful son to this old woman, for as long as she shall live?" asked the governor.

The tiger raised his right paw, and replied solemnly, "I do."

So the governor ordered the tiger unbound, and the little old woman took her stick in her hand, and led the tiger back to the village of Gwai-lin-di. And all the villagers came out of their houses, and went down the road to meet them. The old woman introduced them all to the tiger by name, and they all said that they were very glad to meet him—in a social way.

Then the tiger bounded up into the mountains. He returned with a perfectly enormous bundle of faggots, which he dumped by the old woman's door. Then he went hunting, and returned with a freshly killed deer. The old woman invited all her neighbors in, and there was a great feast in honor of the dutiful tiger.

And every day after that, the tiger brought plenty of faggots and fresh meat for the old woman. And the old woman lived in plenty and happiness for much longer than anyone would have thought possible.

Then one morning, the tiger bounded up to the old woman's door, and heard a great sound of weeping and wailing inside the house. And the neighbor woman came to the door and said, "Tiger, tiger, your mother is dead." The tiger gave a great howl of sorrow and grief.

On the day of the old woman's funeral, the tiger walked in the front of the procession with a white mourning band around his head. After the funeral, he lay down beside the old woman's grave with his head on his paws. For three whole days and nights, he neither ate nor drank nor slept. At the end of that time, he arose and ran around the grave three times.

Then, with a tremendous roar, he bounded off into the mountains. And he was never again seen by anyone in the village of Gwai-lin-di.

Digging For Treasure

E. Nesbit

I have often thought that if the people who write books for children knew a little more, it would be better. I shall not tell you anything about us except what I should like to know about, if I was reading the story and you were writing it. Albert's uncle says I ought to have put this in the preface, but I never read prefaces, and it is not much good writing things just for people to skip. I wonder why other authors have never thought of this.

Well, when we had agreed to dig for treasure we all went down into the cellar and turned on the light. Oswald would have liked to dig there, but it is flagstone. We looked among the old boxes and broken chairs and fenders and empty bottles and things, and at last we found the spades we had used to dig in the sand when we went to the seashore three years ago. They are not silly, babyish, wooden spades, that split if you look at them, but good iron, with a blue mark across the top of the iron part, and yellow wooden handles. We wasted a little time getting them dusted, because the girls wouldn't dig with spades that had cobwebs on them. Girls would never do for African explorers, or anything like that, they are too particular.

It was no use doing the thing by halves. We marked out a sort of square in the moldy part of the garden about three yards across, and began to dig. But we found nothing except worms and stones—and the ground was very hard.

So we thought we'd try another part of the garden, and we found a place in the big, round flower bed, where the ground was much softer. We thought we'd make a smaller hole to begin with, and it was much better. We dug, and dug, and dug, and it was hard work! We got very hot digging, but we found nothing.

Presently Albert-next-door looked over the wall. We do not like him very much, but we let him play with us sometimes, because his father is dead, and you must not be unkind to orphans, even if their mothers are alive. Albert is always very tidy. He wears frilly collars and velvet knee pants. I can't think how he can bear to.

So we said, "Hullo!"

And he said, "What are you up to?"

"We're digging for treasure," said Alice, "An ancient scroll told us the hiding place. Come over and help us. When we have dug deep enough we shall find a great pot of red clay, full of gold and precious jewels."

Albert-next-door only sniggered and said, "What silly nonsense!"

He cannot play properly at all. It is very strange, because he has a very nice uncle. You see, Albert-next-door doesn't care for reading, and he has not read nearly so

many books as we have, so he is very foolish and ignorant. But it cannot be helped, and you just have to put up with it when you want him to do anything. Besides, it is wrong to be angry with people for not being so clever as yourself. It is not always their fault.

So Oswald said, "Come and dig! Then you shall share the treasure when we've found it."

But he said, "I shan't—I don't like digging—and I'm just going in."

"Come along and dig," Alice said. "You can use my spade. It's much the best—"

So he came along and dug, and when once he was over the wall we kept him at it. We worked as well, of course, and the hole got deep. Pincher worked too—he is our dog and he is very good at digging. He digs for rats sometimes, and gets very dirty. But we love our dog, even when his face needs washing.

"I expect we shall have to make a tunnel," Oswald said, "to reach the rich treasure." So he jumped into the hole and began to dig at one side.

After that we took turns digging at the tunnel. Pincher was most useful in scraping the earth out of the tunnel. He does it with his back feet when you say "Rats!" and he digs with his front ones, and burrows with his nose as well.

At last the tunnel was nearly a yard long, and big enough to creep along to find the treasure, if only it had been a bit longer. Now it was Albert's turn to go in and dig, but he refused.

"Take your turn like a man," said Oswald. Nobody can say that Oswald doesn't take his turn like a man. But Albert wouldn't. So we had to make him, because it was only fair.

"It's quite easy," Alice said, "you just crawl in and dig with your hands. Then when you come out, we can scrape out what you've done, with the spades. Come—be a man. You won't notice it being dark in the tunnel if you shut your eyes tight. We've all been in except Dora—and she doesn't like worms."

"I don't like worms neither." Albert-next-door said. But we remembered how he had picked a fat red and black worm up in his fingers, and thrown it at Dora only the day before.

So we put him in.

But he would not go in head first, the proper way, and dig with his hands as we had done. Though Oswald was angry at the time, for he hates snivelers, afterwards he admitted that perhaps it was just as well. You should never be afraid to admit that perhaps you were mistaken, but it is cowardly to do it unless you are quite sure you are in the wrong.

"Let me go in feet first," said Albert-next-door. "I'll dig with my boots. I will truly, honor bright."

So we let him go in feet first. He did it very slowly but at last he was in, with only his head sticking out into the hole, and all the rest of him in the tunnel.

"Now dig with your boots," said Oswald, "and Alice, do catch hold of Pincher. He'll be digging again in another minute, and perhaps it would be uncomfortable for Albert, if Pincher threw the dirt into his eyes."

You should always try to think of these little things. Thinking of other people's comfort makes them like you. Alice held Pincher, and we all shouted, "Kick! dig with your feet for all you're worth!"

So Albert-next-door began to dig with his feet, and we stood on the ground over him waiting. All of a sudden the ground gave way, and we tumbled together in a heap. When we got up there was a little shallow hollow where we had been standing, and Albert-next-door was underneath, stuck quite fast, because the roof of the tunnel had tumbled in on him. He is a horribly unlucky boy to have anything to do with.

It was dreadful the way he cried and screamed, though he had to admit it didn't hurt, only it was rather heavy and he couldn't move his legs. We would have dug him out in time, but he screamed so we were afraid the police would come. So Dicky climbed over the wall to tell Albert-next-door's uncle he had been buried by mistake, and to come and help dig him out.

Dicky was gone a long time. We wondered what had become of him. All the while the screaming went on and on, for we had taken the loose earth off Albert's face so that he could scream quite easily and comfortably.

Presently Dicky came back and Albert-next-door's uncle came with him. He has very long legs, and his hair is light, and his face is brown. He has been to sea, but now he writes books. I like him.

He told his nephew to stop it, so Albert did, and then he asked him if he was hurt. Albert had to say he wasn't, for though he is a coward and very unlucky, he is not a liar.

"This promises to be a long job," said Albert-next-door's uncle, rubbing his hands and looking at the hole with Albert's head in it. "I will get another spade," so he got the big spade out of the garden tool shed, and began to dig his nephew out.

"Mind you keep very still," he said, "or I might take a bit out of you with the spade." After a while he said, "I confess that I should like to know how my nephew happened to be buried. But don't tell me if you'd rather not. I suppose no force was used?"

"Only moral force," said Alice. They used to talk a lot about moral force at the school where she went. In case you don't know what it means, I'll tell you that it is making people do what they don't want to, just by laughing at them or promising them things if they're good.

"Only moral force, eh?" said Albert-next-door's uncle. "Well?"

"Well," Dora said, "I'm very sorry it happened to Albert —I'd rather it had been one of us. It would have been my turn to go into the tunnel, only I don't like worms, so they let me off. You see we were digging for treasure."

"Yes," said Alice, "and I think we were just coming to the underground passage that leads to the secret hoard when the tunnel fell in on Albert. He is so unlucky," she sighed.

Then Albert-next-door began to scream again, and his uncle wiped his face—his own face, not Albert's—with his handkerchief, and he put it in his pants pocket. Digging is warm work.

He told Albert-next-door to stop screaming, or he wouldn't go any further in the matter, so Albert did, and presently his uncle finished digging him out. Albert did look so funny, with his hair all dusty, and his velvet suit covered with dirt, and his face muddy with earth and crying.

We all said how sorry we were, but he wouldn't say a word back to us. He was most awfully sick to think he'd been the one buried, when it might just as well have been one of us. I felt myself that it had been hard.

"So you were digging for treasure," said Albert-next-door's uncle, wiping his face again with his handkerchief. "Well, I fear that your chances of success are small. I have made a careful study of the whole subject. What I don't know about buried treasure is not worth knowing. And I never knew more than one coin buried in any one garden —and that is generally—Hullo—what's that?"

He pointed to something shining in the hole he had just dragged Albert out of. Oswald picked it up. It was a half-dollar. We looked at each other, speechless with surprise and delight, like in books.

"Well, that's lucky, at all events," said Albert-next-door's uncle. "Let's see, that's about eight cents for each of you."

"It's seven cents," said Dicky. "There are seven of us, you see."

"Oh, you count Albert as one of yourselves on this occasion, eh?"

"Of course," said Alice. "He was buried after all. Why don't we let him have eight cents and we'll have seven each."

We all agreed to this, and told Albert-next-door we would bring his share as soon as we could get the half-dollar changed. His uncle wiped his face again—he did look hot—and began to put on his coat.

When he had done it he stooped and picked up something. He held it up, and you will hardly believe it, but it is quite true—it was another half-dollar!

"To think that there should be two!" he said. "In all my experience of buried treasure I never heard of such a thing!"

I wish Albert-next-door's uncle would come treasure hunting with us regularly. He must have very sharp eyes, for Dora says she was looking just the minute before at the very place where the second half-dollar was picked up and she never saw it.

Dr. Dolittle and the Pushmi-Pullyu

Hugh Lofting

Dr. John Dolittle lived in a little town called Puddleby-on-the-Marsh. He kept his house so full of pets that his patients stopped coming to him. So he became an animal doctor and learned to speak animal languages. Chee-Chee, his pet monkey, received word of a terrible sickness among the monkeys of Africa. So the good Doctor traveled to Africa and cured the monkeys.

John Dolittle told the monkeys that he must now go back to Puddleby.

They were very surprised at this; for they had thought that he was going to stay with them forever. And that night all the monkeys got together in the jungle to talk it over.

And the Chief Chimpanzee rose up and said,

"Why is it the good man is going away? Is he not happy here with us?"

But none of them could answer him.

Then the Grand Gorilla got up and said,

"I think we should all go to him and ask him to stay. Perhaps if we make him a new house and a bigger bed, and promise him plenty of monkey servants to work for him and to make life pleasant for him—perhaps then he will not wish to go."

Then Chee-Chee got up, and all the others whispered, "Sh! Look! Chee-Chee, the great Traveler, is about to speak!"

And Chee-Chee said to the other monkeys, "My friends, I am afraid it is useless to ask the Doctor to stay. He owes

money in Puddleby; and he says he must go back and pay it."

And the monkeys asked him, "What is *money?*"

Then Chee-Chee told them that in the Land of the White Men you could get nothing without money; you could *do* nothing without money—that it was almost impossible to *live* without money.

And some of them asked, "But can you not even eat and drink without paying?"

But Chee-Chee shook his head. And then he told them that even he, when he was with the organ-grinder, had been made to ask the children for money.

And the Chief Chimpanzee turned to the Oldest Orang-outang and said, "Cousin, surely these Men be strange creatures! Who would wish to live in such a land? My gracious, how paltry!"

Then Chee-Chee said,

"When we were coming to you, we had no boat to cross the sea in and no money to buy food to eat on our journey. So a man lent us some biscuits; and we said we would pay him when we came back. And we borrowed a boat from a sailor; but it was broken on the rocks when we reached the shores of Africa. Now the Doctor says he must go back and get the sailor another boat—because the man was poor and his ship was all he had."

And the monkeys were all silent for a while, sitting quite still and thinking hard.

At last the Biggest Baboon got up and said, "I do not think we ought to let this good man leave our land till we have given him a fine present to take with him, so that he may know we are grateful for all that he has done for us."

And a little, tiny red monkey who was sitting up in a tree shouted down,

"I think that too!"

And then they all cried out, making a great noise, "Yes, yes. Let us give him the finest present a White Man ever had!"

Now they began to wonder and to ask one another what would be the best thing to give him. And one said, "Fifty bags of coconuts!" And another—"A hundred bunches of bananas! At least he shall not have to buy his fruit in the Land Where You Pay To Eat!"

But Chee-Chee told them that all these things would be too heavy to carry so far and would go bad before half was eaten.

"If you want to please him," he said, "give him an animal. You may be sure he will be kind to it. Give him some rare animal they have not got in the menageries."

And the monkeys asked him, "What are *menageries?*"

Then Chee-Chee explained to them that menageries were places in the Land of the White Men, where animals were put in cages for people to come and look at. And the monkeys were very shocked, and said to one another,

"These Men are like thoughtless young ones—stupid and easily amused. Sh! It is a prison he means."

So then they asked Chee-Chee what rare animal it could be that they should give the Doctor—one the White Men had not seen before. And the Major of the Marmosettes asked,

"Have they an iguana over there?"

But Chee-Chee said, "Yes, there is one in the London Zoo."

And another asked, "Have they an okapi?"

But Chee-Chee said, "Yes. In Belgium, where my organ-grinder took me five years ago, they had an okapi in a big city they call Antwerp."

And another asked, "Have they a pushmi-pullyu?"

Then Chee-Chee said, "No. No White Man has ever seen a pushmi-pullyu. Let us give him that."

A Strange Beast

Pushmi-pullyus are now extinct. That means there aren't any more. But long ago, when Doctor Dolittle was alive, there were some of them still left in the deepest jungles of Africa; and even then they were very, very scarce. They had no tail, but a head at each end, and sharp horns on each head. They were very shy and terribly hard to catch. The black men get most of their animals by sneaking up behind them while they are not looking. But you could not do this with the pushmi-pullyu—because, no matter which way you came towards him, he was always facing you. And besides, only one half of him slept at a time. The other head was always awake—and watching.

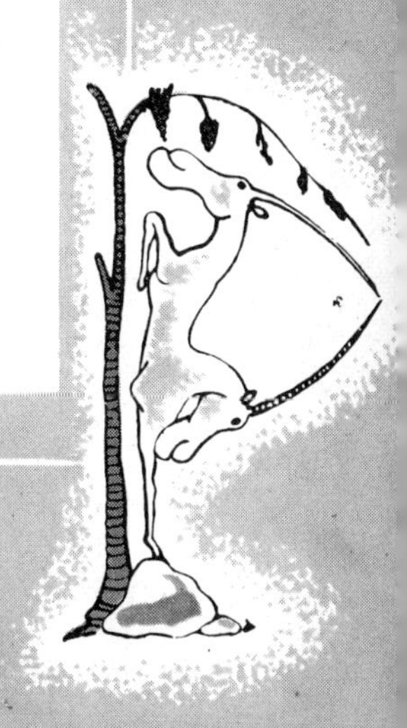

This was why they were never caught and never seen in Zoos. Though many of the greatest huntsmen and the cleverest menagerie-keepers spent years of their lives searching through the jungles in all weathers for pushmi-pullyus, not a single one had ever been caught. Even then, years ago, he was the only animal in the world that had two heads.

Well, the monkeys set out hunting for this animal through the forest. After they had gone a good many miles, one of them found peculiar footprints near the edge of a river; they knew that a pushmi-pullyu must be very near that spot.

Then they went along the bank of the river a little way and they saw a place where the grass was high and thick; and they guessed that he was in there.

So they all joined hands and made a great circle around the high grass. The pushmi-pullyu heard them coming; and he tried hard to break through the ring of monkeys. But he couldn't do it. When he saw that it was no use trying to escape, he sat down and waited to see what they wanted.

They asked him if he would go with Doctor Dolittle and be put on show in the Land of the White Men.

But he shook both his heads hard and said, "Certainly not!"

They explained to him that he would not be shut up in a menagerie but would just be looked at. They told him that the Doctor was a very kind man but hadn't any money; and people would pay to see a two-headed animal

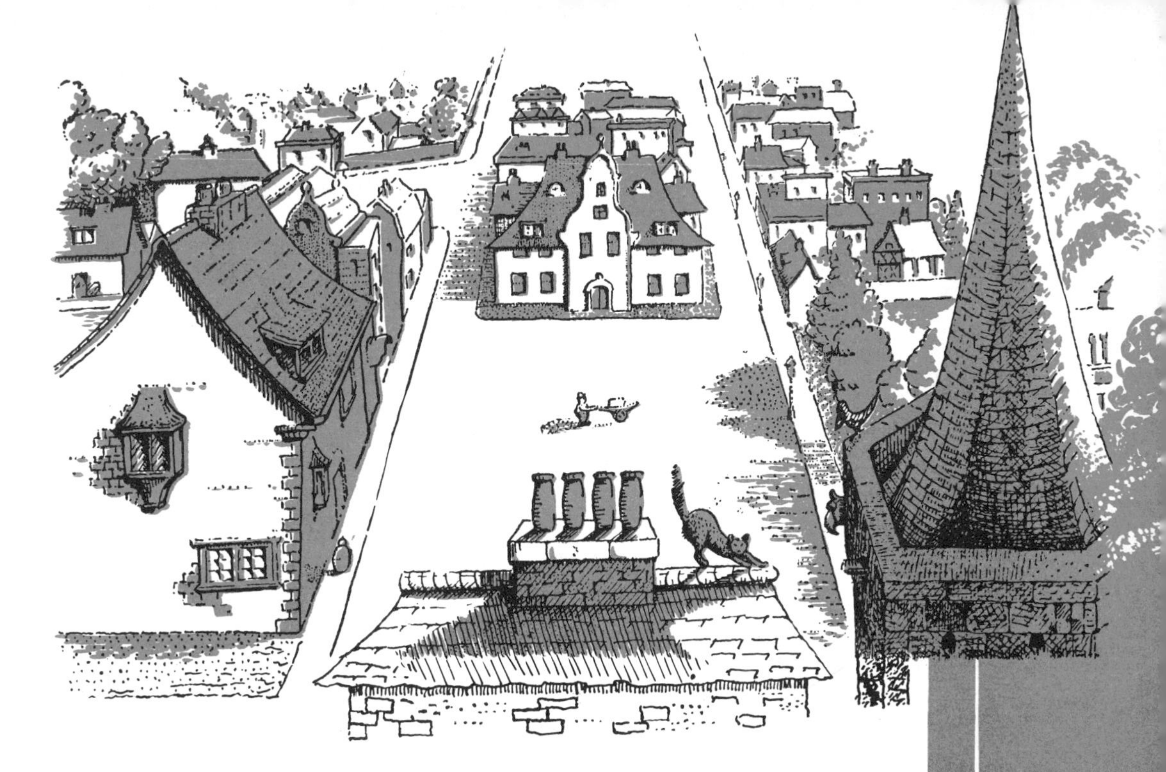

and the Doctor would get rich and could pay for the boat he had borrowed to come to Africa in.

But he answered, "No. You know how shy I am—I hate being stared at." And he almost began to cry.

Then, for three days they tried to persuade him.

And at the end of the third day he said he would come with them and see what kind of a man the Doctor was, first.

So the monkeys traveled back with the pushmi-pullyu. And when they came to where the Doctor's little house of grass was, they knocked on the door.

The duck, who was packing the trunk, said, "Come in!"

And Chee-Chee very proudly took the animal inside and showed him to the Doctor.

"What in the world is it?" asked John Dolittle, gazing at the strange creature.

"Lord save us!" cried the duck. "How does it make up its mind?"

"It doesn't look to me as though it had any," said Jip, the dog.

A New Pet for the Doctor

"This, Doctor," said Chee-Chee, "is the pushmi-pullyu—the rarest animal of the African jungles, the only two-headed beast in the world. Take him home with you and your fortune's made. People will pay any money to see him."

"But I don't want any money," said the Doctor.

"Yes, you do," said Dab-Dab, the duck. "Don't you remember how we had to pinch and scrape to pay the butcher's bill in Puddleby? And how are you going to get the sailor the new boat you spoke of—unless we have the money to buy it?"

"I was going to make him one," said the Doctor.

"Oh, do be sensible!" cried Dab-Dab. "Where would you get all the wood and the nails to make one with?—And besides, what are we going to live on? We shall be poorer than ever when we get back. Chee-Chee's perfectly right: take the funny-looking thing along, do!"

"Well, perhaps there is something in what you say," murmured the Doctor. "It certainly would make a nice new kind of pet. But does the er—what-do-you-call-it really want to go abroad?"

"Yes, I'll go," said the pushmi-pullyu, who saw at once, from the Doctor's face, that he was a man to be trusted. "You have been so kind to the animals here—and the monkeys tell me that I am the only one who will do. But you must promise me that if I do not like it in the Land of the White Men you will send me back."

"Why, certainly—of course, of course," said the Doctor. "Excuse me, surely you are related to the Deer Family, are you not?"

"Yes," said the pushmi-pullyu—"to the Abyssinian Gazelles and the Asiatic Chamois—on my mother's side. My father's great-grandfather was the last of the Unicorns."

"Most interesting!" murmured the Doctor; and he took a book out of the trunk which Dab-Dab was packing and began turning the pages. "Let us see if Buffon says anything—"

"I notice," said the duck, "that you only talk with one of your mouths. Can't the other head talk as well?"

"Oh, yes," said the pushmi-pullyu. "But I keep the other mouth for eating—mostly. In that way I can talk while I am eating without being rude. Our people have always been very polite."

When the packing was finished and everything was ready to start, the monkeys gave a grand party for the Doctor, and all the animals of the jungle came. And they had pineapples and mangoes and honey and all sorts of good things to eat and drink.

After they had all finished eating, the Doctor got up and said,

"My friends: I am not clever at speaking long words after dinner, like some men; and I have just eaten many fruits and much honey. But I wish to tell you that I am very sad at leaving your beautiful country. Because I have things to do in the Land of the White Men, I must go. After I have gone, remember never to let the flies settle on your food before you eat it; and do not sleep on the ground when the rains are coming. I—er—er—I hope you will all live happily ever after."

When the Doctor stopped speaking and sat down, all the monkeys clapped their hands a long time and said to one another, "Let it be remembered always among our people that he sat and ate with us, here, under the trees. For surely he is the Greatest of Men!"

And the Grand Gorilla, who had the strength of seven horses in his hairy arms, rolled a great rock up to the head of the table and said,

"This stone for all time shall mark the spot."

And even to this day, in the heart of the jungle, that stone still is there. And monkey-mothers, passing through the forest with their families, still point down at it from the branches and whisper to their children, "Sh! There it is—look—where the Good White Man sat and ate food with us in the Year of the Great Sickness!"

Then, when the party was over, the Doctor and his pets started out to go back to the seashore. And all the monkeys went with him as far as the edge of their country, carrying his trunk and bags, to see him off.

About Elizabeth Eliza's Piano

Lucretia P. Hale

The Peterkins as a family were not noted for their brains. Indeed, if it hadn't been for the lady from Philadelphia, who was visiting in their town, the Peterkins would have had a hard time.

Elizabeth Eliza had a present of a piano. She was to take lessons from the postmaster's daughter.

They decided to have the piano set across the window in the parlor. The carters brought it in, and went away.

After they had gone, the family all came in to look at the piano. But they found the carters had placed it with its back turned towards the middle of the room, standing close against the window.

How could Elizabeth Eliza open it? How could she reach the keys to play upon it?

Solomon John proposed that they should open the window. Agamemnon could do this with his long arms. Then Elizabeth Eliza should go round upon the piazza, and open the piano. Then she could have her music-stool on the piazza, and play upon the piano there.

So they tried this. They all thought it was a very pretty sight to see Elizabeth Eliza playing on the piano, while she sat on the piazza, with the honeysuckle vines behind her.

It was very pleasant, too, moonlight evenings. Mr. Peterkin liked to take a doze on his sofa in the room. The rest of the family liked to sit on the piazza. So did Elizabeth Eliza, only she had to have her back to the moon.

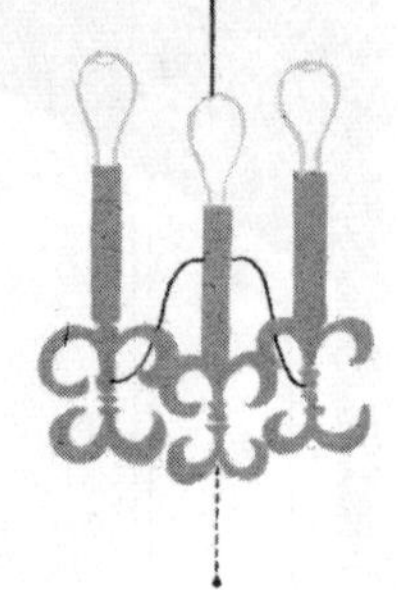

All this did very well through the summer. But, when the fall came, Mr. Peterkin thought the air was too cold from the open window. The family did not want to sit out on the piazza.

Elizabeth Eliza practiced in the mornings with her cloak on. But she was obliged to give up her music in the evenings, the family shivered so.

One day, when she was talking with the lady from Philadelphia, she spoke of this trouble.

The lady from Philadelphia looked surprised. Then she said, "But why don't you turn the piano around?"

One of the little boys pertly said, "It is a square piano."

But Elizabeth Eliza went home directly, and, with the help of Agamemnon and Solomon John, turned the piano round.

"Why did we not think of that before?" said Mrs. Peterkin. "What shall we do when the lady from Philadelphia goes home again?"

Jimmy Takes Vanishing Lessons

Walter Brooks

The school bus picked up Jimmy Crandall every morning. Every afternoon it dropped him again. And so twice a day, on the bus, he passed the entrance to the mysterious road.

It wasn't much of a road any more. It was choked with weeds and blackberry bushes. The woods on both sides pressed in so closely that it was dark and gloomy, even on bright days. The bus driver once pointed it out.

"There's a haunted house about a quarter of a mile down that road." He paused. "But you ought to know about that, Jimmy. It was your grandfather's house."

Jimmy knew about it, and he knew that it now belonged to his Aunt Mary. But Jimmy's aunt would never talk to him about the house. She said the stories about it were silly nonsense and there were no such things as ghosts. If all the villagers weren't a lot of superstitious idiots, she would be able to rent the house. Then she would have enough money to buy Jimmy some decent clothes and take him to the movies.

Jimmy thought it was all very well to say that there were no such things as ghosts. But how about the people who had tried to live there? Aunt Mary had rented the house three times, but every family had moved out within a week. They said the things that went on there were just too queer.

Jimmy thought about the house a lot. If he could only prove that there wasn't a ghost . . . And one Saturday when his aunt was in the village, Jimmy took the key to the haunted house from its hook on the kitchen door, and started out.

It had seemed like a fine idea when he had first thought of it—to find out for himself. Even in the silence and damp gloom of the old road, it still seemed pretty good. Nothing to be scared of, he told himself. Ghosts aren't around in the daytime. But when he came out in the clearing and looked at those blank, dusty windows, he wasn't so sure.

"Oh, come on!" he told himself. And he squared his shoulders and waded through the long grass to the porch.

Then he stopped again. His feet did not seem to want

to go up the steps. But when at last they did, they marched right up and across the porch to the front door. Jimmy set his teeth hard and put the key in the keyhole. It turned with a squeak. He pushed the door open and went in.

He was in a long dark hall with closed doors on both sides. On the right, the stairs went up. He had left the door open behind him, and the light from it showed him that, except for the hatrack and table and chairs, the hall was empty. And then as he stood there, listening to the bumping of his heart, gradually the hall grew darker and darker —as if something huge had come up on the porch behind him. He swung round quickly, but there was nothing there.

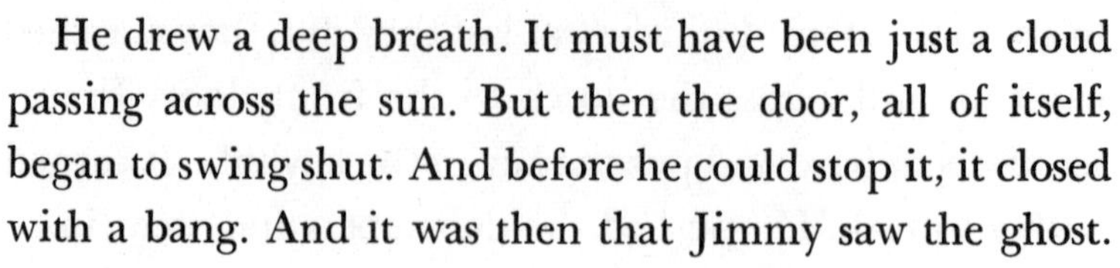

He drew a deep breath. It must have been just a cloud passing across the sun. But then the door, all of itself, began to swing shut. And before he could stop it, it closed with a bang. And it was then that Jimmy saw the ghost.

It behaved just as you would expect a ghost to behave. A tall, dim, white figure, it came gliding slowly down the stairs towards him. Jimmy gave a yell, yanked the door open, and tore down the steps.

He didn't stop until he was well down the road. Then he had to get his breath. He sat down on a log. "Boy!" he said. "I've seen a ghost! Golly, was that awful!" Then, after a minute, he thought, "What was so awful about it? He was trying to scare me, like that smart aleck who was always jumping out from behind things. Pretty silly business for a grown-up ghost to be doing."

It always makes you mad when someone deliberately tries to scare you. And Jimmy began to get angry. And pretty soon he got up and started back. "I must get that key, anyway," he thought, for he had left it in the door.

This time he approached very quietly. He thought he'd just lock the door and go home. But as he tiptoed up the steps and reached out cautiously for the key, he heard a faint sound. He drew back and peeked around the side of the door.

The ghost was going back upstairs, but he wasn't gliding now. He was doing a sort of dance. Every other step he would bend double and shake with laughter. His thin

cackle was the sound Jimmy had heard. Evidently he was enjoying the joke he had played.

A Timid Ghost

That made Jimmy madder than ever. He yelled "Boo!" at the top of his lungs. The ghost gave a thin shriek and leaped two feet in the air. Then he collapsed on the stairs.

As soon as Jimmy saw he could scare the ghost even worse than the ghost could scare him, he wasn't afraid any more. The ghost was hanging on to the banisters and panting. "Oh, my goodness!" he gasped. "Oh, my gracious! Boy, you can't do that to me!"

"I did it, didn't I?" said Jimmy. "Now we're even."

"Nothing of the kind," said the ghost crossly. "Ghosts are supposed to scare people. People aren't supposed to scare ghosts." He glided down and sat on the bottom step. "But look here, boy. This could be pretty serious for me if people got to know about it."

"You mean you don't want me to tell anybody about it?" Jimmy asked.

"Suppose we make a deal," the ghost said. "You keep still about this, and in return I'll—well, let's see. How would you like to know how to vanish?"

"Oh, that would be swell!" Jimmy exclaimed. "But—can you vanish?"

"Sure," said the ghost, and he did. All at once he just wasn't there. Jimmy was alone in the hall.

But the ghost's voice went right on. "It would be pretty handy, wouldn't it?" he said persuasively. "If your aunt called you to do something—well, she wouldn't be able to find you."

"I don't mind helping Aunt Mary," Jimmy said.

"H'm. High-minded, eh?" said the ghost. "Well, then—"

"I wish you'd please reappear," Jimmy interrupted. "It makes me feel funny to talk to somebody who isn't there."

"Sorry, I forgot," said the ghost. There he was again, sitting on the bottom step. Jimmy could see the step, dimly, right through him. "Good trick, eh? Well, maybe I could teach you to go through keyholes. Like this." He floated over to the door and went right through the keyhole, the

way water goes down the drain. Then he came back the same way.

"That's useful, too," he said. "Getting into locked rooms and so on. You can go anywhere the wind can."

"No," said Jimmy. "There's only one thing you can do to get me to promise not to tell about scaring you. Go live somewhere else. There's Miller's, up the road. Nobody lives there any more."

"That old shack!" said the ghost, with a nasty laugh. "Doors and windows half off, roof leaky—no thanks! Peace and quiet, that's really what a ghost wants out of life."

"Well, I don't think it's very fair," Jimmy said, "for you to live in a house that doesn't belong to you and keep my aunt from renting it."

"Pooh!" said the ghost. "I'm not stopping her from renting it. I don't take up any room. It's not my fault if people get scared and leave."

"It certainly is!" Jimmy said angrily. "You don't play fair. I'm going to tell everybody how I scared you."

"Oh, you mustn't do that!" The ghost seemed quite disturbed and he vanished and reappeared rapidly several times. "If that got out, every ghost in the country would be in terrible trouble."

So they argued about it. The ghost said if Jimmy wanted money he could learn to vanish. Then he could join a circus and get a big salary. Jimmy said he didn't want to be in a circus. He wanted to go to college and learn to be a doctor. He was very firm. And the ghost began to cry. "But this is my *home,* boy," he said. "Thirty years I've lived here. Now you want to throw me out into the cold world! And for what? A little money! That's pretty heartless." And he sobbed, trying to make Jimmy feel cruel.

Jimmy didn't feel cruel at all. But he didn't really think it would do much good for him to tell anybody that he had scared the ghost. How could he prove it? So after a minute he said, "Well, all right. You teach me to vanish and I won't tell." They settled it that way.

Jimmy didn't say anything to his aunt. But every Saturday he went to the haunted house for his vanishing lesson. It is really quite easy when you know how. In a couple of weeks he could flicker. In six weeks the ghost gave him an examination and he got a B plus, which is very good for a human. So he thanked the ghost and shook hands with him and said, "Well, good-by now. You'll hear from me."

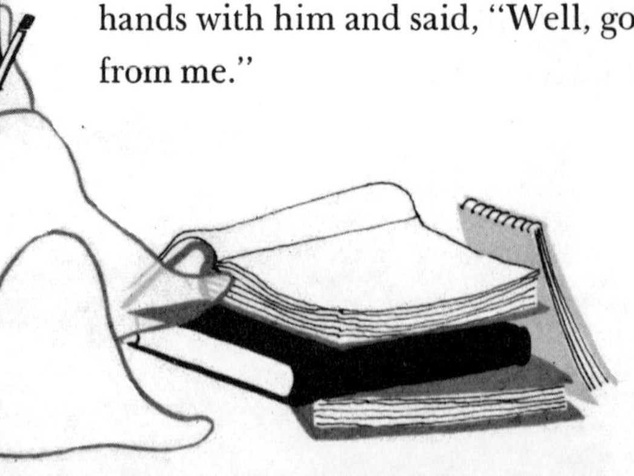

"What do you mean by that?" said the ghost suspiciously. But Jimmy just laughed and ran off home.

Jimmy Plans a Campaign

That night at supper, Jimmy's aunt said, "Well, what have you been doing today?"

"I've been learning to vanish."

His aunt smiled and said, "That must be fun."

"Honestly," said Jimmy. "The ghost up at grandfather's taught me."

"I don't think that's very funny," said his aunt. "And will you please not—why, where are you?" she demanded, for he had vanished.

"Here, Aunt Mary," he said as he reappeared.

"Merciful heavens!" she exclaimed. She rubbed her eyes hard. Then she looked at him again.

Well, it took a lot of explaining and he had to do it twice more before he could persuade her that he really could vanish. But at last she calmed down and they had a long talk. Jimmy kept his word and didn't tell her that he had scared the ghost, but he said he had a plan. At last she agreed to help him.

So, the next day, she went up to the old house and started to work. She opened the windows and swept and dusted and aired the bedding, and made as much noise as possible. This disturbed the ghost. Pretty soon he came floating into the room where she was sweeping. She was scared all right. She gave a yell and threw the broom at

him. As the broom went right through him and he came nearer, waving his arms and groaning, she shrank back.

And Jimmy, who had been standing there invisible all the time, suddenly appeared and jumped at the ghost with a "Boo!" And the ghost fell over in a dead faint.

As soon as Jimmy's aunt saw that, she wasn't frightened any more. She found some smelling salts and held them under the ghost's nose, and when he came to she tried to help him into a chair. Of course, she couldn't help him much because her hands went right through him. But at last he sat up and said reproachfully to Jimmy, "You broke your word!"

"I promised not to tell about scaring you," said the boy.

"But I didn't promise that I wouldn't scare you again."

And his aunt said, "You really are a ghost, aren't you? I thought you were just stories people made up. Well, excuse me, but I must get on with my work." And she began sweeping harder than ever.

The ghost put his hands to his head. "All this noise," he said. "Couldn't you work more quietly, ma'am?"

"Whose house is this, anyway?" she demanded. "If you don't like it, why don't you move out?"

The ghost sneezed violently several times. "Excuse me," he said. "You're raising so much dust. Where's that boy?" he asked suddenly. For Jimmy had vanished again.

"I'm sure I don't know," she replied. "Probably getting ready to scare you again."

"You ought to have better control of him," said the ghost severely. "If he was my boy, I'd take a hairbrush to him."

"You have my permission," she said. She reached right through the ghost and pulled the chair cushion out from under him and began banging the dust out of it. "What's more," she went on, as he got up and glided wearily to another chair, "Jimmy and I are going to sleep here nights from now on. I don't think it would be very smart of you to try any tricks."

"Ha, ha," said the ghost nastily. "He who laughs last—"

"Ha, ha, yourself," said Jimmy's voice from close behind him. "And that's me laughing last."

The ghost muttered and vanished.

Jimmy's aunt put cotton in her ears and slept that night in the best bedroom with the light lit. The ghost screamed for a while down in the cellar. Nothing happened, so he came upstairs. He thought he would appear to her as two glaring, fiery eyes, which was one of his best tricks. But first he wanted to be sure where Jimmy was. He hunted all over the house, and though he was invisible himself, he got more and more nervous. He kept imagining that at any moment Jimmy might jump out at him. Finally, he got so jittery that he went back to the cellar and hid in the coal bin all night.

The following days were just as bad for the ghost. Several times he tried to scare Jimmy's aunt while she was working, but she didn't scare worth a cent. Twice, Jimmy managed to sneak up on him and appear suddenly with a loud yell, frightening him dreadfully. He was, I suppose, rather timid even for a ghost. He began to look quite worn out. He had several arguments with Jimmy's aunt, in which he wept and appealed to her sympathy. But she was firm. There was the abandoned Miller farm two miles up the road. Why didn't he move there?

When the house was all in apple-pie order, Jimmy's aunt went down to the village to see a Mr. and Mrs. Whistler, who were living at the hotel because they couldn't find a house to move into. She told them about the old house, but they said, "No thank you. We've heard about that house. It's haunted. I'll bet," they said, *"you* wouldn't dare spend a night there."

She told them that she had spent the last week there, but they evidently didn't believe her. So she said, "You know my nephew, Jimmy. He's twelve years old. I am so sure that the house is not haunted that I will let Jimmy stay there with you every night until you are sure everything is all right."

"Ha!" said Mr. Whistler. "The boy won't do it."

They sent for Jimmy. "Why, I've spent the last week there," he said. "Sure, I'd just as soon."

A Ghost Goes West

So the Whistlers moved in. Jimmy stayed there for a week, but he saw nothing of the ghost. And then one day one of the boys in his grade told him that somebody had seen a ghost up at the Miller farm. So Jimmy knew the ghost had taken his aunt's advice.

A day or two later, he walked up to the Miller farm. There was no front door and he walked right in. There was some groaning and thumping upstairs, and then after a minute the ghost came floating down.

"Oh, it's you!" he said. "Goodness sakes, boy, can't you leave me in peace?"

Jimmy said he'd just come up to see how the ghost was getting along.

"Getting along fine," said the ghost. "From my point of view, it's a very desirable property. Peaceful. Quiet. Nobody playing silly tricks."

"Well," said Jimmy, "I won't bother you if you don't bother the Whistlers. But if you come back there—"

"Don't worry," said the ghost.

So, with the rent money, Jimmy and his aunt had a much easier life. They went to the movies sometimes twice a week. Jimmy had all new clothes, and on Thanksgiving, for the first time in his life, Jimmy had a turkey.

Once a week, he would go up to the Miller farm to see the ghost. They got to be very good friends. The ghost even came down to the Thanksgiving dinner, though of course he couldn't eat much. He taught Jimmy several more tricks. The best one was how to glare with fiery eyes, which was useful later on when Jimmy became a doctor and had to look down people's throats to see if their tonsils ought to come out.

The ghost was really a pretty good fellow as ghosts go, and Jimmy's aunt got quite fond of him. When the real winter weather began, she even used to worry about him, because of course there was no heat in the Miller place. And when he accepted their invitation for Christmas dinner, she knitted him some red woolen slippers. He was so pleased that he broke down and cried. And that made Jimmy's aunt so happy, *she* broke down and cried.

Jimmy didn't cry, but he said, "Aunt Mary, don't you think it would be nice if the ghost came down and lived with us this winter?"

"I would feel very much better about him if he did," she said.

So he stayed with them that winter, and then he just stayed on. It must have been a peaceful place, for the last I heard he was still there.

Well-Loved Tales

In dreams, I sometimes make my way
To the Limpopo, green and gray;
Or aim the arrow, speed it well,
With great, heroic William Tell;
Drink in the tales told at the feast
Of Sinbad in the gorgeous East;
And look with hopeful eyes upon
Each duckling that may be a swan.

—Dorothy Hall

Master of All Masters

Joseph Jacobs

A girl once went to the fair to hire herself for a servant. At last, a funny-looking old gentleman engaged her, and took her home to his house. When she got there, he told her that he had something to teach her. In his house, he said, he had his own names for things.

He said to her, "What will you call me?"

"Master or mister, or whatever you please, sir," said she.

He said, "You must call me 'master of all masters.' And what would you call this?"—pointing to his bed.

"Bed or couch, or whatever you please, sir."

"No, that's my 'barnacle.' And what do you call these?" said he, pointing to his pantaloons.

"Breeches or trousers, or whatever you please, sir."

"You must call them 'squibs and crackers.' And what would you call her?"—pointing to the cat.

"Cat or kit, or whatever you please, sir."

"You must call her 'white-faced simminy.' And this now," showing the fire, "what would you call this?"

"Fire or flame, or whatever you please, sir."

"You must call it 'hot cockalorum,' and what this?" he went on, pointing to the water.

"Water or wet, or whatever you please, sir."

"No, 'pondalorum' is its name. And what do you call this?" asked he as he pointed to the house.

"House or cottage, or whatever you please, sir."

"You must call it 'high topper mountain.' "

That very night the servant woke her master up in a fright and said, "Master of all masters, get out of your barnacle and put on your squibs and crackers. For white-faced simminy has got a spark of hot cockalorum on its tail, and unless you get some pondalorum high topper mountain will be all on hot cockalorum." . . . That's all.

The Apple and the Arrow

Mary and Conrad Buff

William Tell, a legendary hero of Switzerland, stands for the heroic spirit of the Swiss people when they were trying to gain their independence from Austria. The best-known tale about the bowman, Tell, concerns his refusal to obey the hated ruler, Gessler. It happened on a day when Tell and his son were visiting the town of Altdorf, where Gessler dwelt.

Suddenly Walter saw his father and grandfather step from the inn. His father looked very angry. Even his grandfather did not smile as Walter ran up to him.

"Come at once, Son. Let us go," was all that his father commanded. "Quiet, and stay beside me."

"Yes," Walter answered, wondering. They passed through a narrow way between high houses, and soon the village square or market place opened before them. Walter saw the familiar fountain in the center of the square. Today, two soldiers were beside it. One of them, an old fellow, was munching an apple. The other soldier was whittling on a stick with his dagger. They looked tired and bored.

Then Walter noticed a long pole set in the ground beside the fountain. He had never seen that before. On the top of the pole fluttered a velvet hat with a feather in it, such a hat as Walter had often seen well-born people wear. He wondered why no children were playing in the fountain. No dogs lay in the dirt. No women came with water jars to draw water and to gossip together.

Then a well-dressed villager passed by. Nodding to the soldiers, he doffed his cap and bent his knee to the hat on the pole. Walter felt his father's hand stiffen against his and heard him mutter, "Traitor!" Nevertheless, William Tell walked proudly on, looking neither to left nor to right. His great bow hung from one sturdy shoulder. Past the fountain he strode, Walter clinging to him—past the soldiers, past the pole with the hat on it.

Suddenly Walter heard the younger soldier shout, "Stop, you! Are you blind? See that hat on the pole, *you.* That's the hat of Austria, the ducal hat."

But father and son walked on. The soldier munching the apple grabbed his spear and ran toward the mountaineer, yelling, "You knave, you blockhead, *bow to that hat!* Or I'll run you through with this." And he lowered his great spear.

Only then did William Tell stop and eye the soldier fearlessly, as he shouted, "Hat, what hat? I see no hat. I have business with the tanner."

Tell's words made the soldiers very angry. One yelled, "Bend your knee to that hat, or we will crush your skull like a nutshell." The mountaineer took one more step forward without answering, but the shouting of the soldiers had brought many townsfolk into the square. His way was blocked by soldiers with spears and by shouting people.

Suddenly a guard blew on his bugle. Other soldiers streamed in from narrow streets. Walter and his father were surrounded by a mob of people.

"Now for the last time, bow before the ducal hat of Austria. Show you are a loyal subject of our governor, Gessler."

The name of Gessler seemed to make Tell even more rebellious. He laughed in defiance, as Walter clung to him and shrank back before the lowered spears of the soldiers. "Why should I bow before a silly hat? A hat is

not a lord. A hat is a thing of rags and feathers. It is nothing to bow down before."

The mountaineer held his son's hand tightly and shouted these words so that all heard. The townsfolk milled around the soldiers in a crowd.

"Poor wretch, he'll get it now," said a villager.

"Take your hands from me," commanded Tell as a guard seized him. "I have done no wrong. Take your hands from me, I say. I will not bow before that hat. We've had enough of bowing and scraping in the land of Uri."

As they heard his scornful words, three angry soldiers grabbed the mountain man and pinned back his arms. "We dare you to insult the governor thus, you herder of goats!"

A bugle sounded again. The crowd scattered as mounted knights galloped into the market place. "Out of our way, you dumb brutes," they commanded. Walter, almost in tears now, glanced up at them. And then he saw Gessler—the governor, Gessler. It could be no one else. The knight wore fine clothing, and rode a beautiful and spirited horse. But Walter thought he looked evil.

"What goes on here?" demanded Gessler. The crowd was now deathly quiet. "Oh, so it is you, William Tell, the man of the mountains," jeered Gessler. "In trouble again, I see. For what do my men now hold you?"

The mountaineer did not reply. Then a soldier spoke. "He will not bow before the ducal hat, my lord."

"Oh, so he is too fine to bow before the hat of Albrecht of Austria, is he? Bow, I say, or we will run you through," warned Gessler.

Tell was silent. He did not move. He looked at Gessler and his eyes were like black coals, burning with hatred. Walter trembled. But he held himself proudly, like his father.

"So you have no tongue now. Speak, or you will be sorry."

Now the great bowman was really angry. He bellowed like a mad bull. The people could hear every word that he said.

"I will not bend my knee before a hat. I will bow only to those more truly noble than I. Men of gentle birth. Wise men. The man of God and the good Lord Himself. I will

not bend my knee before a hat of rags and feathers. A hat is nothing to worship. A well-born man, a noble, is something else."

How angry Gessler became at these words! He knew that Tell was jeering at his common birth.

Trial by Arrow

"Oh, so you are too fine to bow!" snarled Gessler, white with fury. Then a sly look came into his face. He glanced sharply down at Walter, who was clinging to his father.

"Who is that cowardly brat that clings to you, Tell?" asked Gessler.

"My son, Walter. My elder son," replied Tell, looking at Walter and pressing his hand.

"I see you have your crossbow with you, Tell. I have heard it said you are a good bowman, the best in the canton of Uri. Is that true?"

"I know not if it is true," answered Tell, modestly. "There are many good bowmen in Uri. But some folk have said so."

A townsman shouted, "Tell is the best of us all."

"Let us see, then, how good a bowman you really are. Take that cowardly boy, men, and place him against yonder linden tree. Put an apple on his head. Tell, if you can shoot the apple from your son's head, you shall go free. But . . . if any harm comes to the boy or you miss the apple, you will *both* die."

A gasp of horror went through the crowd. Walter heard people cry, "The wretch . . . knave . . ." But Gessler only smiled an evil smile as he pointed to the linden tree.

At last Tell found his voice. "You cannot ask this of me, Governor," he pleaded. "This is an innocent lad, and my first-born. He has done no harm to anyone."

"But I thought you were such a great bowman, Tell," retorted the governor. "I see you are just a bag of wind with the face of a lion and the heart of a deer."

At these stinging words, Walter shouted in his high boyish voice, so that all heard—"Father, I am not afraid. I will stand at the linden tree and they need not bind me. I will stand as still as a rock. You will hit the apple, Father. I am not afraid."

"See the boy, Gessler, how he believes in his father!" shouted a woman. The soldiers seized Walter and bound him to the linden tree, while mothers clutched their children to them, as if to protect them from the evil governor.

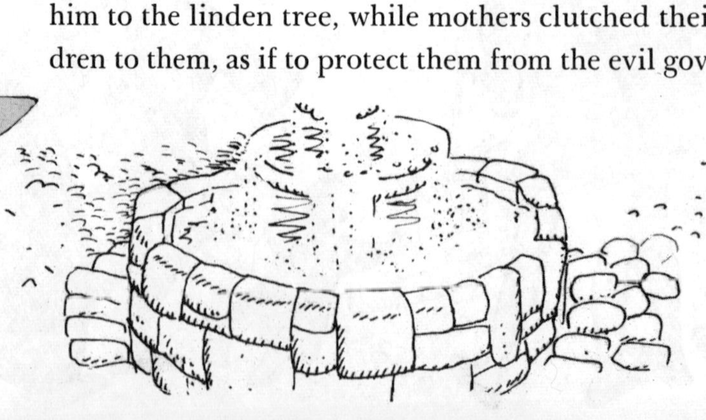

As a guard placed a large apple upon Walter's head, the boy could see the townsfolk brandishing sticks and threatening the knights. A boy threw a stone and a horse reared.

Gessler commanded, "Quiet, you people of Altdorf. Quiet." Then, looking down at Tell, he said, "This is your chance to show how skilled you are with the bow."

The soldiers freed the mountaineer. He slipped his bow from his shoulder and raised it. He placed the arrow. Then, standing quietly, he looked at his son tied to the linden tree.

William Tell knelt on the ground. He raised his heavy crossbow to his shoulder and took careful aim. Not a sound was heard. Even the dogs stopped barking; the horses prancing. The mountaineer was about to press the trigger

of his crossbow, when the sight of his slender son, standing so quietly at the linden tree, overcame him. He put down his bow and groaning aloud, he pleaded, "My lord, have pity. Spare my son. I cannot do this to an innocent, trusting child. I cannot. Have pity on us, my lord."

"Ho, ho, so it is 'my lord' at last, Tell. So you cannot. The strong mountain man cannot. He trembles like the leaves of that linden tree yonder. See how pale he is! What a rare sight! Tell is trembling like a frightened woman. Where is your boasted skill with the bow, Tell?"

As Walter heard these bitter words, he shouted above the noise, "Shoot, Father. God is watching over us."

Walter's voice seemed to bring back his father's courage. Tell took another arrow from his quiver and slipped it into his girdle. Then he quickly raised the heavy crossbow to his shoulder as muscles rippled on his brown arms. He sighted the apple on his son's head. He pulled back the drawstring. Many of the townsfolk were now on their knees praying. Gessler eyed every move that Tell made.

Then, with a grim smile and almost without warning, the great bowman quickly and surely squeezed the trigger of his bow. The arrow sped like a ray of light. Walter suddenly felt the apple on his head split, tremble, and fall to the ground. The nose of the arrow buried itself in the gnarled trunk of the old tree.

A great sigh of relief, like a sudden wind, passed over the heads of the people. Then all at once sounds of jubilation burst forth. "The mighty Tell! Tell, the hero!" the

people shouted, surging toward the bowman as he stood there, his dark body glistening with sweat. The people tried to reach him to carry him on their shoulders, but soldiers barred their way.

When guards unbound Walter, he picked up the two halves of the apple and ran toward his father, crying, "See, Father, you cut the apple in two pieces!"

A soldier blew on a horn to quiet the crowd. In the silence, Walter heard Gessler shout, "You *are* a bowman, Tell, as men say. But what of that second arrow you thrust so quickly into your girdle?"

William Tell, feeling suddenly weak and tired, just looked at the governor. He said, "That is the custom of bowmen."

"Answer me, Tell. I want the truth. Why was the second arrow hidden in your girdle?"

William Tell was a simple, trustful man of the mountains. So he replied honestly, "Had I killed my son, Governor, this arrow would have found your heart."

The Elephant's Child

Rudyard Kipling

In the High and Far-Off Times the Elephant, O Best Beloved, had no trunk. He had only a blackish, bulgy nose, as big as a boot, that he could wriggle about from side to side; but he couldn't pick up things with it. But there was one Elephant—a new Elephant—an Elephant's Child—who was full of 'satiable curtiosity, and that means he asked ever so many questions. *And* he lived in Africa, and he filled all Africa with his 'satiable curtiosities.

He asked his tall aunt, the Ostrich, why her tail-feathers grew just so, and his tall aunt the Ostrich spanked him with her hard, hard claw. He asked his tall uncle, the Giraffe, what made his skin spotty, and his tall uncle, the Giraffe, spanked him with his hard, hard hoof. And still he was full of 'satiable curtiosity! He asked his broad aunt, the Hippopotamus, why her eyes were red and his

broad aunt, the Hippopotamus, spanked him with her broad, broad hoof; and he asked his hairy uncle, the Baboon, why melons tasted just so, and his hairy uncle, the Baboon, spanked him with his hairy, hairy paw. And *still* he was full of 'satiable curtiosity! He asked questions about everything that he saw, or heard, or felt, or smelt, or touched, and all his uncles and his aunts spanked him. And still he was full of 'satiable curtiosity!

One fine morning in the middle of the Precession of the Equinoxes this 'satiable Elephant's Child asked a new fine question that he had never asked before. He asked, "What does the Crocodile have for dinner?" Then everybody said, "Hush!" in a loud and dretful tone, and they spanked him immediately and directly, without stopping, for a long time.

By and by, when that was finished, he came upon Kolo-

kolo Bird sitting in the middle of a wait-a-bit thorn-bush, and he said, "My father has spanked me, and my mother has spanked me; all my aunts and uncles have spanked me for my 'satiable curtiosity; and *still* I want to know what the Crocodile has for dinner!"

Then Kolokolo Bird said, with a mournful cry, "Go to the banks of the great gray-green, greasy Limpopo River, all set about with fever-trees, and find out."

That very next morning, when there was nothing left of the Equinoxes, because the Precession had preceded according to precedent, this 'satiable Elephant's Child took a hundred pounds of bananas (the little short red kind), and a hundred pounds of sugar-cane (the long purple kind), and seventeen melons (the greeny-crackly kind), and said to all his dear families, "Good-bye. I am going to the great gray-green, greasy Limpopo River, all set about with fever-trees, to find out what the Crocodile has for dinner." And they all spanked him once more for luck, though he asked them most politely to stop.

Then he went away, a little warm, but not at all astonished, eating melons, and throwing the rind about, because he could not pick it up.

He went from Graham's Town to Kimberley, and from Kimberley to Khama's Country, and from Khama's Country he went east by north, eating melons all the time, till at last he came to the banks of the great gray-green, greasy Limpopo River, all set about with fever-trees, precisely as Kolokolo Bird had said.

Now you must know and understand, O Best Beloved, that till that very week, and day, and hour, and minute, this 'satiable Elephant's Child had never seen a Crocodile, and did not know what one was like. It was all his 'satiable curtiosity.

The first thing that he found was a Bi-Colored-Python-Rock-Snake curled round a rock.

" 'Scuse me," said the Elephant's Child most politely, "but have you seen such a thing as a Crocodile in these promiscuous parts?"

"Have I seen a Crocodile?" said the Bi-Colored-Python-Rock-Snake, in a voice of dretful scorn. "What will you ask me next?"

" 'Scuse me," said the Elephant's Child, "but could you kindly tell me what he has for dinner?"

Then the Bi-Colored-Python-Rock-Snake uncoiled himself very quickly from the rock, and spanked the Elephant's Child with his scalesome, flailsome tail.

"That is odd," said the Elephant's Child, "because my father and my mother, and my uncle and my aunt, not to mention my other aunt, the Hippopotamus, and my other uncle, the Baboon, have all spanked me for my 'satiable curtiosity—and I suppose this is the same thing."

So he said good-bye very politely to the Bi-Colored-Python-Rock-Snake, and helped to coil him up on the rock again, and went on, a little warm, but not at all astonished, eating melons, and throwing the rind about, because he could not pick it up, till he trod on what he thought was

a log of wood at the very edge of the great gray-green, greasy Limpopo River, all set about with fever-trees.

Really the Crocodile

But it was really the Crocodile, O Best Beloved, and the Crocodile winked one eye—like this!

" 'Scuse me," said the Elephant's Child most politely, "but do you happen to have seen a Crocodile in these promiscuous parts?"

Then the Crocodile winked the other eye, and lifted half his tail out of the mud; and the Elephant's Child stepped back most politely, because he did not wish to be spanked again.

"Come hither, Little One," said the Crocodile. "Why do you ask such things?"

" 'Scuse me," said the Elephant's Child most politely, "but my father has spanked me, my mother has spanked me, not to mention my tall aunt, the Ostrich, and my tall uncle, the Giraffe, who can kick ever so hard, as well as my broad aunt, the Hippopotamus, and my hairy uncle, the Baboon, *and* including the Bi-Colored-Python-Rock-Snake, with the scalesome, flailsome tail, just up the bank, who spanks harder than any of them; and *so,* if it's quite all the same to you, I don't want to be spanked any more."

"Come hither, Little One," said the Crocodile, "for I am the Crocodile," and he wept crocodile-tears to show it was quite true.

Then the Elephant's Child grew all breathless, and panted, and kneeled down on the bank and said, "You are the very person I have been looking for all these long days. Will you please tell me what you have for dinner?"

"Come hither, Little One," said the Crocodile, "and I'll whisper."

Then the Elephant's Child put his head down close to the Crocodile's musky, tusky mouth, and the Crocodile caught him by his little nose, which up to that very week, day, hour, and minute, had been no bigger than a boot, though much more useful.

"I think," said the Crocodile—and he said it between his teeth, like this—"I think today I will begin with Elephant's Child!"

At this, O Best Beloved, the Elephant's Child was much annoyed, and he said, speaking through his nose, like this, "Led go! You are hurtig be!"

Then the Bi-Colored-Python-Rock-Snake scuffled down from the bank and said, "My young friend, if you do not now, immediately and instantly, pull as hard as ever you can, it is my opinion that your acquaintance in the large-pattern leather ulster" (and by this he meant the Crocodile) "will jerk you into yonder limpid stream before you can say Jack Robinson."

This is the way Bi-Colored-Python-Rock-Snakes always talk.

Then the Elephant's Child sat back on his little haunches, and pulled, and pulled, and pulled, and his nose began to stretch. And the Crocodile floundered into the water, making it all creamy with great sweeps of his tail, and *he* pulled, and pulled, and pulled.

And the Elephant's Child's nose kept on stretching; and the Elephant's Child spread all his little four legs and pulled, and pulled, and pulled, and his nose kept on stretching; and the Crocodile threshed his tail like an oar, and *he* pulled, and pulled, and pulled, and at each pull the Elephant's Child's nose grew longer and longer—and it hurt him hijjus!

Then the Elephant's Child felt his legs slipping, and he said through his nose, which was now nearly five feet long, "This is too butch for be!"

Then the Bi-Colored-Python-Rock-Snake came down from the bank, and knotted himself in a double-clove-hitch around the Elephant's Child's hind legs, and said, "Rash and inexperienced traveler, we will now seriously devote ourselves to a little high tension, because if we do not, it is my impression that yonder self-propelling man-of-war with the armor-plated upper deck" (and by this, O Best Beloved, he meant the Crocodile) "will permanently vitiate your future career."

This is the way all Bi-Colored-Python-Rock-Snakes always talk.

So he pulled, and the Elephant's Child pulled, and the Crocodile pulled; but the Elephant's Child and the Bi-

Colored-Python-Rock-Snake pulled hardest; and at last the Crocodile let go of the Elephant's Child's nose with a plop that you could hear all up and down the Limpopo.

Then the Elephant's Child sat down most hard and sudden; but first he was careful to say "Thank you" to the Bi-Colored-Python-Rock-Snake; and next he was kind to his poor pulled nose, and wrapped it all up in cool banana leaves, and hung it in the great gray-green, greasy Limpopo to cool.

"What are you doing that for?" said the Bi-Colored-Python-Rock-Snake.

" 'Scuse me," said the Elephant's Child, "but my nose is badly out of shape, and I am waiting for it to shrink."

"Then you will have to wait a long time," said the Bi-Colored-Python-Rock-Snake. "Some people do not know what is good for them."

How To Use a Trunk

The Elephant's Child sat there for three days waiting for his nose to shrink. But it never grew any shorter, and, besides, it made him squint. For, O Best Beloved, you will see and understand that the Crocodile had pulled it out into a really truly trunk, same as all Elephants have today.

At the end of the third day a fly came and stung him on the shoulder, and before he knew what he was doing he lifted up his trunk and hit that fly dead with the end of it.

" 'Vantage number one!" said the Bi-Colored-Python-Rock-Snake. "You couldn't have done that with a mere-smear nose. Try and eat a little now."

Before he thought what he was doing, the Elephant's Child put out his trunk and plucked a large bundle of grass, dusted it clean against his fore-legs, and stuffed it into his own mouth.

" 'Vantage number two!" said the Bi-Colored-Python-Rock-Snake. "You couldn't have done that with a mere-smear nose. Don't you think the sun is very hot here?"

"It is," said the Elephant's Child, and before he thought what he was doing he schlooped up a schloop of mud from the banks of the great gray-green, greasy Limpopo, and slapped it on his head, where it made a cool schloopy-sloshy mud-cap all trickly behind the ears.

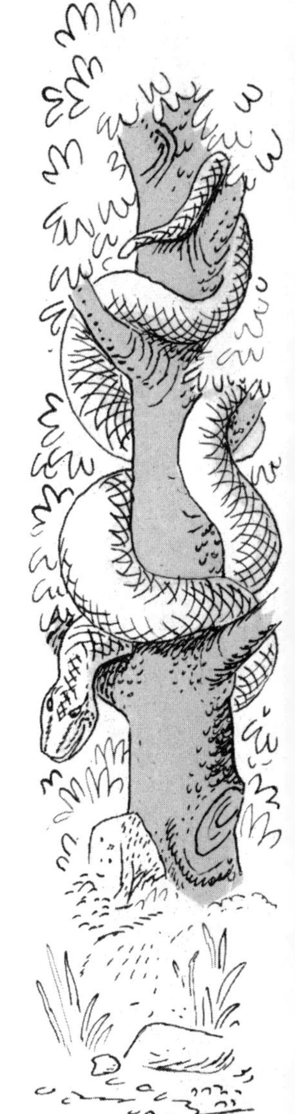

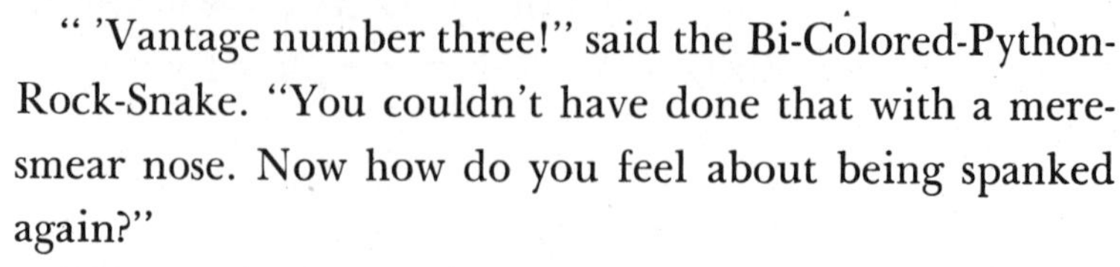

" 'Vantage number three!" said the Bi-Colored-Python-Rock-Snake. "You couldn't have done that with a mere-smear nose. Now how do you feel about being spanked again?"

" 'Scuse me," said the Elephant's Child, "but I should not like it at all."

"How would you like to spank somebody?" said the Bi-Colored-Python-Rock-Snake.

"I should like it very much indeed," said the Elephant's Child.

"Well," said the Bi-Colored-Python-Rock-Snake, "you will find that new nose of yours very useful to spank people with."

"Thank you," said the Elephant's Child, "I'll remember that; and now I think I'll go home to all my dear families and try."

So the Elephant's Child went home across Africa frisking and whisking his trunk. When he wanted fruit to eat, he pulled fruit down from a tree, instead of waiting for it to fall as he used to do. When he wanted grass, he plucked grass up from the ground, instead of going down on his knees as he used to do. When the flies bit him, he broke off the branch of a tree and used it as a fly-whisk; and he made himself a new, cool, slushy-squashy mud-cap whenever the sun was hot. When he felt lonely walking through Africa, he sang to himself down his trunk, and the noise was louder than several brass bands. He went especially out of his way to find a broad Hippopotamus (she was no relation of his), and he spanked her very hard, to make sure that the Bi-Colored-Python-Rock-Snake had spoken the truth about his new trunk. The rest of the time he picked up the melon rinds that he had dropped on his way to the Limpopo—for he was a Tidy Pachyderm.

One dark evening he came back to all his dear families, and he coiled up his trunk and said, "How do you do?" They were very glad to see him, and immediately said, "Come here and be spanked for your 'satiable curtiosity."

"Pooh," said the Elephant's Child. "I don't think you peoples know anything about spanking; but *I* do, and I'll show you."

Then he uncurled his trunk and knocked two of his dear brothers head over heels.

"O Bananas!" said they. "Where did you learn that trick, and what have you done to your nose?"

"I got a new one from the Crocodile on the banks of the great gray-green, greasy Limpopo River," said the Elephant's Child. "I asked him what he had for dinner, and he gave me this to keep."

"It looks very ugly," said his hairy uncle, the Baboon.

"It does," said the Elephant's Child. "But it's very useful," and he picked up his hairy uncle, the Baboon, by one hairy leg, and hove him into a hornet's nest.

Then that bad Elephant's Child spanked all his dear families for a long time, till they were very warm and greatly astonished. He pulled out his tall Ostrich aunt's tail-feathers; and he caught his tall uncle, the Giraffe, by the hind-leg, and dragged him through a thorn-bush; and he shouted at his broad aunt, the Hippopotamus, and blew bubbles into her ear when she was sleeping in the water after meals; but he never let any one touch Kolokolo Bird.

At last, things grew so exciting that his dear families went off one by one in a hurry to the banks of the great gray-green, greasy Limpopo River, all set about with fever-trees, to borrow new noses from the Crocodile. When they came back nobody spanked anybody any more; and ever since that day, O Best Beloved, all the Elephants you will ever see, besides all those that you won't, have trunks precisely like the trunk of the 'satiable Elephant's Child.

The Second Voyage of Sinbad the Sailor

From *The Arabian Nights*

In the magnificent city of Bagdad, in the reign of the good Caliph Haroun-al-Raschid, there lived a merchant named Sinbad. He had sailed around the world, men said. He was enormously wealthy. Every day at his house a banquet was spread, with the finest and most tempting foods, and beautiful and agreeable music.

Now one day, a poor porter named Hinbad happened to be in that part of town where Sinbad had his home. Only wealthy people lived in that quarter, and Hinbad's errands seldom took him there. So when he saw the fine large mansion of Sinbad, and smelled the rich food and heard the music, he had to ask a servant at the gate whose house it was.

"Do you live in Bagdad and not know the house of Sinbad, the famous sailor?" asked the servant, amazed.

"Oh, Heaven!" exclaimed the porter. "Everyone has indeed heard of Sinbad. And why should it be that every day I must labor, and scarcely get bread for myself and my family, while Sinbad may spend vast riches and lead a life of pleasure?"

Picking up his load, Hinbad was about to go on. Just then a servant came out of the house and stopped him.

"My master, Sinbad, desires to speak with you," said the servant. And he led the poor porter through the courtyard into the dining hall. There sat a large company of people richly dressed, around a table loaded with good things. And at the head of the table was Sinbad himself, in a gorgeous turban, with many servants behind him.

Hinbad trembled with fear and embarrassment. But Sinbad called Hinbad to a seat at his own right hand. He himself served Hinbad with the best and most delicious food. And after the meal was over, Sinbad asked Hinbad his name and business.

"My lord, I am a poor porter. They call me Hinbad."

"And perhaps you would repeat for me the words you spoke in the street a while ago." For Sinbad had happened to overhear Hinbad complaining, through the window, and had sent the servant out to fetch him.

Hinbad was more embarrassed than ever. "My lord," he said, hanging his head, "my weariness made me say what I should not have said. I beg you to pardon me."

"I am not so unjust as to be angry with you," said Sinbad. "But I was just going to relate to this company the story of my second voyage. Stay and hear. Then you can judge for yourself whether my riches were acquired without labor, and whether I deserve the life of ease and pleasure which I now enjoy."

So saying, Sinbad settled himself more comfortably. All the company stopped talking and looked at him, waiting to hear the tale.

"After my first voyage, of which I told you yesterday," Sinbad began, "I planned to spend the rest of my days in Bagdad. But I soon grew weary of doing nothing. So I bought goods for a voyage, and gathered together a company of merchants upon whom I could depend.

"From island to island we sailed, trading with great

profit. One day we landed on an island fair to see, but apparently uninhabited by man or beast. We wandered about, each at his own pleasure, some here and some there. I ate my noon meal, and lay down in the shade to sleep. But when I awoke, alas, the ship was gone! I ran down to the shore. Her sail was just disappearing over the horizon.

"I was ready to die of grief. I tore my beard, threw dust upon my head, and lay down upon the ground in despair. Why had I not been content to stay at home, with the riches already acquired? Now it was too late.

"At length I felt calmer. Girding my robes about me, I climbed to the top of a tall tree to look about. Toward the sea, I could see nothing but sky and water. Looking over the land, however, I could see, far off, something white. Coming down from the tree and gathering up the scraps from my meal into a leather bag, I started off toward it.

"As I came up to the thing after a long while, I thought it was some sort of great white dome. I touched it. The walls were very smooth. I walked around it. But there was no door, no window, nor any other opening. Nor was there any way of climbing up the side.

"It was nearly sunset. All of a sudden the sky was darkened, as if by a thick black cloud. I looked up. There, flying toward me, was a bird of enormous size.

"Suddenly I remembered hearing sailors speak of a marvelous great bird called the roc. Immediately I saw that the white dome must be the creature's egg. I crept close to the egg. Soon one of the bird's legs, as big as the trunk of a tree, was beside me. I tied myself firmly to the leg with my unrolled turban, gave myself into the hands of Heaven, and went to sleep.

The Vale of the Serpents

"The next morning, before it was yet full day, the bird rose from the egg and flew away. She carried me so high I could not see the earth. Then she came down so rapidly that I lost my senses. Presently I found myself on the ground and hastily untied myself. The roc, having taken up an enormous serpent in her bill, flew away.

"I found myself within a fearful and gloomy valley. On all sides, the mountains rose up so high that their tops were in the clouds. Their sides were too steep to climb. There seemed to be no way to escape.

"As I walked about, I found that the floor of the valley

was paved with sharp jagged stones. Looking closer, I discovered that the stones were diamonds, larger and more beautiful than any I had ever seen. But I had no pleasure in walking among the diamonds, since the valley was likely to be my grave.

"Then I became aware that in the valley also were great numbers of enormous serpents, like the serpent the roc had carried away. Now that day had come, they had stolen away to their dens. The smallest of them could easily have swallowed an elephant.

"All that day I wandered sadly about. When night fell, I went into a cave and rolled a stone into the opening. I ate some of the scraps of food in my leather sack, and tried to sleep. But now the serpents had come from their dens. They hissed so fearfully that I could only lie there trembling. When day broke and I could at last come out of the cave, I was so weary that I lay down in the open and at once went to sleep.

"But suddenly I was awakened by a loud noise. Several large pieces of raw meat had been thrown from the cliffs above, and one had fallen very near me.

"I had heard stories before of this valley, and had always thought them to be idle tales. But now I remembered that to get the diamonds, merchants were said to throw down large pieces of meat, to which the diamonds would stick. Eagles living in the mountains would snatch the meat for their young ones. Then the merchants, who had climbed up to the nests, would drive away the eagles with shouts, and take the diamonds from the meat.

"Now I saw how I should be saved. I began to gather the largest diamonds I could find, and put them in the leather sack in which my food had been. Then, tying the sack and the largest piece of meat firmly to me by my girdle, I lay face down and waited.

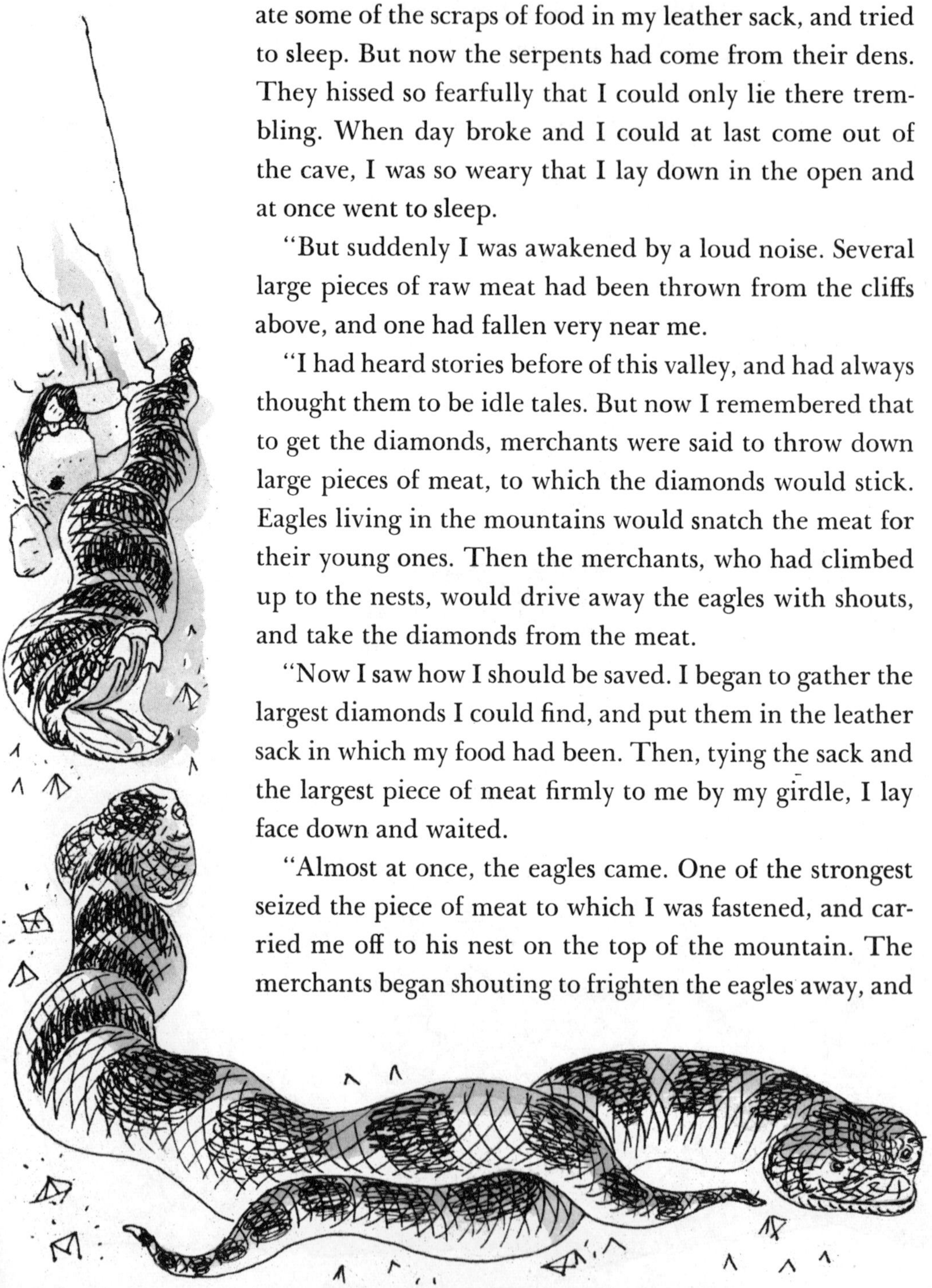

"Almost at once, the eagles came. One of the strongest seized the piece of meat to which I was fastened, and carried me off to his nest on the top of the mountain. The merchants began shouting to frighten the eagles away, and one of the merchants soon came to the nest where I was.

"Seeing me, he was alarmed and angry. 'Why did you come here?' he asked. 'Was it to steal my goods?'

" 'You will not be angry with me when you have heard my story,' I replied calmly. 'I have here enough diamonds for both of us, more than all the other merchants together. They have only the diamonds that stuck to their meat. But I gathered these myself in the bottom of the valley.'

"The other merchants came up, then. They were surprised to see me, but even more surprised when I had told my story.

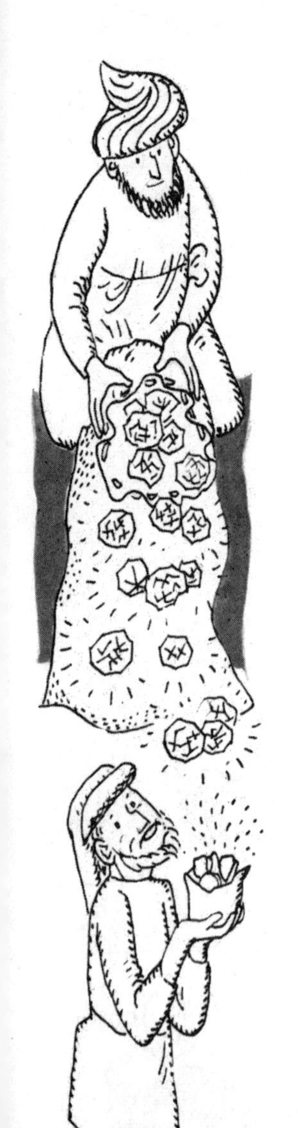

"At their camp, I opened the leather sack and showed them the diamonds I had brought. All the merchants said they had never seen such diamonds before—no, not in all their travels to foreign courts and places. I begged the merchant who had rescued me to take as many of the diamonds for his share as he pleased. However, he would take only one, and that the very smallest. 'This will be enough,' he said, 'to make my fortune for the rest of my days.'

"A day or two later, the merchants being satisfied with their luck, we left that place. We took ship at the first port we reached, and sailed away to the Isle of Roha, where the camphor trees grow. The tree is bored and the camphor juice is collected in a vessel. Then the tree withers and dies.

"On this island I exchanged some of my diamonds for goods to trade, and we went for a time from port to port. At length, enormously wealthy, I again reached Bagdad. Immediately, I gave large presents to the poor, and then lived honorably upon the riches I had acquired with so much risk. I think even you, friend Hinbad, will agree that I have done something to deserve the ease which I now enjoy."

So saying, Sinbad gave the poor porter a hundred pieces of gold. "Come tomorrow, friend Hinbad, and hear the tale of my third voyage," Sinbad invited him. And Hinbad left, scarcely able to believe in his good fortune, and that it was not all a dream.

The Ugly Duckling

Hans Christian Andersen

It was summer. The country was lovely. Golden wheat and green oats ripened in the fields, and the rich green meadows were dotted with haystacks. Beyond the fields and meadows stretched wide woods, hiding deep lakes.

In the bright sunshine stood an old castle, surrounded by a deep moat, and all overgrown with burdock. Down at the moat, the thicket was just as wild as in the deepest woods. And there a duck was sitting on her nest, hatching her young. She was growing weary of it, because it took so long.

But now, one after another, the eggs cracked open. "Peep, peep," said the babies. "Quack, quack," said Mother Duck. The babies all scrambled out from under her, looking in wonder at the green world. Mother let them have a good look, for she knew how good green is for the eyes.

"How large the world is!" said her babies.

"So you think this is the whole world? Let me tell you, the world stretches far and wide," she said. "Why, it goes as far as the other side of the garden and over to the churchyard."

She got up and said, "I hope all the eggs are hatched. Oh, my, the largest egg is still there. I am sick and tired of it." But she sat down again.

"How are you coming along?" asked the old duck who stopped in to visit.

"The last egg is taking so long," said Mother Duck. "It just won't crack. But look at the others. They are the handsomest ducklings I've ever seen."

"I'm sure the egg that won't crack is a turkey egg," said the old duck. "I was fooled just the same way once. Did I have trouble with that brood! They are afraid of the water, you see. I scolded them and pecked them, but no, they wouldn't go into it. Now, let me look. Yes, that certainly *is* a turkey egg. Leave it alone and go teach the others to swim."

"Oh, I think I'll sit here just a little longer."

"Do as you please. I don't care," said the old duck, and she left.

And then the big egg cracked. "Peep, peep," it said, and out came the last child. It was big and ugly.

Mother Duck looked at it and said, "This really is awfully big for a duckling. Can it be a turkey chick? We'll soon find out. It shall go into the water even if I have to push it in myself!"

The next day was perfectly beautiful. Mother Duck came down to the water with all her family. She splashed in first. "Quack, quack," she commanded, and they all followed. They all swam admirably, even the ugly gray one.

"That surely is no turkey chick," said Mother. "Just look how prettily it uses its legs and how straight it holds itself. It *is* my very own child! Now come, children, and I'll show you the world and introduce you in the duck yard. Keep near me so that no one kicks you, and beware of the cat!"

So they came into the duck yard. There was a noise and a din going on, for two families were fighting over an eel's head. But the cat stole it and went off with it.

"That's how things go in the world," said Mother Duck. "Now pull yourselves together and curtsy nicely before that old duck there at the back. She is the most distinguished of us all, being of Spanish ancestry. That's why she is so fat. And if you look closely, you'll see she's wearing a red string around her leg. That's something very beautiful and the highest distinction a duck can get. It means that no one shall overlook her and that all animals, including men, shall know her. Come on, now. And don't turn your toes in! A well-educated duckling turns his toes out in walking, just as his father and mother do. Now, make a bow and say 'Quack.' "

And so they did. But the ducks of the yard looked them over, saying, "Goodness gracious! Do we have to have this brood here too? Look at that ugly one! No, no, we won't have that!" And one of them came right over and bit the ugly duckling's neck.

"Leave him alone," said Mother Duck. "He doesn't harm anybody, does he?"

"But he is so big and strange," said the duck who bit him. "So he must be cuffed about!"

"She really has nice children," said the old duck, "except that one. That one didn't turn out so well."

"He has been too long in the egg, that's why," said the mother. "He may not be handsome, but he's kindhearted. And he swims as well as the rest. And what's more, he's a drake. So his looks don't matter so much."

"Make yourselves at home, now," said the old duck. "And if you happen to find an eel's head, you may bring it to me."

They felt quite at home, except the ugly one who had been hatched last. He was bitten and teased by all the ducks and the hens in the yard.

Things went from bad to worse. Everybody chased the poor duckling wherever he went. Even his sisters and brothers treated him miserably. The ducks would bite him, the hens peck him, and the girl kick him when she came with their feed.

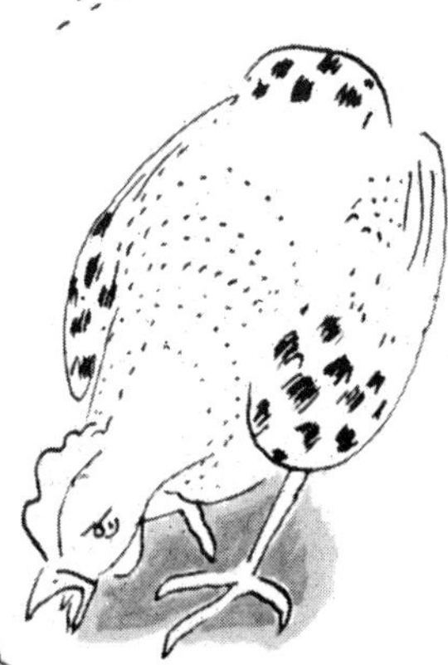

In the Marsh

The duckling couldn't bear it any longer, and ran away. As he flew over the fence, the little birds fluttered out of the bushes in fright.

"It's my ugliness that frightens them," the duckling thought. Closing his eyes, he kept running till he reached the great marsh where the wild ducks lived. There he rested for the night, tired and discouraged.

In the morning, when the wild ducks saw the newcomer, they asked, "What kind of bird are you? You certainly are ugly! But little do we care as long as you don't marry into our tribe."

Poor duckling! He didn't even dream of marriage. All he wanted was to be allowed to lie in the reeds and have a sip of marsh water now and then.

He had been there for a couple of days when two wild geese—or rather, ganders—came by.

"Listen, young fellow," they said, "you are so ugly it even makes us like you. Don't you want to come with us and be a rover?"

Just then, "Bang, bang!" rang out above their heads, and two shots brought down the two ganders. "Bang! Bang! Bang!" Flocks of wild geese flew up from the reeds. A great hunt was on. The bird dogs—the setters—splashed through the marsh, right through the mud and rushes.

The poor duckling trembled with fear. He twisted his head to hide it under his wing, but right at his side appeared a big setter with frightfully glaring eyes and sharp, bright teeth. He looked and sniffed, and "Splash, splash!"—off he went without harming the duckling.

"Thank heaven," sighed the duckling. "I'm so ugly that even the dogs won't bite me." And he lay quite still while the shots whizzed through the reeds.

It was late afternoon before all became quiet again. The poor duckling looked around cautiously and then hurried out of the marsh, across fields and meadows, as fast as his legs would carry him. Out in the open, the wind was very strong. He could hardly struggle along.

Before dusk, he reached a peasant's hut. It was so ramshackle it didn't know which way to fall—and that's why it still stood. The wind grew stronger and stronger. The duckling noticed that the door to the hut was hanging on only one hinge, leaving a crack, through which he quickly slipped into the room.

In the hut lived an old woman with a tomcat and a hen.

The tomcat, called "Sonny," could arch his back and purr —and even make his fur spark, though for that stunt you had to stroke his fur the wrong way. The hen had very short legs, so she was called "Chicky Shortleg." She was an excellent egg-layer, and the woman loved her as she would have loved a child.

The Cat and the Hen

In the morning, they all noticed the little stranger right away. The cat began to purr and the hen to cluck.

"Well, what do we have here?" said the old woman, looking at the duckling. But her eyesight was not good. She thought it was a fat duck who had got lost. "I call that good fortune," she said. "Now I can have duck eggs, too— if it doesn't turn out to be a drake. We'll have to try it."

The cat was master, and the hen mistress, in this house.

"Can you lay eggs?" the hen asked the duckling.

"No."

And the cat asked, "Can you arch your back and purr, and send sparks off your fur?"

"No."

Timidly the poor duckling sat down in a corner. He began to think of the fresh air and the sunshine outdoors, and such a longing came over him to be in the water that he could not help telling the hen about it.

'Are you crazy?" she said. "That's what comes of doing nothing. Lay eggs or purr, and then this whim of yours will quickly pass."

"But it's so wonderful to swim!" said the duckling. "So wonderful when you dive to the bottom and feel the water closing over your head!"

"What a pleasure *that* must be!" said the hen. "You must be completely out of your mind. Ask the cat, who is

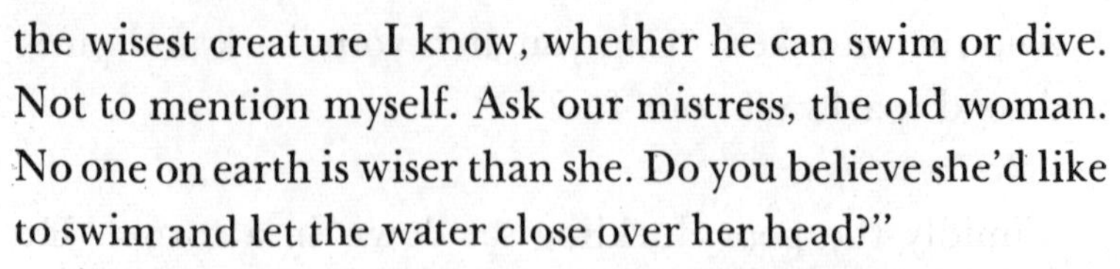

the wisest creature I know, whether he can swim or dive. Not to mention myself. Ask our mistress, the old woman. No one on earth is wiser than she. Do you believe she'd like to swim and let the water close over her head?"

"You don't understand," said the duckling.

"My, if we don't, who would?" said the hen. "You don't mean to say you are wiser than the cat and the old woman—not to mention myself? Stop boasting, youngster, and thank heaven you are here. And now see to it that you lay eggs. And learn to purr and make sparks."

"I think I'd prefer to go out into the world," said the duckling.

"All right, then—go!" said the hen.

And the duckling went. He swam and he dived marvelously. But no animal paid any attention to him because he was so ugly.

Autumn came, and the leaves in the woods turned yellow and brown. The dark clouds threatened hail and snow. On the fence sat the crow, cawing of cold. The poor duckling had a hard time of it.

One evening, as the sun was setting in splendor and glory, there came a flock of fine large birds out of the bushes. Such beautiful birds the duckling had never seen before.

They were swans, dazzling white, with long, graceful necks. They spread their wide, wide wings and flew off with a strange cry. They soared up so high that the duckling felt strangely moved.

He swam round and round in the water, craning his neck after them, himself uttering so strange and eerie a cry that it made him shiver with fright.

When he could no longer see the swans, he dived deep down to the bottom, and he was still all upset when he came up again. He loved these birds as he had never loved anything before. He did not envy them their beauty—how could he ever think of even wishing such beauty for himself? He, poor ugly creature, would have been happy had the ducks let him stay among them!

The winter was so cold, so bitter cold, that the duckling had to swim round and round to keep the water from freezing over. But night after night, the hole where he swam got smaller and smaller. The duckling couldn't let his legs rest for a moment, lest the water freeze entirely. But at last his strength failed him, and he lay quite still, frozen fast in the ice.

In the early hours of the morning, a peasant came by. Seeing what had happened, he went out, cracked the ice with his wooden shoe, lifted the duckling out, and carried him home to his wife. And they brought him back to life.

The children would have liked to play with him, but the duckling thought they wanted to harm him. Afraid, he flew away from them and right into the milk pail, spilling the milk all over the floor. The woman threw her hands up in despair. The duckling flew into the kneading trough—right into the butter—and then into the meal tub. He certainly looked awful now! The woman shrieked and chased him with the fire tongs. Laughing and screaming, the children ran into one another trying to catch him. By luck, he found the door open. He fluttered out and lay underneath the bushes in the fresh snow, almost unconscious.

It would be too distressing to tell of all the misery he had to suffer through that winter. He lay in the reeds of the marsh when the sun began to shine warm again. The larks sang a joyful greeting to the glorious spring.

All at once, the duckling lifted his wings. Their beat was much more powerful than ever before. They carried him aloft, and before he knew it he landed in a big garden. There the apple trees were in full bloom, and the sweet

scent of lilacs filled the air. It was beautiful here—fresh and lovely along the winding channels of a little stream, overhung by clusters of blossoming lilac.

And then, out from the thicket right in front of him, appeared three lovely white swans. Their wing feathers rustled as they moved over the water. The duckling recognized these marvelous birds, and a strange sadness took hold of him.

"I shall fly over to these royal birds," he said to himself. "They will surely peck me to death for having dared to show myself before them in all my ugliness. But that won't matter. Better to end amongst them than to be nipped by the ducks, pecked by the hens, and kicked by the hen-yard girl."

And he flew over to them. The swans saw him coming and with rustling wings sailed toward him.

"Kill me!" said the poor duckling, and he bent his head down to the water to wait.

But what did he see in the clear mirror below? His own reflection! No longer did it show a dark, ugly, and unlovely bird. No, he himself was a swan!

The big swans pressed close to him, stroking him with their bills. Children came into the garden to throw the swans bread and seeds. And the smallest child cried, "Look, a new one is here!"

The others echoed, "Yes, yes, a new one has come!" They clapped their hands and danced merrily and ran to tell their father and mother, "The new one is the loveliest of all!" And the old swans bowed before him.

He felt bashful and happy, but not a bit haughty. With his feathers rustling and his graceful neck up high, he said from the bottom of his heart, "Of so much happiness I dared not even dream, when I was the ugly duckling!"

Other Lands and Other Faces

Other lands and other faces,
Other names and ways,
Strange processions in strange places,
Other nights and days . . .

Same imagining and dreaming–
Courage, friends, and fame–
Hearts, no matter what the seeming,
Everywhere the same.

–Dorothy Hall

The Shark

Armstrong Sperry

Mafatu was a boy of the South Seas. His mother had been drowned in a storm when he was a baby, and he was deathly afraid of the ocean. Cowards were not liked among Mafatu's people. All the boys made fun of him. Finally, in desperation, he sailed in a boat to a far, uninhabited island, to prove to himself his own courage. His only companion was his dog, Uri.

One morning, far down the beach, Mafatu came upon a sheltered cove. His heart gave a leap of joy; for there, white-gleaming in the sun, was all that remained of the skeleton of a whale. It might not have meant very much to you or to me. But to Mafatu it meant knives and fishhooks, bone for darts and spears, a shoulder blade for an ax. It was a real treasure. The boy leaped up and down in his excitement. "Uri!" he shouted. "We're rich! Come—help me drag these bones home!"

His hands seemed all thumbs in his eagerness. He tied as many bones as he could manage into two bundles. One bundle he shouldered himself. The other, Uri dragged behind him. And thus they returned to the camp, weary but filled with happiness. Even the dog seemed to have some understanding of what this discovery meant, or he was at least excited by his master's high spirits. He leaped about like a puppy, yapping until he was hoarse.

Now began the long task of grinding the knife and the ax. Hour after long hour, squatting before a slab of rock, Mafatu worked and worked, until his hands were raw and blistered and the sweat ran down into his eyes. The knife came first, since that was the most needful. Its blade was ten inches long, its handle a knob of bone. It was sharp enough to cut the fronds of coconut trees, to slice off the end of a green nut. *Ai,* but it was a wonderful knife! All Mafatu's skill went into it. It would be a fine weapon as well, the boy thought grimly, as he ground it down to a sharp point. Some sea robber had been breaking into his bamboo trap, and he was going to find out who the thief was! Was it that old hammerhead shark who was always swimming around, just as if he owned the lagoon?

Fishing with a line took too long when you were working against time. Mafatu could not afford to have his trap robbed. Twice it had been broken into, the bamboos crushed, and the fish inside it eaten. It was the work either of a shark or of an octopus. That was certain. No other fish was strong enough to snap the bamboo.

Mafatu's mouth was set in a grim line as he worked away on his knife. That old hammerhead—of course he *was* the thief! Mafatu had come to know him; for every day when the boy went out with his trap, that shark, larger than all the others, was circling around watchfully. The other sharks seemed to treat the hammerhead with great respect.

Hunger alone drove Mafatu out to the reef to set his trap. He knew that if he was to keep his strength to do all that lay ahead, he must have fish to add to the fruit he ate. But often, as he set his trap far out by the reef, the hammerhead would approach and roll over slightly in passing. The cold gleam of its eye filled Mafatu with fear and anger.

"Wait, you!" the boy threatened darkly, shaking his fist at the *ma'o* (shark). "Wait until I have my knife! You will not be so brave then, Ma'o. You will run away when you see it flash."

The Test of Courage

But the morning that the knife was finished, Mafatu did not feel so brave as he would have liked. He hoped he would never see the hammerhead again. Paddling out to the reef, he glanced down from time to time at the long-bladed knife where it hung about his neck by a cord. It wasn't, after all, such a dangerous weapon. It was only a knife made by a boy from a whale's rib.

Uri sat on the edge of the raft, sniffing at the wind. Mafatu always took his dog along, for Uri howled loudly if he were left behind. And Mafatu had come to depend on the companionship of the little yellow dog. The boy talked with the animal as if he were another person, consulting with him, playing when there was time for play. They were very close, these two.

This morning, as they approached the spot where the fish trap was, Mafatu saw the polished dorsal of the hated hammerhead circling slowly in the water. It was like a black triangle, making a little furrow in the water as it passed.

"Aiá, Ma'o!" the boy shouted roughly, trying to get up his courage. "I have my knife today, see! Coward who robs traps—catch your own fish!"

The hammerhead approached the raft without haste; it rolled over slightly, and its jaws seemed to curve in a grin. Uri ran to the edge of the raft, barking furiously. The hair on the dog's neck stood up stiffly. The shark, paying no attention, moved away. Then, with a whip of its powerful tail, it rushed at the bamboo fish trap and grabbed it in its jaws. Mafatu was struck dumb. The hammerhead shook the trap as a dog might shake a rat. The boy watched, fascinated, unable to make a move. He saw the muscles work in the fish's neck as the great tail beat the water to foam. The trap splintered into bits, while the fish within escaped, only to vanish into the shark's mouth. Mafatu was filled with helpless anger. The hours he had spent making that trap! But all he could do was shout threats at his enemy.

Uri was running from one side of the raft to the other, furious with excitement. A large wave sheeted across the reef. At that second, the dog's shift in weight tipped the raft dangerously. With a yelp, Uri slid off into the water. Mafatu sprang to catch him, but he was too late.

Instantly, the hammerhead whipped about. The wave pushed the raft away. Uri, swimming frantically, tried to regain it. There was desperation in the brown eyes so faithful and true. Mafatu leaned forward. His dog, his companion. . . . The hammerhead was moving in slowly. A mighty anger stormed through the boy. He gripped his knife. Then he was over the side in a clean-curving dive.

Mafatu came up under his enemy. The shark whirled

about. Its rough hide scraped the flesh from the boy's shoulder. In that instant, Mafatu stabbed. Deep, deep into the white belly. There was a terrific shock. Water lashed to foam. Gasping, the boy fought for life and air.

It seemed that he would never reach the surface. *Aué,* his lungs would burst! . . . At last his head broke water. Putting his face to the surface, he saw the great shark turn over, fathoms deep. Blood flowed from the wound in its belly. Instantly, gray shapes rushed in—other sharks, tearing the wounded hammerhead to pieces.

Uri—where was he? Mafatu saw his dog then. Uri was trying to pull himself up on the raft. Mafatu caught him by the neck and dragged him up to safety. Then he pulled his dog to him and hugged him close, talking to him foolishly. Uri yelped for joy and licked his master's cheek.

It wasn't until Mafatu reached shore that he realized what he had done. He had killed the *ma'o* with his own hand, with nothing but a bone knife. He could never have done it for himself. Fear would have robbed his arm of all strength. He had done it for Uri, his dog. And he felt suddenly humble, with gratitude.

At the Grandfather's House

Johanna Spyri

Heidi's parents had died when she was a baby, and her Aunt Dete had taken care of her. Now Dete wished to take a new job. So she brought Heidi to her grandfather's. The old man had lived by himself for many years high on one of the beautiful Swiss mountains, and was thought to be fierce and stern. The people in the village below were worried about how he would treat the little girl.

After Dete had gone, the grandfather sat down again on the bench. He smoked his pipe without saying a word, his eyes fixed on the ground. In the meantime, Heidi was busily looking about her. She saw the goats' shed near the hut and peeped into it. It was empty.

Continuing to explore, she came to the fir trees back of the hut. The wind was blowing hard. It roared through

the branches, high up in the very tops. Heidi stood still and listened. When the sound died down a little, she went on around to the other side of the hut, coming back to her grandfather. She stood directly in front of him, put her hands behind her back, and gazed steadily at him. Her grandfather looked up.

"What do you want?" he asked.

"I want to see what you have inside the house," said Heidi.

"Come along, then!" And the grandfather got up and started to go in.

"Bring your bundle of clothes," he said, as he reached the door.

"I won't need them any more," replied Heidi.

The old man turned around and looked sharply at the child. Her black eyes sparkled as she waited to see what was inside the house.

"She's not stupid," he said, half to himself. Then he asked aloud, "Why won't you need them any more?"

"Because I want to go like the goats, with their thin, quick legs."

"So you shall. But bring the things anyhow," commanded the grandfather. "We can put them away in the cupboard."

Heidi obeyed. The old man opened the door, and Heidi followed him into a fairly large room. The room made up the whole hut. It was furnished with a table and a chair, and—in one corner—the grandfather's bed. In another corner was the fireplace, where a large kettle hung. On the other side of the room, in the wall, was a door. The grandfather opened the door, and there was the cupboard. His clothes hung there. On one shelf were his shirts, stockings, and linen. On another shelf stood plates, cups, and glasses. On the highest shelf of all were a loaf of bread, smoked meat, and cheese. As soon as he opened the door, Heidi hurried in with her bundle and pushed it as far back as she could, so that it would be hard to find again.

Then, looking carefully around the room, she asked, "Where shall I sleep, Grandfather?"

"Wherever you like," was the answer.

The idea suited Heidi. She examined every corner of the room. Beside her grandfather's bed was a little ladder, leading up to the hayloft. Heidi climbed the ladder. The loft was full of fresh, fragrant hay. Through a round window, she could see far down into the valley below.

A Room With a View

"I'll sleep up here," Heidi called down. "It is beautiful! Just come and see how beautiful it is here, Grandfather."

"Oh, I know all about it," the grandfather's voice said from below.

"I'm going to make me a bed," called out the child again, trotting busily to and fro in the loft. "But you must come up and bring a sheet. The bed needs a sheet for me to sleep on."

"Well, well," said the grandfather, below. He went to the cupboard and rummaged about. Finally, he pulled out from under his shirts a coarse, heavy piece of cloth,

which might do for a sheet. When he came up the ladder, he found that Heidi had indeed made a very neat little bed. It was turned so that she could look from it straight out through the round open window.

"That is very nicely made," said the grandfather. "Next comes the sheet—but wait a moment—". And he took up a big armful of hay and made the bed twice as thick, so that Heidi would not feel the hard floor through it. "There, now put the sheet on."

Heidi quickly took hold of the cloth, but she could not lift it because it was so heavy. However, this was all to the good, because the sharp ends of hay could not prick through its firm weave. So Heidi and the grandfather together spread the sheet over the hay, and Heidi tucked the ends under. It looked quite nice, and Heidi stood gazing at it thoughtfully.

"We have forgotten something, Grandfather," she said.

"And what is that?" he asked.

"The cover. When we go to bed, we creep in between the sheet and the cover."

"Is that so? But what if I haven't any cover?"

"Oh, that's all right," said Heidi, soothingly. "We can use more hay for a cover." She was about to run to the piled hay again, but her grandfather stopped her.

"Wait a minute," he said, and disappeared down the ladder to his own bed. When he came back, he laid a large, heavy linen sack on the floor.

"Isn't that better than hay?" he asked her. Heidi pulled

at the sack as hard as ever she could, trying to straighten it out. Her grandfather helped, and when it, too, was spread out on the bed, everything looked very neat and comfortable. Heidi regarded it admiringly. "That is a splendid cover," she said, "and the whole bed is beautiful! I wish it were night so that I could sleep in it!"

"I think we might have some lunch first," said the grandfather. "What do you say?"

Heidi had been so excited about the bed that she had forgotten everything else. But now that food was mentioned, she was suddenly very hungry. She had eaten nothing but a piece of bread and a cup of weak coffee early in the morning, and on top of that she had made a long journey. "Yes, I think so, too."

"Well, since we think the same thing, let us go down," said the old man. Following Heidi down the ladder, he went to the fireplace, pushed aside the large kettle, and pulled forward the little one that hung on the chain. He sat down on a three-legged wooden stool and built a fire. After a while, the kettle began to boil, and the old man toasted a large piece of cheese over the fire, at the end of a long iron fork. He turned the cheese this way and that, until it was golden yellow on all sides.

Heidi watched him. Suddenly an idea came to her. She jumped up and ran to the cupboard, and made several trips between it and the table. When the grandfather brought the toasted cheese, the table was already neatly laid with the round loaf of bread, two plates, and two knives. Heidi's bright eyes had seen everything in the cupboard. She knew what would be needed for the meal.

"That is right, to see for yourself what has to be done," said the grandfather. He laid the cheese on the bread and put the teapot on the table. "But there is still something else."

Heidi ran back to the cupboard. She spied a small bowl, and behind it, two glasses. She came back at once with the bowl and the glasses, and put them on the table also.

"Very good. But where are you going to sit?"

The grandfather himself was sitting in the only chair. Heidi flew like an arrow to the fireplace, carried back the little three-legged stool, and sat down on it.

"Well, you have a chair, sure enough. But it is rather a low one," the grandfather said.

He got up, filled the little bowl with milk, put it on his own chair, and pushed it up to the three-legged stool, so that Heidi had a table in front of her. He put a large slice of bread and a piece of the golden cheese on the chair and said, "Now eat!"

Sitting on the corner of the table, the grandfather began his own dinner. Heidi picked up the bowl of milk and drank and drank without stopping. Drawing a long breath, she finally set the bowl down.

"Do you like the milk?" her grandfather asked.

"I never tasted such good milk before," Heidi told him.

"Then you must have some more." The grandfather filled the bowl again and put it in front of the child. Contentedly, she began to eat her bread, spreading it with the toasted cheese, soft as butter. It tasted very good, with frequent drinks of milk.

When lunch was over, the grandfather went out to clean the goat-shed. Heidi watched while he swept it with a broom and laid down fresh straw for the animals to sleep

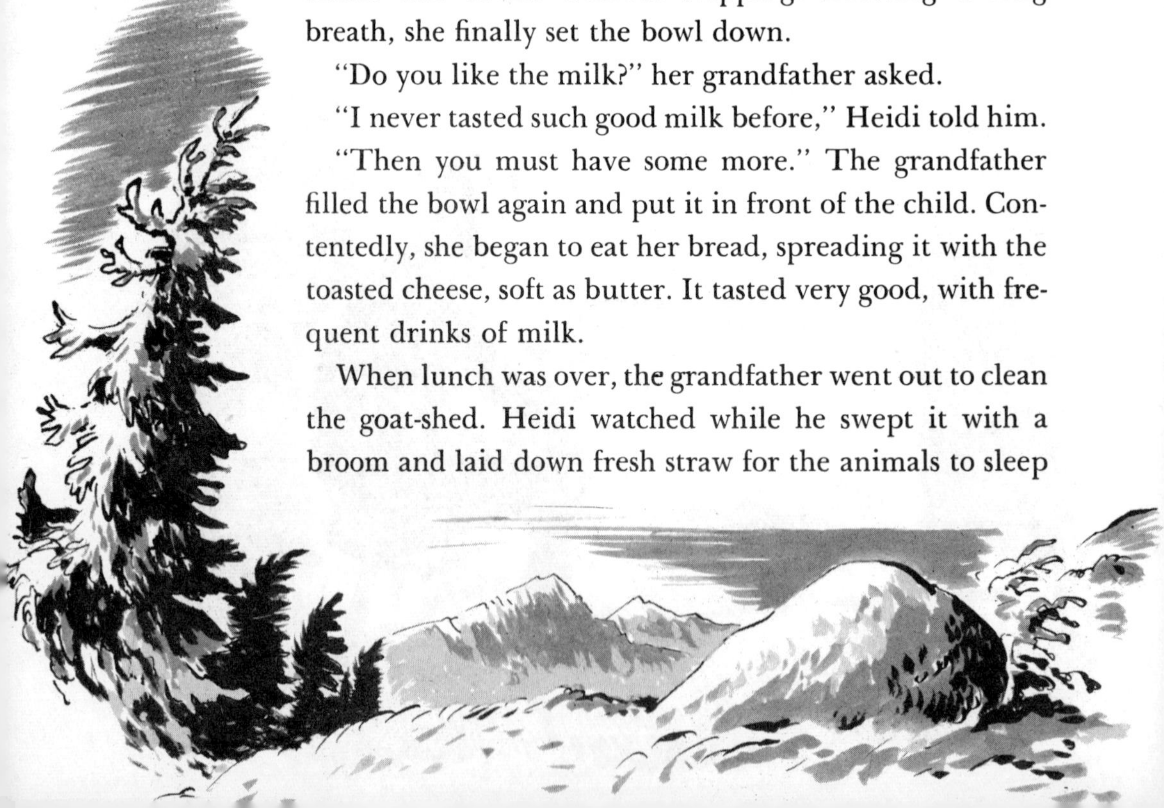

on. Then he went into his little workshop. He found some round sticks, cut and shaped a board, bored some holes in it, and put the round sticks into them. Suddenly it was a stool like the fireplace one, only higher. Heidi was speechless with amazement.

"Do you know what this is, Heidi?" asked the grandfather.

"It is a stool for me. I know, because it is so high. You made it so quickly!" said the child. She was still deeply astonished.

"She understands what she sees. Her eyes are in the right place," the grandfather said to himself. He went around the hut, driving a nail here and there, and mending wherever it was needed. Heidi followed him step by step, and watched every move.

The Goats

Evening was coming on. The sound was getting deeper in the old fir trees, for a strong wind had come up and was

blowing through their thick tops. To Heidi, the sound was so beautiful that she skipped and jumped in delight, under the trees. The grandfather stood in the doorway, watching the child.

Suddenly, there came a shrill whistle. Down from the mountain above, the goats came leaping, with Peter in the midst of them. With a shout of joy, Heidi rushed in among them.

At the hut, two pretty, slender goats—one white, the other brown—left the others and went over to the grandfather. They licked his hands, in which he had brought some salt to welcome them, as he did every evening. Peter went on with his flock. Heidi gently petted first one goat and then the other. She was wild with delight.

"Are they ours, Grandfather? Are they both ours? Will they sleep in the shed? Will they stay with us for always?" asked Heidi.

When the goats had finished their salt, the old man said, "Go and bring out your little bowl and the bread."

Heidi obeyed and came back at once. Milking one of the goats, the grandfather filled the bowl and cut off a piece of bread. "Now eat your supper and go on up to bed!" he said. "Your Aunt Dete left another bundle for you. Your nightgown and other night things are in it. You will find it in the cupboard. I must take care of the goats now, so sleep well!"

"Good-night, Grandfather! Good-night—oh, what are their names, Grandfather? What are they called?" cried the child, running after the old man and the goats as they went into the shed.

"The white one is called Little Swan. The brown one is Little Bear," answered the grandfather.

"Good-night, Little Swan! Good-night, Little Bear!" Heidi sang after them. Sitting down on the bench, she ate the bread and drank the milk. But the wind was so strong that it almost blew her off the seat. So she hurried to finish; then went in and climbed the ladder to her bed. At once she fell asleep, and slept as soundly and as well as if she had been in the bed of some royal princess.

Simba's First Lion

Alden G. Stevens

Perhaps no place in all the world is as beautiful as Eastern Africa on a dewy morning just after the season of long rains. Mountain tops, forest, and veldt are gilded with the gentle light of the newly risen sun. Millions of flowers make masses of color on the face of the plains. Across the vast sweep of the land, zebra, wildebeeste, kongoni, and gazelle numbering beyond the power to count feed into the wind. High against the blue heavens, vultures wheel on motionless wings.

On such a morning, at the hour of letting out of cattle, which the People of the Mountain call mafunglulia, the boy, Simba, stood near the gate of his mud-walled village. In his hand was a herding spear about five feet long. About him were other boys of his own age equipped with similar spears, and all of them were shouting at the cattle which were crowding through the narrow opening in the wall. Occasionally, when some wayward cow would turn back into the village itself, a boy would leap nimbly after her, prodding her sides and yelling shrilly until she would turn, with tossing horns and rolling eyes, to join the others on their way through the gate.

Dust rose in clouds. Simba's slender body was covered with it, for it clung to the sweat that rolled down his ribs and stomach. For a week now, Simba had been given the responsibility of herding his father's animals and he was a proud boy. He was no longer a child. With his hunting bow he could bring down a monkey from the tallest tree, driving the bamboo arrow clean through its body. Across hard ground he could track game by way of signs only visible to eyes trained to observe the tiniest details—a scratch on the rocks, a turned pebble, a blade of grass out of place.

Watching the skilled warriors of his village, listening to the tales of his people, trained by his father, he had learned the things that would get him food and save his life from savage men and beasts. Simba was only eleven years old and his body was the slender, slim-muscled one of a boy, but he knew and could do many things, for his school had been the hard one of his race, savage and primitive, where death and hunger and suffering are the price of mistakes.

Finally, with low bellowings, the cattle were all out in the open and the boys started cutting out their own particular cows from the herd. Wielding his spear, Simba darted into and about the beasts, avoiding horns and trampling hoofs, pricking the stubborn ones, joining his shrill voice with the cries of his companions until magically, it seemed, some sort of order began to appear and the cattle were sorted into family groups. Driven by their herders, they began moving off toward the hills, where they would graze all day on the grassy hillsides. When the shadows of the mountains began to creep across the plains, they would be driven back again to spend the night where no lions or leopards could kill them, safe within the thorn and mud walls of the village.

Most of the boys joined their herds and moved away in groups of three or four, but Simba started out alone. Some of the boys called to him to ask that he go with them, but he shook his head. He liked to play the games of the village with his friends and did not ordinarily like to be alone, but this guarding of his father's property was a new and great responsibility. With the other boys, he might not watch closely, and a hyena could kill and carry off one of the young calves. So he preferred to be alone, and run no risk of being distracted from his herding.

Simba strode along behind his herd of some twenty humpbacked cows with three or four calves straggling at their mothers' heels. His objective was a long slope of sun-drenched hill a mile distant. From the top of it, he would be able to look to the northward over the plains and forest strips while his cattle grazed in plain view before him.

Arriving finally at the hilltop, Simba sat down in the grass, his spear beside him. The animals fed close to him in little groups down the slope. Sitting there, Simba looked out over the land he knew so well. Partridges and spur fowl rustled through the grass about him. The plains were dotted with feeding game. At his left a few yards, tiny gazelles frisked on the hillside. Far below, at the edge of the jungle that bordered a stream, five giraffes moved along the forest background where great clumps of poinsettia flamed against the green foliage. Simba's eyes took in all this in a sweeping glance, coming to rest again on the feeding cattle.

With special fondness he watched Madoadoa and her calf. The little creature was only five days old. Madoadoa, the spotted one, was his mother. She was a large cow who seemed to have no sense of her maternal duties. When the calf tried to get at her udder to feed, she would swing away from him, never ceasing her own greedy eating of the grass. The little fellow stumbled constantly after her, bawling forlornly for the dinner that was rightfully his.

Simba became quite annoyed with Madoadoa keeping her calf hungry and unfed. Simba loved this calf with passionate devotion. It was his very own, presented to him by his father the day it was born. But there was nothing he could do at the moment to change Madoadoa's treatment of her calf, so he lay back on his elbow and gave himself to the thoughts and daydreams of his age.

Perhaps it was because his stomach was full, or it may have been the warmth of the sun and the coolness of the grass roots, but at any rate, the truth must be told that Simba's head nodded and he fell asleep. He had not slept long when he woke suddenly, guiltily aware that he had failed in his duty. Suddenly he knew, with the instinct of all wild creatures, that he was not alone. He rose in a single movement and whirled, the slender spear in his hand. There immediately behind him stood old Kibeti, the dwarfed cripple. His black eyes were fixed on the boy sternly. Ashamed, Simba relaxed and sat down. Kibeti limped forward and sat beside him.

"So," grunted the old man, "you sleep while guarding your father's cattle. Had I been a lion I could have killed you, and killed that worthless Madoadoa as well."

"I am sorry, Kibeti," replied Simba. "I deserve to be eaten by a lion. Perhaps you will tell my father and he will beat me." Simba eyed Kibeti anxiously.

"This time I will not tell him. You are young, and it is hard for the young to sit still through the long day. To sit without sleeping, here in the sun, is hard for a boy. Perhaps I should say that it is hard for a child, because a boy who would be a hunter and a warrior would not sleep."

Simba's cheeks burned with shame, for he knew that there was justice in what Kibeti said. "Oh, Kibeti," he said miserably, "I know well that what you say is true. If the warrior who sits by the village night fire should sleep, then enemies could enter our village and spear us on our mats where we slumber. I will never sleep again when I should stay awake."

"That is well and as it should be," said Kibeti. "Listen now, and I will tell you of my younger days when I was a great warrior. Do not look surprised, Simba, for indeed I was truly a hunter and a fighter in our tribe. Of course the time was before the elephant caught me and made me a twisted man. He broke me with his trunk and left me as you see me now." The old man's face cracked into a bitter smile as he looked down at his withered legs, which lay like black, broken sticks on the grass before him.

Simba smiled gravely. "We have many warriors and hunters, Kibeti. If the elephant had not broken you with his trunk, then you would not be a teller of stories. There would be no man, then, to tell us magic things. Who but Kibeti can sit with the chiefs in council and tell them of the things that happened long ago, so they may know how to deal with these same matters when they happen now?"

Kibeti nodded. "Perhaps you are right, my boy. As you say, I am indeed a great man, but sometimes I think it is better to be young and strong than it is to be great." The old man's eyes burned in the wrinkled mask of his face as he thought of the days of his youth.

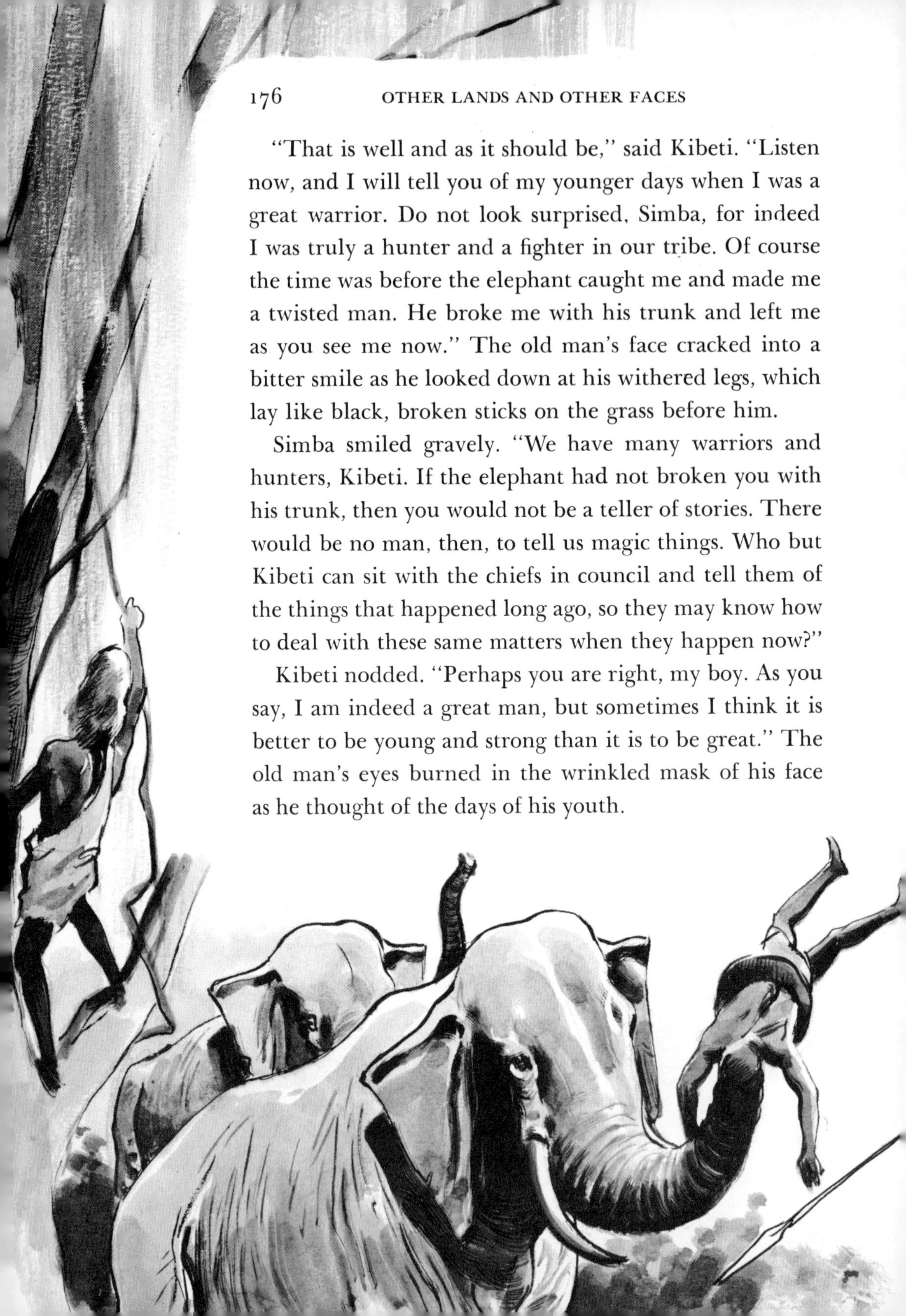

Presently he spoke again. "I had almost forgotten that I wanted to speak to you of duty," he continued. "There is the duty of the hunter who follows a long hard trail so that his people may have meat. There is the duty of women, who cook and raise our crops, of the warrior who watches and sleeps not, lest enemies come in the night. And then, too, there is the duty of the boy who watches his father's cattle. He must not sleep. Now me, I never sleep except at night. Old though I am, I never—I never—" Kibeti's voice trailed away and stopped. His head nodded and the aged body relaxed. He slept.

It was very still there on the sunny hilltop. Simba smiled and looked at Kibeti as he slept, noting the gray color of his wrinkled skin where ashes from his fire clung to it. He looked at the twisted, broken body, and thought of the elephant who had made Kibeti a cripple. Simba made a note in his mind to ask for the story some day soon. It was one that Kibeti had never told. The moments passed until Simba thought of the cattle. He looked up at them.

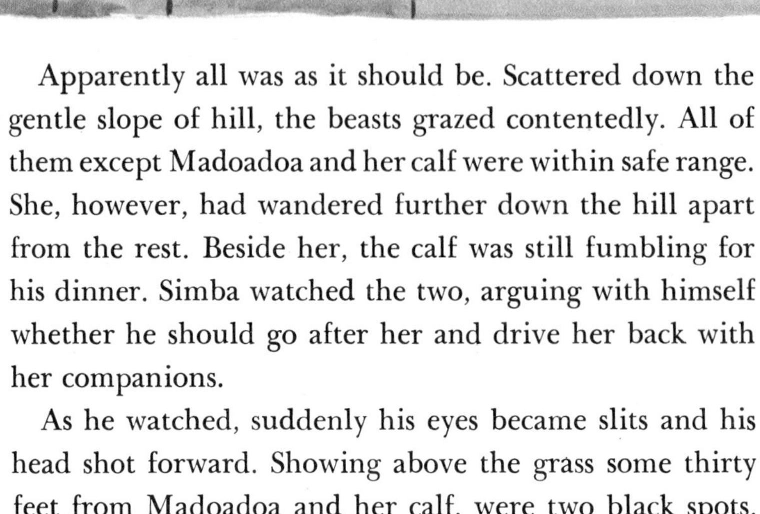

Apparently all was as it should be. Scattered down the gentle slope of hill, the beasts grazed contentedly. All of them except Madoadoa and her calf were within safe range. She, however, had wandered further down the hill apart from the rest. Beside her, the calf was still fumbling for his dinner. Simba watched the two, arguing with himself whether he should go after her and drive her back with her companions.

As he watched, suddenly his eyes became slits and his head shot forward. Showing above the grass some thirty feet from Madoadoa and her calf, were two black spots. They were about a foot apart. Now Simba knew that two such motionless black spots as these were not a natural part of the landscape. As the fact of their being there swiftly became part of his consciousness, he instantly knew what they were and his heart tightened with fear.

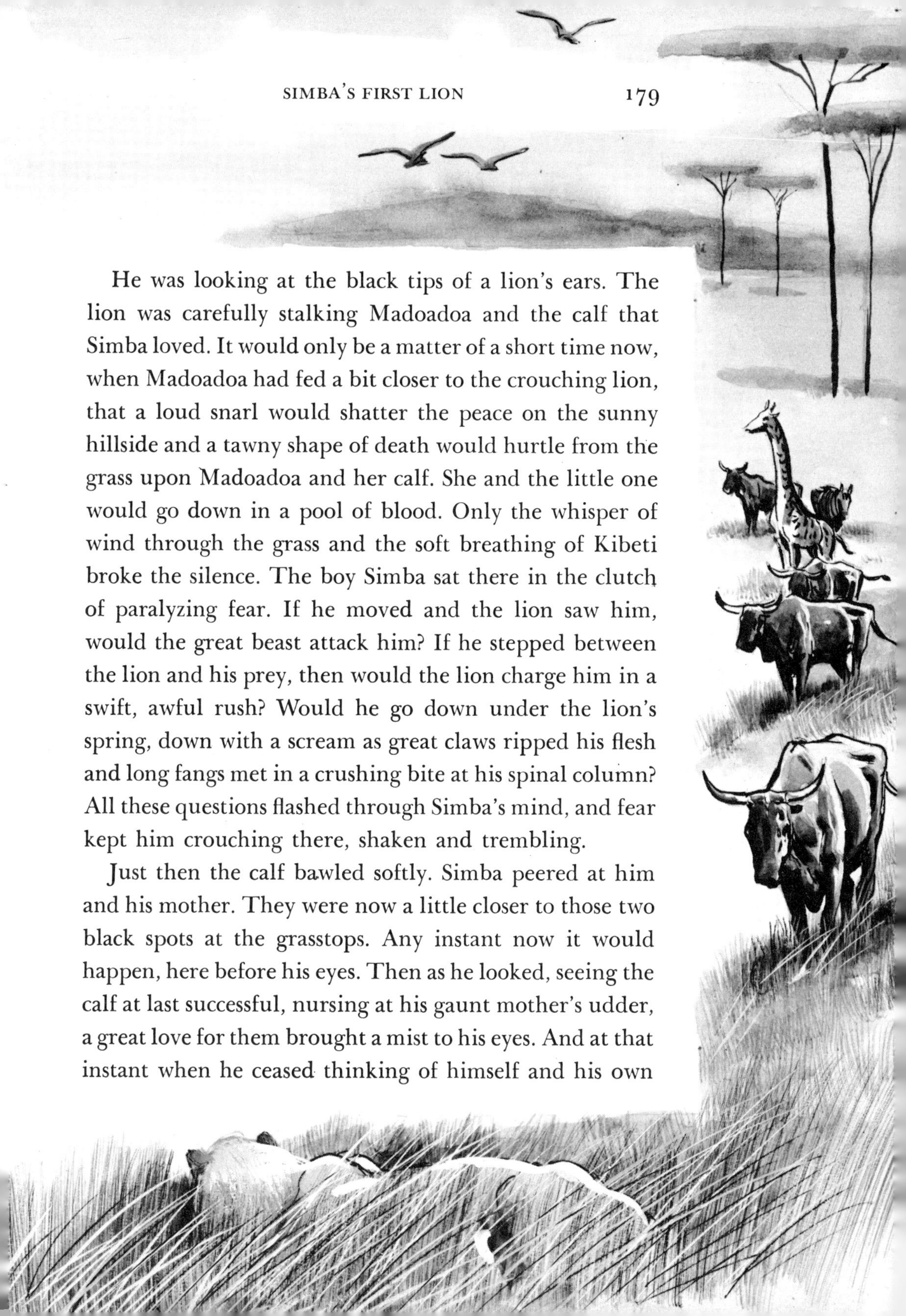

He was looking at the black tips of a lion's ears. The lion was carefully stalking Madoadoa and the calf that Simba loved. It would only be a matter of a short time now, when Madoadoa had fed a bit closer to the crouching lion, that a loud snarl would shatter the peace on the sunny hillside and a tawny shape of death would hurtle from the grass upon Madoadoa and her calf. She and the little one would go down in a pool of blood. Only the whisper of wind through the grass and the soft breathing of Kibeti broke the silence. The boy Simba sat there in the clutch of paralyzing fear. If he moved and the lion saw him, would the great beast attack him? If he stepped between the lion and his prey, then would the lion charge him in a swift, awful rush? Would he go down under the lion's spring, down with a scream as great claws ripped his flesh and long fangs met in a crushing bite at his spinal column? All these questions flashed through Simba's mind, and fear kept him crouching there, shaken and trembling.

Just then the calf bawled softly. Simba peered at him and his mother. They were now a little closer to those two black spots at the grasstops. Any instant now it would happen, here before his eyes. Then as he looked, seeing the calf at last successful, nursing at his gaunt mother's udder, a great love for them brought a mist to his eyes. And at that instant when he ceased thinking of himself and his own

fears, and thought of his love for those two so close to death, some measure of fright left him. He poked Kibeti, grasped his little spear, and rose to his feet.

The old man got up and stood beside him. At once he took in the situation. "Down, Simba," he whispered. "Down, or we, too, will die."

"No, Kibeti, I am going forward," cried Simba. "Have I not my spear?" He raised the slender, inadequate weapon above his head.

As his voice broke the stillness, Simba stepped forward. Unarmed and afraid, the old warrior went with him. Side by side these two, the shuffling crippled one and the slim boy, advanced toward Madoadoa. Simba shouted bravely, although his voice quivered a bit. His legs trembled and there was a strange shaking in the pit of his stomach. The instant Simba's voice rang out, the lion stood up from the grass. He knew he was discovered and he growled deeply in his throat.

Madoadoa now saw the danger that threatened her and her calf. If in the past few days she had appeared to be a poor sort of mother, she made up for her sins in this moment. Swiftly she thrust her calf behind her. Her eyes rolled with terror, but she stood firm between her calf and the lion, horns down, ready to give her life for the little creature cowering in terror behind her.

Simba advanced steadily. The lion, at the sight of these human enemies, bared his fangs and crouched to face them. Less than forty feet now separated the man and boy from the great muscular beast before them. It was close enough. Simba halted, placed the shaft of the spear under his right arm, advanced the sharp tip, and braced himself. The lion crouched lower and dropped his shaggy head. It was the sign of a charge. In that moment, Simba knew for certain that the spear would break under the impact of the lion's spring, knew that he was going to die, he and old Kibeti. The lion rasped out a snarl and Simba saw the mighty muscles gather themselves for the spring.

And at this moment, Madoadoa let go a furious bellow, put down her head, and charged at the lion. It was so unexpected that Simba dropped his spear. The lion may have remembered suddenly that the scar on his shoulder had come from the dagger-like point of a mother eland's horn. Perhaps a quick recollection of the pain of that old, deep wound flashed across his mind. At any rate, his savage form lifted in a mighty leap and he hung for a moment in arched splendor against the sky. When he came down to earth, he turned in a flash and went off down the hill in long bounds to disappear in the forest below.

Madoadoa stood, shaking her horns, and bawled defiance after the fleeing lion. The calf, now over his fright and quite unaware that his mother had narrowly escaped committing suicide, was sucking happily at her udder. Kibeti and Simba sat down and laughed until tears came to their eyes. Through the afternoon Simba watched the cattle, and when the long shadows drew across the plains from the mountains, drove them back to his village.

That night the tale was told by Kibeti and all the people heard it. Warriors looked at Simba, and knew that some day he would be a great one among them. The boys with whom he played looked, too, and with a respect they did not quite understand. If Simba's chest swelled a bit and if there was a slight strut to his walk that night, he must surely be forgiven. After all, the thing he had done had taken the courage of a man and a warrior.

Jiya Makes a Choice

Pearl S. Buck

A big tidal wave from the ocean has taken the lives of Jiya's family. Now Jiya, a Japanese boy, is living with his friend Kino and Kino's family, who have a farm high up on the mountain.

While Kino and his father were talking, the dusk had deepened. Now, coming up the mountainside, they saw a flickering light. This light was steadily climbing the pathway toward their house.

"I wonder who comes!" Kino exclaimed.

"A visitor," his father replied. "But who can it be?"

In a few minutes, they saw the visitor was Old Gentleman, coming from the castle. His manservant carried the lantern, but Old Gentleman walked behind him very sturdily, with the help of a long staff. They heard Old Gentleman's voice in the dusk.

"Is this the house of Uchiyama the farmer?" Old Gentleman asked.

"It is," his servant replied. "And the farmer sits there at his door with his son."

At this, Kino's father stood up, and Kino stood up too.

"Please, Honored Sir," Kino's father said, "what can I do for you?"

Old Gentleman came forward. "Do you have a lad here by the name of Jiya?"

"He lies sleeping inside my house," Kino's father said.

"I wish to see him," Old Gentleman said. Anyone could see that this old gentleman was one who expected to be obeyed. But Kino's father only smiled.

"Sir, the lad is asleep and I cannot wake him. He suffered the loss of his whole family when the big wave came. Now sleep heals him."

"I will not wake him," Old Gentleman said. "I only want to see him."

So Kino's father led Old Gentleman tiptoe into the room where Jiya slept. Kino went too. The servant held the light, shaded by his hand so it would not fall on Jiya's closed eyes.

Old Gentleman looked down on the sleeping boy. Jiya was very beautiful, even though so pale and weary. He was tall for his age and his body was strong, and his face showed intelligence as well as beauty.

Old Gentleman gazed at him and then motioned to the servant to lead him away. They went again to the dooryard and there Old Gentleman turned to Kino's father.

"It is my habit when the big wave comes to care for those who are orphaned. Three times the wave has come.

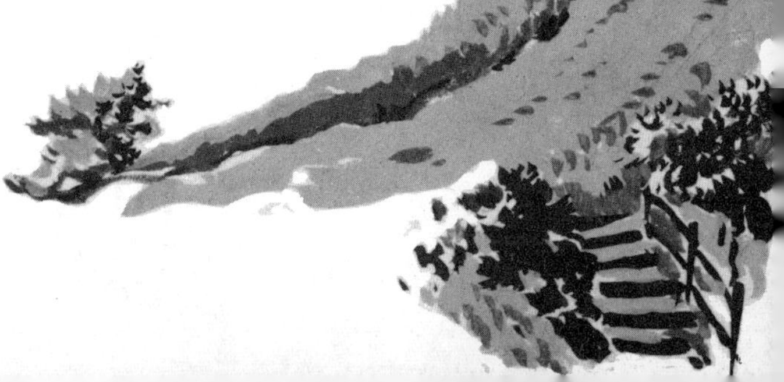

Three times I have searched out the orphans and the widows and I have fed them and sheltered them. But I have heard of this boy Jiya and I wish to do more for him. If he is as good as he is handsome, I will make him my own son."

"But Jiya is ours!" Kino cried.

"Hush," his father cried. "We are only poor people. If Old Gentleman wants Jiya, we cannot say we will not give him up."

"Exactly," Old Gentleman said. "I will educate him and give him fine clothes and send him to a good school. He may become a great man and an honor to our whole province and even to the nation."

"But if he lives in the castle we can't play together any more," Kino said.

"We must think of Jiya's good," Kino's father said. Then he turned to Old Gentleman. "Sir, it is very kind of you to propose this for Jiya. I had planned to take him for my own son, now that he has lost his birth parents. But I am only a poor farmer. I cannot pretend that my house is as good as yours, or that I can afford to send Jiya to a fine school. Tomorrow when he wakes, I will tell him of your kind offer. He will decide."

"Very well," Old Gentleman said. "But let him come and tell me himself, so that I will know how he feels."

"Certainly," Kino's father replied proudly. "Jiya will speak for himself."

How unhappy Kino was to think that Jiya might leave this house and go and live in the castle! "If Jiya goes away, I shan't have a brother," he told his father.

"You must not be so selfish, Kino," his father replied. "You must allow Jiya to make his own choice. I forbid you to speak to Jiya of this matter. When he wakes, I shall speak to him myself."

When his father was so stern, Kino did not dare to disobey, and so he went sadly to bed. He thought, when he drew his quilt over him, that he would not sleep all night. But being young and tired, he slept almost at once.

Day of Decision

Yet, as soon as Kino woke in the morning, he remembered Jiya and the choice he had to make. He got up and washed and dressed and folded his quilt and put it into the closet where it stayed during the day. His father was already out in the field, and there Kino went and found him. It was a beautiful, mild morning. A soft mist covered the ocean so that no water could be seen.

"Is Jiya awake yet?" Kino asked his father, when they had exchanged morning greetings.

"No, but he will wake soon, I think," his father replied. He was weeding the cabbage bed carefully. Kino knelt down to help him.

"Must you tell him about Old Gentleman today?" Kino pleaded.

"I must tell him as soon as he wakes," his father replied. "It would not be fair to let Jiya grow used to thinking of this as his home. He must make the choice today, before he has time to put down his new roots."

"May I be there when you talk with him?" Kino asked next.

"No, my son," his father replied. "I shall talk to him alone and tell him all the benefits that a rich man like Old Gentleman can give him and how little we who are poor can give him."

Kino could not keep from wanting to cry. He thought his father was very hard. "But Jiya will certainly want to go away!" he sobbed.

"Then he must go," his father said.

They went into the house to have breakfast, but Kino could scarcely eat. After breakfast, he went back to the field. His father stayed in the house, and they could hear Jiya getting up.

For a long time, Kino stayed in the field working alone. The warm tears dropped from his eyes upon the earth. When the sun was nearing its height, he heard his father's voice. He got up at once and walked along the path between the terraces until he reached the doorway. There his father stood with Jiya. Jiya's face was still pale and his eyes were red.

The father turned to Kino. "I have told Jiya that he must not decide until he has seen the inside of the castle. I want him to see all that Old Gentleman can give him for a home. Jiya, you know how our house is—these four rooms and the kitchen, this little farm, upon which we have to work so hard for our food. We have only what our hands can earn for us."

Kino's father held out his two hard, work-worn hands. Then he went on, "Kino, you are to go with Jiya. When you see the castle, you must persuade him to stay there, for his own sake."

Kino felt the task laid upon him was very hard. But he only said, "I will go and wash myself, Father, and put on my good clothes."

"No," his father said. "Go as you are—you are a farmer's son."

So the two boys went down the mountainside. Avoiding

the empty beach, they climbed to the castle. The gate was open and the garden was most beautiful. A gardener was sweeping the green moss.

When he saw them he came over to them. "What do you want?" he asked.

"My father sent us to see the honored Old Gentleman," Kino faltered.

"Are you the Uchiyama boy?" the gardener asked.

"Yes," Kino replied, "and this is Jiya, whom Old Gentleman wants to come and live here."

"Follow me, if you please," the gardener said. He bowed to Jiya and his voice was polite.

The two boys followed him along a wide, pebbled path. Over their heads, the ancient pines leaned their crooked branches. In the distance beyond the forest, the sun poured down upon a flower garden and a pool with a waterfall.

"How beautiful it is!" Kino whispered sadly.

Jiya did not answer. He walked along, his head held high. When they reached the house, they took off their shoes and followed the gardener through a great door. Inside this, the gardener paused. A manservant came forward and asked what they wanted. The gardener whispered and the manservant nodded. "Follow me," he said to the boys.

In the Castle

So they followed him through wide passageways. The walls were of fine polished wood, unpainted, but smooth

and silvery. Under their feet, fine-woven, padded mats were softer than the moss beneath the trees. On both sides of this passageway, panels slid back to show beautiful rooms. In each room were a vase of flowers, an exquisite scroll, a few pieces of dark polished furniture. Neither Jiya nor Kino had ever seen such a house. Kino was speechless. How could he hope now that Jiya would not want to stay in the castle?

Then, far in the distance, they saw Old Gentleman sitting beside a small table. The table was set in front of the

open sliding panels that looked into the garden. Old Gentleman was writing. He held a brush upright in his right hand and he was carefully painting letters on a scroll, his silver-rimmed spectacles sliding down on his nose.

When the two boys came near, he looked up and took off his spectacles and laid down his brush. "Would you like to know what I have been writing?" he asked.

Neither Kino nor Jiya could answer. The great house, the silence, the beauty—all of this fell into place as the background for Old Gentleman himself. He was tall and thin, and his hair and beard were white. His face and hands were beautiful. The bones were delicate and the skin was smooth and brown. He looked as proud as a king, but his dark eyes were wise as an old scholar's eyes are wise.

"It is not my own poem," he said. "It is the saying of a man of India. But I like it so much that I have painted it on this scroll to hang where I can see it every day." He took up the scroll and read these words:

The Children of God are very dear,
but very queer—
Very nice, but very narrow.

He looked at the boys. "What do you think of it?" he said.

They looked at one another. "We do not understand it, sir," Jiya said at last. Since he was a little older than Kino, he felt he should speak.

Old Gentleman shook his head and laughed softly. "Ah, we are all the children of God," he said. Then he put on his spectacles and looked hard at Jiya. "Well?" he said. "Will you be my son?"

Jiya turned very red. He had not expected to have the question put to him so suddenly and so directly.

Old Gentleman saw he found it hard to speak. "Say yes or no," he told Jiya. "Those are not hard words to say."

"I will say—no!" Jiya said. Then he felt this was harsh. "I thank you but I have a home—on the farm," he added.

Ah, how Kino felt when he heard these words! He forgot entirely about the big wave and all the sorrow it had brought. For a moment, he was filled with pure joy. Then

he remembered the small farmhouse, the four little rooms and the old kitchen.

"Jiya," he said solemnly, "remember how poor we are."

Old Gentleman was smiling a half-sad little smile. "They are certainly very poor," he said to Jiya. "And here, you know, you would have everything. You can even invite this farm boy to come and play sometimes, if you like. And I am quite willing for you to give the family some money. It would be suitable, as my son, for you to help the poor."

"Where are the others who were saved from the big wave?" Jiya asked suddenly.

"Some wanted to go away, and the ones who wanted to stay are out in the back yard with my servants," Old Gentleman replied.

"Why do you not invite them to come into this big house and be your sons and daughters?" Jiya asked.

"Because I don't want them for my sons and daughters," Old Gentleman replied rather crossly. "You are a bright, handsome boy, and they told me you were the best boy in the village."

Jiya looked about him. Then he shook his head again. "I am no better than the others," he said. "My father was a fisherman."

Old Gentleman took up his spectacles and his brush again. "Very well," he said. "I will do without a son."

The manservant motioned to them and they followed. Soon they were out in the garden again.

"How foolish you are!" the manservant said to Jiya.

"Our Old Gentleman is very kind indeed. You would have everything here."

"Not everything," Jiya replied.

They went out of the gate and across the hillside again, back to the farmhouse. Setsu, Kino's little sister, was outside. She came running to meet them, the sleeves of her bright kimono flying behind her and her feet clattering in wooden sandals.

"Jiya has come back home!" she cried. "Jiya—Jiya—"

And Jiya, seeing her happy little face, opened his arms and gave her a great hug. For the first time, he felt comfort creep into his sad heart, and this comfort came from Setsu, who was like life itself.

Go West, Young Man

There was a wise fellow
  Who said, "It is best
For ambitious young folks
  To go West, West, West."

Out where the plains
  And the coyotes are,
The eye of a man
  Can see far, far, far.

Out where the mountains
  Stand bare of a tree,
The soul of a man
  Can feel free, free, free.

—Dorothy Hall

Dan Drake's First Patient

Marion Renick and Margaret C. Tyler

"This is the place," Dan Drake said to his father. He pointed to the sign on the wide white front door: *Doctor Wm. Goforth.* As the boy reached up to bang the big brass knocker he told himself that he, too, would someday have a similar sign on his own door. For Dan had wanted to be a doctor ever since he could remember. Now here he was with his father, calling upon Dr. Goforth, of Cincinnati, one of the few doctors in Ohio in that year of 1799.

Dan turned once more to his father with the question he had asked a dozen times as they had made the trip from their home across the Ohio River in Kentucky. "Do you think Dr. Goforth will let me stay and learn about medicine from him?"

Before Mr. Drake could reply, the door was opened by a sweet-faced woman who said she was Mrs. Goforth. A few minutes later, Dan was asking his question of the doctor himself.

At first the boy had high hopes. For Dr. Goforth looked at him with interest and said there was a great need for good doctors in Cincinnati, and indeed in all the Ohio country. But then the physician asked about Dan's schooling. He shook his head as if displeased with Mr. Drake's

explanation that Dan had never been to school because there was no school near enough for him to attend.

"But I can read!" Dan hastened to put in. "Mother taught me. I've read all the books we have at home. The Bible, the Hymn Book, the Almanac, and *Aesop's Fables,* and Montellion's *History of Romance and Chivalry.*"

Dr. Goforth looked at Dan as if he were going to shake his head again. But the look of longing on the boy's face must have made him change his mind. Then Dan said with all his heart in his voice, "I'd study very hard, sir, if you will only accept me as an apprentice."

So the doctor smiled and clapped Dan on the shoulder, promising to give him a trial. "But your life as a frontier doctor will be a hard one," he warned. "You'll have long, cold, lonely trips to make on winter nights. Wolves and wildcats will be your only company as you ride through trackless forests to attend the sick and dying in the cabins of the pioneers."

"I won't mind, sir, I'm *sure,*" was Dan's answer.

"Your earnings will be uncertain," the doctor went on. "And when you do get paid it's likely to be in the shape of a fat hen or a bushel of corn. You'll make many a call miles off in the wilderness. And you'll get a dozen eggs for your pay. Often you won't even take the eggs because the sick person needs them worse than you do."

Dan was grinning now. "You can't scare me off, Dr. Goforth."

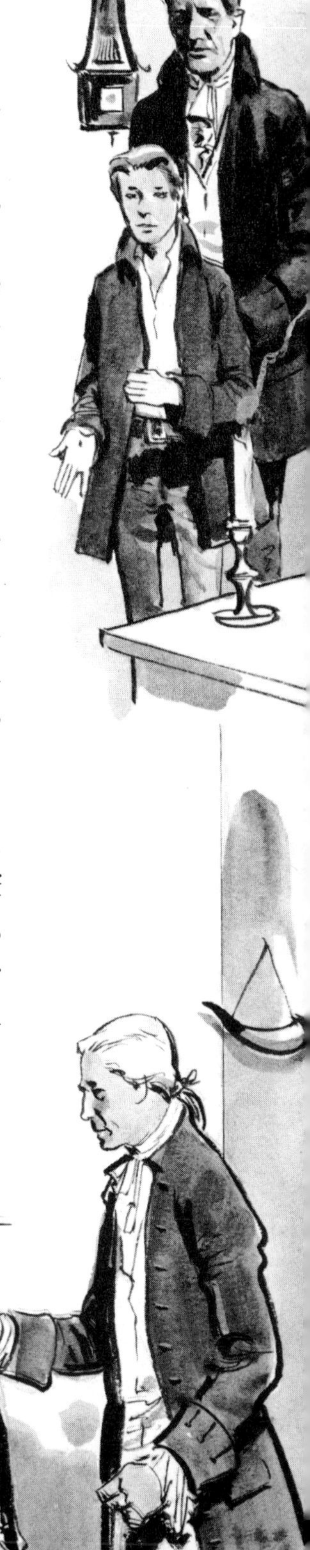

"Good lad!" The doctor nodded as if well satisfied. He turned to Mr. Drake to ask, "When can he start?"

"Can't I start now, father?" Dan spoke as if he couldn't bear to wait a minute longer to enter the thrilling world of medicine.

And a truly thrilling world it was, he soon found. In the weeks that followed, Dr. Goforth gave him medical books to read and even began showing him how to prepare medicines.

In those days, there wasn't a drugstore full of pills on every other corner. A doctor had to make his own medicines from healing herbs, the bark of certain trees, and a few drugs brought by sailing vessels from countries across the sea. Dan soon learned how to stir up cough syrup or shake together a compound that was good for stomach pains. His steady, nimble fingers grew skillful at folding tiny squares of paper and filling them with quinine to cure a fever. He liked this work. It made him feel he was helping the doctor save lives. Many times he saw his medicines in use as he went along with Dr. Goforth to visit the sick. Every evening, he wrote down in a notebook the things he had learned on these visits.

Dan began to dream of the time when he, too, would be allowed to treat the sick. He often imagined how he would doctor his first patient. He wondered if this patient would live in town or in some pioneer's cabin far out in the wilderness. For Dan soon had learned that Dr. Goforth's patients were not all within easy reach. Many of them lived miles away in the Ohio hills. Sometimes at night, Dan would hear the big brass knocker on the front door go *thump-thump-thump*. He would hurry downstairs to find a frightened father or husband who had ridden far and fast to fetch the doctor. Then Dan would hurry to the barn to saddle the doctor's horse, Copper. Quickly he would pack the saddlebags with medicines, bandages, and instruments. Dr. Goforth would gallop off into the darkness with the frightened man hurrying ahead of him.

One night Thad Harper rode in from his father's farm ten miles out of town. The whole family was down with swamp fever, Thad said, just as his knees gave way and he collapsed with the sickness on the doorstep. Dan helped the doctor get the young fellow into bed. Then the doctor looked thoughtfully at his apprentice.

"I hesitate to ask this of you, Dan," he said. "But do you think you could take some medicine out to the Harpers? I'd go myself, but there is too much serious illness here in town just now. I don't dare leave."

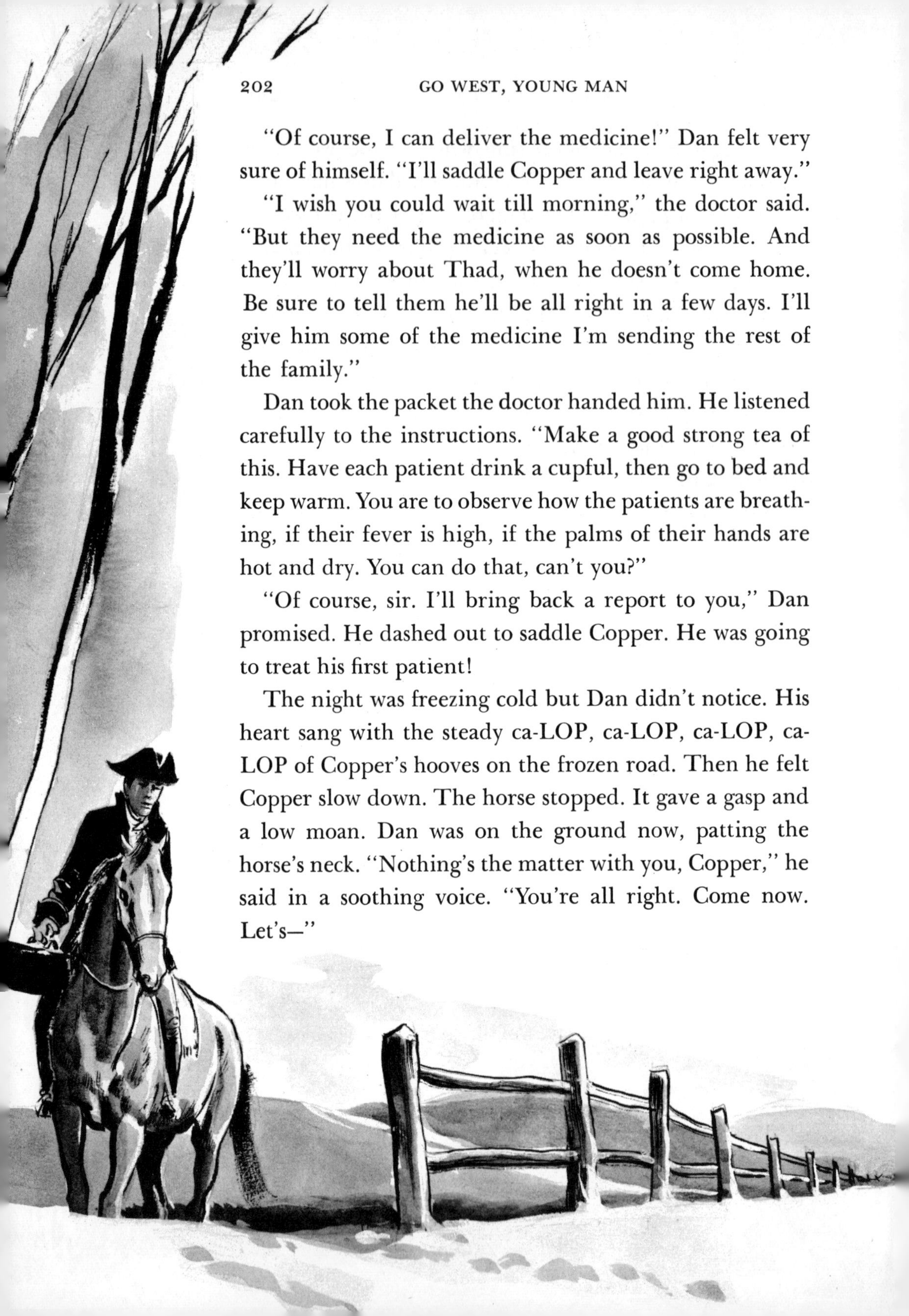

"Of course, I can deliver the medicine!" Dan felt very sure of himself. "I'll saddle Copper and leave right away."

"I wish you could wait till morning," the doctor said. "But they need the medicine as soon as possible. And they'll worry about Thad, when he doesn't come home. Be sure to tell them he'll be all right in a few days. I'll give him some of the medicine I'm sending the rest of the family."

Dan took the packet the doctor handed him. He listened carefully to the instructions. "Make a good strong tea of this. Have each patient drink a cupful, then go to bed and keep warm. You are to observe how the patients are breathing, if their fever is high, if the palms of their hands are hot and dry. You can do that, can't you?"

"Of course, sir. I'll bring back a report to you," Dan promised. He dashed out to saddle Copper. He was going to treat his first patient!

The night was freezing cold but Dan didn't notice. His heart sang with the steady ca-LOP, ca-LOP, ca-LOP, ca-LOP of Copper's hooves on the frozen road. Then he felt Copper slow down. The horse stopped. It gave a gasp and a low moan. Dan was on the ground now, patting the horse's neck. "Nothing's the matter with you, Copper," he said in a soothing voice. "You're all right. Come now. Let's—"

But something *was* the matter. Copper's dark red body was swelling right before Dan's eyes. As fast as he could, he loosened the saddle, tearing at it with his cold stiff fingers. By the time he got the saddle off, the horse's body had swollen until it looked like a huge barrel on four thin sticks of legs. Dan watched those legs anxiously. He was afraid they might double up. He knew if Copper once got down on the cold road, that might be the end.

Dan was almost sure he knew what was wrong. Copper probably had eaten too many oats for supper. Or had drunk too much water. And then Dan had galloped the horse too hard right after it had eaten. So now Copper had the heaves.

With every painful breath Copper drew, Dan grew more frightened. He tried to remember his notebook full of medical learning. When one of Dr. Goforth's human patients swelled up with indigestion, what had the doctor prescribed? Heat, Dan remembered. He shivered as he looked at the icy darkness around him. No heat there! Then he thought of the blanket under the saddle. He spread that over the horse. He took off his own coat and flung that, too, on Copper's back.

"The next thing to do is keep moving," he said aloud. "Come on, Copper. Come on. Just walk along easy-like. I'm right here beside you. Come on. Come on. That's the way, Copper. Keep moving. Keep going."

Step by step the shivering boy and the gasping horse went down the road. The sun was up by the time they came to a farmhouse. Dan was happy to see a large shed in the rear. He stopped and asked the farmer for permission to leave Copper there until he returned. He also explained his errand and asked how far it was to the Harper farm.

"About five miles," said the farmer's wife. "And you'd better have a bite to eat and warm yourself before you start out." She put an extra plate on the table for Dan. As they were eating breakfast, Dan told the farmer and his wife about his dream of becoming a doctor. He ended by saying the Harpers would be his first patients.

The farmer laughed. "You're wrong there," he said with a twinkle in his eyes. "You've already treated your first patient–and it was a horse."

For a moment Dan felt disappointed. Then he began to laugh, too. With a merry heart he set out on foot for the Harpers. He delivered the medicine, made a report for Dr. Goforth, and walked back to the farmer's shed for Copper. The horse was now much bettter. Dan thought he could safely ride the rest of the way home if he went slowly.

As Copper plodded along, Dan began to realize that the short winter day was almost ended. He should have been home long ago. Surely Dr. Goforth would wonder what

had happened. So, the minute he finished making Copper comfortable in the barn, Dan ran to the house. As the door slammed behind him he heard Mrs. Goforth call to her husband, "Oh, Will! Here's Dan!" And both she and the doctor hurried to greet him.

"I'm sorry I was so long," Dan started to say. "I couldn't—"

"Never mind that," the doctor exclaimed. "You're safe, lad! That's all that matters. We feared you might have fallen into a ditch with Copper on top of you."

"It was Copper, sir—" Dan began again.

"Poor lad, you look frozen," Mrs. Goforth interrupted. "Here, let me help you off with your boots. And I'll make you a cup of hot tea."

At last Dan was allowed to tell what had happened. The doctor beamed with satisfaction at his account of how he had taken care of Copper. Later, after he had gone to the barn to have a look at his horse, he said, "Well, Dan, your first patient is getting along fine. You have the makings of a real doctor, my lad."

Four years later, Dan began to really practice medicine as a junior partner to Dr. Goforth. He had been well-trained by the older doctor. In his education, practical experience had taken the place of study in a college or a hospital, so Daniel Drake was given a diploma in medicine. It was the first doctor's diploma ever given west of the Allegheny Mountains. It said:

Cincinnati, State of Ohio, August first, 1805.

I do hereby certify that Mr. Daniel Drake has pursued under my direction, for four years, the study of Physics, Surgery and Midwifery. From his good abilities and marked attention to the prosecution of his studies, I am fully convinced that he is qualified to practice in the above branches of his profession.

William Goforth, Surgeon General
First Division Ohio Militia

The Shindig

Shannon Garst

Twelve-year-old Bob was spending the summer on his Uncle John's Wyoming cattle ranch. Bob had never been on a ranch before, and he had a lot to learn.

One Saturday morning, Bob noticed that the Circle K cowboys plunged into their work with unusual energy. That night there was to be a big "shindig" at the neighboring Flying V Ranch. During breakfast, the men could talk of nothing else. They gulped down hot cakes, bacon and eggs, and scalding coffee, eager to get at their day's work and finish it in plenty of time to slick up for the occasion.

"What is a shindig?" Bob asked.

"You don't know what a shindig is?" Crowbait asked in amazement. And all the men looked shocked at such ignorance.

"I never heard of such a thing," Bob confessed.

Finally Montana took pity on him. "A shindig is—well, it's just a shindig," he said lamely. "A big hoedown. A get-together. Everyone comes from miles around. Some fellows bring their fiddles. Happy, here, will take his guitar. They play music for the square dances. The ladies and gals bring sandwiches and cakes and pies. And everyone has a high old time."

"It sounds like fun!" Bob turned to his uncle. "May I go to the shindig, Uncle John?" he asked eagerly.

John Benton pursed his lips and studied the matter for a long moment. Bob held his breath.

"He can go in the pickup truck with me," Happy offered. "I'll keep my eye on him."

"We-ll," the words came out slowly. "I believe he can go. I don't see how any harm can come to him."

"Oh, thanks!" Bob exclaimed.

Supper was a hurried affair that night, with much talk and banter about the shindig. Bob never had seen the men spend so much time cleaning themselves up. They polished their boots, doused oil on their hair, and put on their brightest silk shirts and neckerchiefs.

Most of the men rode horseback to the Flying V, but Happy drove the pickup because he was to take some of the food. Bob saw him wrap his guitar case tenderly in a

blanket before he carefully stowed it away in the car.

"Aren't you going?" Bob asked his uncle.

"No," Mr. Benton said. "Someone has to stay at the ranch, and the job suits me very well. Have a good time, Bob. When you get tired, go out and sleep in the pickup. The boys always stay until morning."

Cookie rode with Bob and Happy. As they spun along, he and Happy told Bob that the Flying V was a dude ranch that made a business of entertaining city people who wanted a taste of ranch life without any of the hardships. Bob noticed a touch of scorn in their tone as they spoke of the Flying V hands as "dude wranglers."

When they got to the big barn where the dance was being held, the place was a gay sight. Electrically-wired lanterns hung from the rafters, and bales of hay had been placed along the walls for seats. Bob was amused to see that the dude wranglers were dressed much like the cowboys he had seen in the movies. They wore bright-colored, braid-trimmed silk shirts, brighter neckerchiefs, and tight-fitting trousers trimmed with braid. Their hats were extra wide, with fancy bands. Some of them wore chaps decorated with large silver conchas. Most of the dudes were also fixed up in fancy Western clothes.

"Howdy, stranger!" A voice beside him made Bob start. He turned to look into the most thoroughly freckled face he had ever seen, on a boy about his own age.

"Oh, howdy!" Bob returned, smiling.

"I'm Jerry Bates. I live on the ranch just north of your

uncle's," the freckled boy said with a friendly grin. "I hear you're spending the summer on the Circle K. Why don't you ride over sometime?"

Bob felt his face turn red. He didn't want to admit that he wasn't allowed to ride outside the ranch.

"Oh, I don't know my way around very well yet," he finally found words. "Why don't you ride over to the Circle K?"

"I might do that," Jerry answered.

Swing Your Partner!

The two boys stood watching the square dancers. Bob had never seen dancing like this before. The cowboys

entered into the spirit of the thing with enthusiasm and considerable hilarity. The "caller" stood on a chair and bellowed directions:

Rope your cow and brand your calf,
Swing your honey a loop and a half.
Come on now with the old mess wagon,
Hind wheel's broke and the axle's draggin'.
Swing, swing! Everybody swing!

The cowboys stamped and whooped to liven things up. Bob noticed that Shorty was the liveliest and noisiest of them all.

"He's really having a good time," Jerry observed.

Bob watched Montana, whirling around gracefully in the complicated figures of the square dances. It seemed only natural to him that the foreman should excel at everything he did. And he noticed that, although most

of the musicians smiled and stamped their feet as they played, Happy strummed his guitar with as much dead seriousness as he did everything else.

As the two boys wandered around the great barn, Bob was surprised to see in one corner a dozen or more babies and small children, fast asleep on hard benches.

"I don't see how they do it," he said—"sleep with all this music and whooping and laughing going on!"

"I don't either," Jerry laughed, "but I used to do it myself. My folks began to drag me to these shindigs when I was only knee high to a grasshopper. So I practically grew up sleeping in places like this."

Bob stared down at the small children lying there.

"Ever hear how some cowpokes switched babies at one of these dances?" Jerry asked.

"No. Tell me about it."

"It really happened not very far from here," Jerry said. "My father read me the story out of a book called *The Virginian.* They had all the babies asleep in one of the bedrooms, and these fellows went in and changed the babies around. There was quite a mix-up when their mamas went to get them."

Bob laughed.

Jerry looked thoughtful for a moment. Then he whispered, "I have an idea. A humdinger!" He seized Bob's arm. "Come along with me."

Bob followed him outside. Near the barn there was a long rail to which the cowboys' horses were tied.

"We'll switch the ponies," whispered Jerry. "It's so dark out here the fellows can't see their animals. Each cowboy will just come to where he tied his pony and climb on without thinking. They dance till nearly daylight and by then the men are so dead tired they generally go to sleep while they're riding. They depend on their ponies to take them home."

Bob put his hand over his mouth to keep back a shout of mirth. "Most of the cowboys will wake up on some other ranch—not their own," he whispered.

"Yeh," Jerry chuckled. "Each pony will go to his home ranch. There'll be an awful mix-up of cowboys in the morning."

"This is a better joke than mixing up the babies," Bob said, in deep admiration over Jerry's genius. "This really should be in a book, too."

A Joke—and the Morning After

Bob settled himself cozily between Happy and Cookie as the shindig broke up in that dark hour just before dawn. Everyone was groggy with weariness and yawning widely as good nights were said.

Bob chuckled as he thought of the mixed-up horses.

"What's funny, partner?" Cookie asked.

"Oh, I just happened to think of something," Bob answered briefly.

Happy started to sing. Bob promptly went to sleep, to be awakened by Cookie's booming voice, "Here we are

back on the home range. Wake up, Bob, and let's go!"

As Bob climbed stiffly from the pickup, Happy said mournfully, "There won't be time for any snoozing at all. When we have one of these all-night shindigs, we might as well count it a night's sleep lost and let it go at that."

"Then why don't people go home earlier?" Bob asked a trifle crossly. "Why do they stay all night?"

"Oh, we cowmen don't have many social events," Happy yawned. "So when we do, we have to make the most of it." He looked toward the eastern sky which the dawn was beginning to tinge with pink. "Just in time to get in the hosses," he added in gloomy tones.

"And Bob and I are just in time to get breakfast," said Cookie, as spryly as if he had had a full night's sleep. "Shake a leg there, partner, and get the wood and water in and set the places at the table."

Bob's feet dragged as he did his chores, though the smell of cooking bacon and coffee revived him a bit. He heard some of the men coming in, shouting at one another across the barnyard as cheerfully as though they were not tired at all.

As Bob slid sleepily into his place at the table, he suddenly remembered something. He looked about quickly. Then he gasped. He had taken pains to see that Crowbait's horse was changed, but there sat Crowbait, eating as though nothing unpleasant had ever happened to him. It was Montana who was missing! No one had seen him since the party.

"It's possible he might have got his hoss mixed up," Crowbait remarked, and Bob thought he felt a glance in his direction. "I noticed my pony was tied in a different place. Might be, the animals got tired of standing in the same spot and moved about just for fun. I was smart enough to notice. Probably a dumb guy like Montana wouldn't."

Almost as Crowbait spoke, Montana dragged himself into the room. He smiled rather sheepishly, but he looked half-dead with weariness.

A mighty guffaw of laughter greeted him.

Suddenly Bob didn't think the trick was clever at all. If it had been Crowbait who had made the useless ride to some far-away ranch, he wouldn't have minded. But not for anything would he have pulled a trick like this on his friend Montana.

"It's a wise man that knows his own hoss. Especially after a dance." Crowbait laughed in the disagreeable manner he had. "Me, I had sense enough to notice whether I was mounted on my own animal."

Montana grinned wearily. "I reckon I deserve your kidding," he said. "Any cowpoke that don't recognize his own hoss, even in the dark and when he's half asleep, deserves a lot of kidding. But I never thought anyone would pull a skunky trick like that."

He looked straight at Crowbait, and his eyes were like cold steel.

"Don't look at me," Crowbait shrugged. "Why don't you ask Bob if he knows anything about it?"

All eyes turned on Bob.

"You—of all people?" Montana cried.

Bob wished the floor would swallow him.

Montana said nothing more. He sat down and piled hot cakes on his plate. Everyone else went on eating.

When the men went outside, Bob tagged along after Montana. The cowboy paid no attention. Finally Bob plucked him by the sleeve.

"Sa-ay," he blurted, "I'm sure sorry about what I did last night. Changing horses, I mean—"

"Whose idea was it?" Montana asked sharply.

"It was Jerry's really," Bob admitted. "But I thought it was awfully good. That is, at first I did. But I didn't mean to play such a trick on *you.*"

"O.K.," Montana said, and the old familiar grin came back to his face. "I've pulled too many tricks on other fellows to hold any grudge when I'm the victim. I reckon I can take a joke as well as play one."

Something welled up in Bob's heart that made it actually hurt. Gee, but Montana was a swell guy!

Texas Trains and Trails

Whenever I ride on the Texas plains
I never hear the couplings cluck,
I never hear the trains
Go chuck-a-luck, chuck-a-luck, chuck-a-luck,
I never hear the engine snort and snuffle,
I never see the smoke plume, I never watch the rails,
But I see the moving dust where the beef herds shuffle,
And I think I am a cowboy,
A rope and tie 'em cowboy,
Punching Texas longhorns
On the Texas trails.
And the engine goes *Whoop!*
Whoopee, whoopala!
And the cars go *Ki-yi,*
Ki-yi, ki-yi, coma-la ki-yi,
  Whoopala,
Ki-yi!
  Whoop!

No, I never hear the bell, nor the brakeman call
When I ride on the Texas trains;
But I hear the steers bellow and the yearlings bawl,
And the lone wolf howl on the wire grass plains.
And I never play I'm fireman, or anything like that,
For I'm playing I'm a cowboy,
A bronco-bustin' cowboy,
Riding Texas longhorns
In a ten-gallon hat.
And the trains go *Youpi-ya,*
Get a-long, dogies,
Get a-long, get a-long
Youpi-yi, youpi-ya,
Youpi-youpi-youpi-ya
Get a-long, get a-long,
Youpi-ya,
Yo-o-u-u-p!

—*Mary Austin*

The Blizzard

Laura Ingalls Wilder

Seventy years ago, as now, winter on the Great Plains of the West could be cruelly long and cold. Ma, Pa, and the girls had moved from their Dakota homestead into the little prairie town near by, after an old Indian had warned them it was going to be a bad winter. Now, in October, Laura and Carrie were going to the town school.

Laura and Carrie were enjoying school so much that they were sorry when Saturday and Sunday interrupted it. They looked forward to Monday. But when Monday came, Laura was cross because her red flannel underwear was so hot and scratchy.

It made her back itch, and her neck, and her wrists, and where it was folded around her ankles, under her stockings and shoe-tops, that red flannel almost drove her crazy. At noon, she begged Ma to let her change to cooler underthings. "It's too hot for my red flannels, Ma!" she protested.

"I know the weather's turned warm," Ma answered gently. "But this is the time of year to wear flannels. You would catch cold if you took them off."

Laura went crossly back to school and sat squirming because she must not scratch. She held the flat geography open before her, but she wasn't studying. She was trying to bear the itching flannels. The sunshine from the western windows had never crawled so slowly.

Suddenly there was no sunshine. It went out, as if someone had blown out the sun like a lamp. The outdoors was gray, the windowpanes were gray, and at the same moment a wind crashed against the schoolhouse, rattling windows and doors and shaking the walls.

Miss Garland, the teacher, started up from her chair. One of the little Beardsley girls screamed. Carrie turned white.

Laura thought, "It happened this way on Plum Creek, the Christmas when Pa was lost." Her whole heart hoped and prayed that Pa was safe at home now.

Teacher and all the others were staring at the windows, where nothing but grayness could be seen. They all looked frightened. Then Miss Garland said, "It is only a storm, children. Go on with your lessons."

All the heads bent over the books as Teacher had told them to do. But Laura was trying to think how to get home. The schoolhouse was a long way from Main Street, and there was nothing to guide them.

All the others had come from the East that summer.

They had never seen a prairie blizzard. But Laura and Carrie knew what it was. Carrie's head was bowed limply above her book, and the back of it, with the white parting between the braids of fine, soft hair, looked small and helpless and frightened.

There was only a little fuel at the schoolhouse. The school board was buying coal, but only one load had been delivered. Laura thought they might outlive the storm in the schoolhouse, but they could not do it without burning all the desks.

Without lifting her head, Laura looked up at Teacher. Miss Garland was thinking and biting her lip. She could not decide to dismiss school because of a storm, but this storm frightened her.

"I ought to tell her what to do," Laura thought. But

she could not think what to do. It was not safe to leave the schoolhouse and it was not safe to stay there. Even the twelve desks might not last long enough to keep them warm until the blizzard ended. She thought of her wraps and Carrie's, in the entry. Whatever happened, she must somehow keep Carrie warm. Already the cold was coming in.

There was a loud thumping in the entry. Every pupil started and looked at the door.

It opened and a man stumbled in. He was bundled in overcoat, cap, and muffler, all solid white with snow driven into the woolen cloth. They could not see who he was until he pulled down the stiffened muffler.

"I came out to get you," he told Teacher. He was Mr. Foster, who had come in from his claim to stay in town for the winter at Sherwood's, across the street from Teacher's house.

Miss Garland thanked him. She rapped her ruler on the desk and said, "Attention! School is dismissed. You may bring your wraps from the entry and put them on by the stove."

Laura said to Carrie, "You stay here. I'll bring your wraps."

The entry was freezing cold. Snow was blowing in between the rough boards of the walls. Laura was chilled before she could snatch her coat and hood from their nail. She found Carrie's and carried the armful into the schoolhouse.

Crowded around the stove, they all put on their wraps and fastened them. Cap Garland, Teacher's brother, did not smile. His blue eyes narrowed and his mouth set straight while Mr. Foster talked.

Laura wrapped the muffler snugly over Carrie's white face and took firm hold of her mittened hand. She told Carrie, "Don't worry. We'll be all right."

"Now, just follow me," said Mr. Foster, taking Teacher's arm. "And keep close together."

He opened the door and led the way with Miss Garland. Mary Power and Minnie each took one of the little Beardsley girls. Ben and Arthur followed them closely with the Wilmarth boys. Then Laura went out with Carrie into the blinding snow. Cap Garland shut the door behind them.

They could hardly walk in the beating, whirling wind. The schoolhouse had disappeared. Nothing could be

seen but swirling whiteness and now and then a glimpse of each other, disappearing like shadows.

Laura felt that she was smothering. The icy particles of snow whirled scratching into her eyes and smothered her breathing. Her skirts whipped around her, now wrapped so tightly that she could not step, then whirled and lifted to her knees. She held tightly to Carrie. Carrie, struggling and staggering, was pulled away by the wind and then flung back against her.

"We can't go on this way," Laura thought. But they had to.

Lost in the Storm

She was alone in the whirling winds and snow except for Carrie's hand that she must never let go. The others must be somewhere ahead. She must keep up with them or she and Carrie would be lost. If they were lost on the prairie they would freeze to death.

But perhaps they were all lost. Main Street was only two blocks long. If they were going only a little way to north or south, they would miss the block of stores. Beyond was empty prairie for miles. Laura thought they must have gone far enough to reach Main Street, but she could see nothing.

The storm thinned a little. She saw shadowy figures ahead. They were darker gray in the whirling gray-whiteness. She went on as fast as she could, with Carrie, until she touched Miss Garland's coat.

They had all stopped. Huddled in their wraps, they

stood like bundles close together in the swirling mist. Teacher and Mr. Foster were trying to talk, but no one could hear what they said. Then Laura began to know how cold she was.

Her mittened hand was so numb that it hardly felt Carrie's hand. She was shaking all over and deep inside her there was a shaking that she could not stop. Only in her very middle there was a solid knot that ached, and her shaking pulled this knot tighter so that the ache grew worse.

She was frightened about Carrie. The cold hurt too much, Carrie could not stand it. Carrie was so little and thin, she had always been delicate, she could not stand such cold. They must reach shelter soon.

Mr. Foster and Teacher were moving again, going a little to the left. All the others hurried to follow them. Laura took hold of Carrie with her other hand. It had been in her coat pocket and was not quite so numb. Suddenly she saw a shadow go by them. She knew it was Cap Garland.

He was not following the others to the left. With hands in his pockets and head bent, he went trudging straight ahead into the storm. A fury of winds thickened the air with snow and he vanished.

Laura did not dare follow him. She must take care of Carrie, and Teacher had told them to follow her. She was sure that Cap was going toward Main Street. But perhaps she was mistaken.

She kept tight hold of Carrie and hurried to follow Mr. Foster and Teacher as fast as she could. Her chest sobbed for air and her eyes strained open in the icy snow-particles that hurt them like sand. Carrie struggled bravely, stumbling and flopping, doing her best to stay on her feet and keep going.

Laura felt that they were going in the wrong direction. She did not know why she felt so. No one could see anything. There was nothing to go by—no sun, no sky, no direction in the winds blowing fiercely from all directions. There was nothing but the dizzy whirling and the cold.

Then, out of the whiteness, something hit her. The hard blow crashed against her shoulder and all through her. She rocked on her feet and stumbled against something solid. It was high, it was hard, it was the corner of two walls. Her hands felt it, her eyes saw it. She had walked against some building. With all her might she yelled, "Here! Come here! Here's a house!"

Main Street at Last

At first no one heard her. She pulled the icy stiff muffler from her mouth and screamed into the blinding storm. At last she saw a shadow in it, two tall shadows thinner than the shadowy wall she clung to—Mr. Foster and Teacher. Then other shadows pressed close around her. They were all there—Mary Power and Minnie, each with a little Beardsley girl, and Arthur Johnson and Ben Woodworth and the small Wilmarth boys. Only Cap Garland was missing.

They followed along the side of that building till they came to the front of it. It was Mead's Hotel, at the very north end of Main Street. Beyond it was nothing but the railroad track covered with snow, the lonely depot and the wide, open prairie. If Laura had been only a few steps nearer the others, they would all have been lost on the endless prairie north of town.

For a moment, they stood by the hotel's lamplit windows. Warmth and rest were inside. But the blizzard was growing worse and they must all reach home.

Main Street would guide all of them except Ben Woodworth. No other buildings stood between the hotel and the depot where he lived. So Ben went into the hotel to stay till the blizzard was over. He could afford to do that because his father had a regular job.

Minnie and Arthur Johnson, taking the little Wilmarth boys, had only to cross Main Street to Wilmarth's grocery store. Their home was beside it. The others went down Main Street, keeping close to the buildings. They passed Royal Wilder's feed store, and then they passed Barker's grocery. The Beardsley Hotel was next and there the little Beardsley girls went in.

The journey was almost ended. They passed Couse's Hardware store and they crossed Second Street. Mary Power had only to pass the drugstore now. Her father's tailor shop stood next to it.

Laura and Carrie and Teacher and Mr. Foster had to cross Main Street now. It was a wide street. But if they

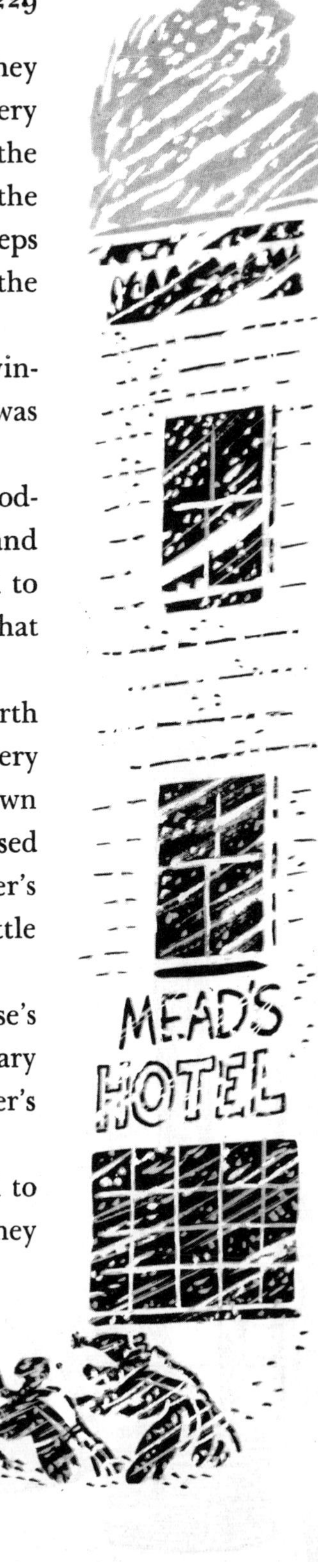

missed Pa's house, the haystacks and the stable were still between them and the open prairie.

They did not miss the house. One of its lighted windows made a glow that Mr. Foster saw before he ran into it. He went on around the house corner with Teacher to go by the clothesline, the haystacks, and the stable to the Garland house.

Laura and Carrie were safe at their own front door. Laura's hands fumbled at the doorknob, too stiff to turn it. Pa opened the door and helped them in. He was wearing an overcoat and cap and muffler. He had set down a lighted lantern and dropped a coil of rope. "I was just starting out after you," he said.

Laura felt Ma's hands breaking away the icy muffler, and she said, "Is Carrie all right?"

"Yes, Carrie's all right," said Pa.

Ma took off Laura's hood and unbuttoned her coat and helped her pull out of its sleeves. Laura could hardly move, but she stooped and with her fingers dug out the caked snow that the wind had driven in between her woolen stockings and the tops of her shoes. Then she staggered toward the stove and sat stiffly down.

She felt numb and stupid. She rubbed her eyes and saw a pink smear on her hand. Her eyelids were bleeding where the snow had scratched them. The sides of the coal heater glowed red-hot and she could feel the heat on her skin, but she was cold inside. The heat from the fire couldn't reach that cold.

Pa sat close to the stove holding Carrie on his knee. He had taken off her shoes and held her wrapped in a shawl. The shawl shivered with Carrie's shivering. "I can't get warm, Pa," she said.

"You girls are chilled through. I'll have you a hot drink in a minute," said Ma, hurrying into the kitchen. She brought them each a steaming cup of ginger tea.

It was wonderful to be there, safe at home, sheltered from the winds and the cold. Laura thought that this must be a little bit like heaven.

"I'm glad you didn't have to come for us, Pa," Laura said drowsily. "I was hoping you were safe."

"So was I," Carrie told Pa, snuggling against him. "I

remembered that Christmas, on Plum Creek, when you didn't get home."

"I did, too," Pa said grimly. "When Cap Garland came into Fuller's and said you were all heading out to the open prairie, you can bet I made tracks for a rope and lantern. We'd have had a posse out looking for you, though we'd have been hunting for a needle in a haystack."

"Best forget about it," said Ma. "And now, Laura and Carrie, you're going to bed and get some rest. A good long sleep is what you need."

Whitey and Jinglebob

Glen Rounds

At the time I speak of, Whitey was ten years old, or thereabouts. He had him a hand-me-down Stetson with a rattlesnake-skin hatband onto it, and a pair of Uncle Torwal's fancy stitched Fort Worth boots.

Jinglebob was about the same size and probably the same age. He got his name from the second-hand Stetson he wore. The brim of it had been tromped on by a horse at some time, so it sort of hung down on one side, the way a jinglebobbed calf's ear does. His father was a freighter. He had left the boy with Torwal and Whitey one trip, and Jinglebob'd just sort of stayed.

Torwal was an old-time cattle man, with legs that were bowed, a drooping red moustache, and a stiff arm from getting an Injun arrow in the early days.

These three lived by themselves, doing their own cooking, dish washing, and the like. They ran the ranch with the help of a sooner dog, name of Confusion.

This particular day, Torwal had gone to Lone Tree to get the mail and some other odds and ends. Whitey and Jinglebob were down in the corral practicing up on their rodeo stuff. You see, they were no great shakes for size, but none the less they figured they were top hands, almost. And it's a well-known fact that if you want to be a top hand in any business, you have to practice.

So, when Torwal came back that afternoon, he saw a considerable cloud of dust raising up over the corral where he was keeping a bunch of long yearlings and two-year-olds, fattening them up for shipping. As he rode closer, he could hear the excitement. He tied his horse and climbed up on the fence to watch.

Jinglebob had just roped a big yearling and got him snubbed up to the snubbing post in the middle of the corral. He held him there while Whitey put a rope around the critter and climbed onto his back. Jinglebob turned his rope loose, and the calf started an imitation of a Brahma bull at the rodeo. Whitey rode about three jumps and then was thrown. After he'd dusted himself off a little, he roped another calf and Jinglebob tried to ride it.

Both boys were plastered with sweat and dirt. The calves likewise. Some were standing around with the tips of their tongues showing and foam on their chops.

"We're practicing to be top hands," Whitey told Uncle Torwal.

"Yessir!" said Jinglebob. "We're practicing on roping and bareback riding today."

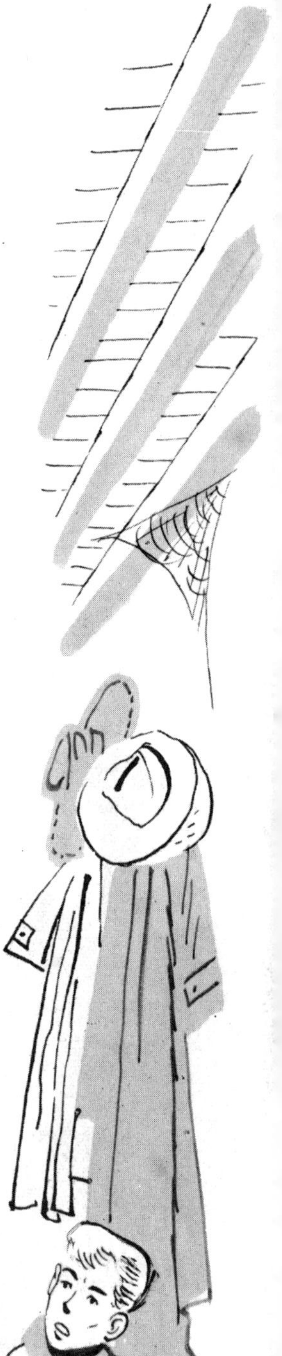

"Fat stock like that gets hot mighty easy," Torwal said, as they walked over to the windmill to get a drink.

"Yessir, it does for a fact," Whitey admitted.

"We'd sort of noticed that," said Jinglebob. "But if we are to be top hands, we have to keep in practice."

Uncle Torwal agreed that it was necessary for a top hand to keep in practice. But it occurred to him that such excitement wasn't exactly the best thing in the world for fattening calves.

Whitey and Jinglebob agreed that there was much in what he said. But how in the world were they to practice their riding, they wanted to know.

Uncle Torwal thought that over a while. Then he said, "It's too late to do anything about it today. But tomorrow, we'll build a contraption like one I saw down on the Reservation one time."

"I just don't see how we can learn to ride on a contraption," Whitey said. Jinglebob agreed with him.

"It'll give you a right brisk bit of practice, and not sweat the fat off the beef," Torwal assured him. From then on, he would tell no more about it.

They talked about the contraption while they peeled potatoes and sliced bacon for supper. Torwal listened to them as he mixed the biscuits, but wouldn't say anything. Even after they'd gone to bed, Whitey and Jinglebob talked of what kind of contraption Uncle Torwal could be thinking of. But they could make nothing of it. So they finally took their Stetsons off and went to sleep.

The next morning, as soon as they'd had breakfast and cleaned up the kitchen, Torwal took them out behind the blacksmith shop. He started the boys digging four deep post holes, set in a square some ten feet across, while he fastened four rings onto the ends of an old oil drum with strap iron and rivets. They finished the holes about the time he was done with the drum.

Then, from the pole pile, Torwal picked out four long, stout ash poles. He helped the boys set these up in the post holes and tamp them solid, after he'd fastened a good length of rope to the top of each. When that was done, he fastened the ropes to the rings in the drum, so it hung on its side some four feet off the ground. After he'd taken an old saddle and strapped it on the drum, he stepped back and looked the thing over.

"There's your contraption," he said, looking right pleased with himself. Whitey and Jinglebob looked at the contraption and then at each other.

After a while, Whitey spoke up. "It looks like a kids' play-toy to me," he said, looking right unhappy.

"Yessir! That's just the way it looks to me," Jinglebob said. "It'd be fine for kids to play with. But I don't see what we can do with it."

"Mebbe you won't feel so disappointed about it when you've given it a whirl," said Torwal. "Supposing you try it out first, Jinglebob."

Jinglebob wasn't at all enthusiastic. But he didn't want to hurt Uncle Torwal's feelings after he'd gone to so much trouble building the thing. So he said it was all right with him. He and Whitey both figured Uncle Torwal must be slipping. As a general thing, he understood how they felt about having to fool with kid stuff.

They hated to think how cowboys roundabout would laugh if the word got around they played with such a sissy contraption! But for now, there was nothing they could

do but make the best of it. So Jinglebob climbed into the saddle. He sat there looking sheepish while Uncle Torwal took up the stirrups to fit him.

"All set?" Torwal asked after a bit.

"Yessir, I reckon so," Jinglebob said, without much enthusiasm.

"Well, hang onto your hat!" And Torwal and Whitey started shoving the limber poles one way and another.

The Lone Tree Killer

That was when Jinglebob got the surprise of his life. With the drum swung from the tops of those limber poles whipping in all directions, it proved to be anything but a solid proposition. In less than no time at all, Jinglebob sailed off and rolled head over heels.

He was somewhat surprised. So was Whitey, for that matter. They looked at one another. They looked at the contraption. Uncle Torwal just looked pleased with himself. "Still think it's a kids' play-toy?" he asked after a while.

"No, sir! That thing bucks worse than Black Diamond at Cheyenne! But of course I wasn't expecting anything so brisk. If I could try it again, I don't reckon I'd have any trouble staying with it."

But the second try was no better than the first. Then Whitey tried it and was piled. After that, they talked Torwal into trying it, and were mighty pleased when he was thrown almost as quick as they had been. They all took

turns from then on. With practice, they found that they could make the contraption do just about anything an outlaw horse could do, and a few that would be right difficult for the best horse that ever wore hair.

While they were still experimenting with the contraption, Smoky Tom Nelson rode up with one of his cowboys to see Torwal about something or other. They were right pleased to see Torwal playing with a kids' contraption, they said, with wide grins.

After some talk back and forth, Torwal invited them to try a ride themselves, provided it was all right with Whitey and Jinglebob.

"Yessir! We'd be right pleased to have you try out our

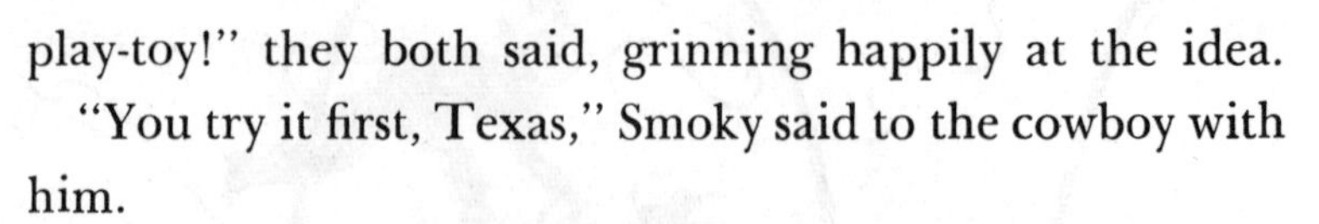

play-toy!" they both said, grinning happily at the idea.

"You try it first, Texas," Smoky said to the cowboy with him.

This cowboy was from Texas, where they go in more for fancy trimmings than is usual in Lone Tree County. Even for a Texas man, he was a sight for sore eyes. His saddle was crusted almost solid, wherever he wasn't sitting on it, with silver conchas and doo-dads of all kinds. He had little looking glasses set into the corners of his saddle skirts, in addition to the silver. His stirrups were covered with long *tapaderos* that near touched the ground. His Stetson was so tall and so wide in the brim, and had so many silver conchas on it, that Whitey and Jinglebob figured he must need both hands to take it off. Altogether, he was so loaded down that it seemed a wonder his horse wasn't sway-backed.

"I'm a man that will ride anything that has four legs and hair on the outside," the Texas man said. "When I set onto an outlaw's back, it's as if I'd suddenly growed there. Many a killer hoss has taken one look at me walking up to him and reformed on the spot, being from then on a perfect mount fer ladies, children, and *dee*-crepit Injuns. I've rode hosses that couldn't be rode, setting straight up, scratching them fore and aft according to Association rules, meanwhile reading the latest copy of *Grit*. But that's no hoss. It's nothing but a kids' contraption."

"Of course, if you're not feeling good . . ." Torwal began.

"I'm in fine fettle," the Texas man said. "Never felt better! Bright-eyed and bushy-tailed, that's me. But I still say that's a complete waste of time for a man of my talents!"

Whitey and Jinglebob were bug-eyed with excitement. They figured that if anybody could ride the contraption, it was the Texas man. A fellow that looked as grand and talked as fancy as that must be about the best in the country.

But the long and short of it was that after Torwal and Smoky talked the Texas man into trying just one ride, he did no better than anyone else. The first time the contraption flung him, he allowed it was an accident. He hadn't expected it to be so brisk, he said.

"Just what I said," Jinglebob whispered to Whitey.

But the second try was no better. The third was as bad. After that, he picked himself up and limped over to the contraption and looked it over close, while nobody said a word.

"Where in the name of all-get-out did you get this infernal machine? What do you use it for?"

"In this country we build such things for the children to learn to ride on," Torwal told him. "To sort of start them on something easy until they can handle a real horse."

The Texas man brushed dust off himself, then spoke up again. "Up to now I've rode everything that come down the pike," he said. "I've rode 'em saddled and I've rode 'em slick. I've rode big hosses down to nubbins and little hosses down to nuthin! And then I get flang by a kids' contraption! All I can say is, yuh should name it the Lone Tree Killer and enter it in the contest at Cheyenne this fall."

And from then on, the Lone Tree Killer's reputation spread. Any Sunday afternoon, you could find half the cowboys in Lone Tree County gathered around and waiting their turn to get thrown by it. Whitey and Jinglebob had to wait their turn at it like everyone else. They no longer felt it was a kids' contraption. And they had plenty of company when they practiced to be top hands.

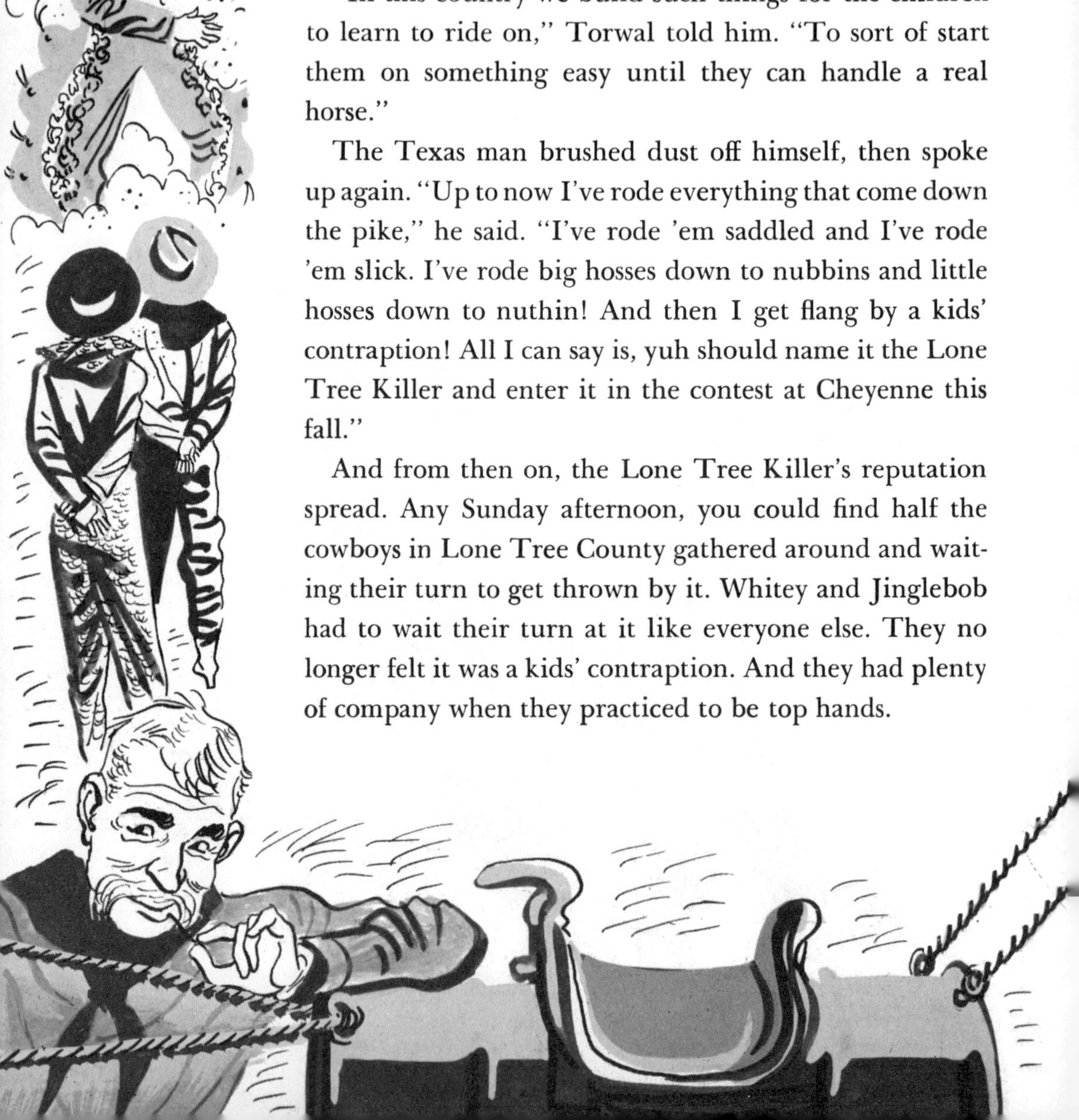

Whistling Down the Street

If I've a tune to whistle
When hurrying down the street,
A rhythm to keep time to
With running, jigging feet—

I'll not be sad or lonely,
While there's a gay refrain
For whistling in the sunshine,
Singing in the rain.

—Dorothy Hall

I Arise

I arise from rest with movements swift
As the beat of the raven's wings.
I arise
To meet the day.
My face is turned from the dark of night
To gaze at the dawn of day
Now whitening in the sky.

—Eskimo Poem

I Will Walk

I will walk with leg muscles
which are strong
as the sinews of the shins of the
little caribou calf.
I will walk with leg muscles
which are strong
as the sinews of the shins
of the little hare.
I will take care not to go towards the dark.
I will go towards the day.

—Eskimo Poem

The Puzzled Centipede

A centipede was happy quite,
Until a frog in fun
Said, "Pray, which leg comes after which?"
This raised her mind to such a pitch
She lay distracted in the ditch
Considering how to run.

—Unknown

The Lion

The Lion is a kingly beast.
He likes a Hindu for a feast.
And if no Hindu he can get,
The lion-family is upset.

He cuffs his wife and bites her ears
Till she is nearly moved to tears.
Then some explorer finds the den
And all is family peace again.

—Vachel Lindsay

The Melancholy Pig

There was a Pig, that sat alone,
  Beside a ruined Pump.
By night and day he made his moan:
It would have stirred a heart of stone
To see him wring his hoofs and groan,
  Because he could not jump.

—Lewis Carroll

The Pirate Don Durk of Dowdee

Ho, for the Pirate Don Durk of Dowdee!
He was as wicked as wicked could be,
But oh, he was perfectly gorgeous to see!
The Pirate Don Durk of Dowdee.

His conscience, of course, was as black as a bat,
But he had a floppety plume on his hat
And when he went walking it jiggled—like that!
The plume of the Pirate Dowdee.

His coat it was crimson and cut with a slash,
And often as ever he twirled his mustache
Deep down in the ocean the mermaids went splash,
Because of Don Durk of Dowdee.

Moreover, Dowdee had a purple tattoo,
And stuck in his belt where he buckled it through
Were a dagger, a dirk and a squizzamaroo,
For fierce was the Pirate Dowdee.

Oh, he had a cutlass that swung at his thigh
And he had a parrot called Pepperkin Pye,
And a zigzaggy scar at the end of his eye
Had Pirate Don Durk of Dowdee.

He kept in a cavern, this buccaneer bold,
A curious chest that was covered with mould,
And all of his pockets were jingly with gold!
Oh jing! went the gold of Dowdee.

His conscience, of course, it was crook'd like a
squash,
But both of his boots made a slickery slosh,
And he went through the world with a wonderful
swash,
Did Pirate Don Durk of Dowdee.

It's true he was wicked as wicked could be,
His sins they outnumbered a hundred and three,
But oh, he was perfectly gorgeous to see,
The Pirate Don Durk of Dowdee.

—Mildred Plew Meigs

Water Noises

When I am playing by myself,
And all the boys are lost around,
Then I can hear the water go;
It makes a little talking sound.

Along the rocks below the tree,
I see it ripple up and wink;
And I can hear it saying on,
And do you think? And do you think?

A bug shoots by that snaps and ticks,
And a bird flies up beside the tree
To go into the sky to sing,
I hear it say, *Killdee, killdee!*

Or else a yellow cow comes down
To splash a while and have a drink.
But when she goes I still can hear
The water say, *And do you think?*

—Elizabeth Madox Roberts

Dust of Snow

The way a crow
Shook down on me
The dust of snow
From a hemlock tree

Has given my heart
A change of mood
And saved some part
Of a day I rued.

—*Robert Frost*

Song for a Little House

I'm glad our house is a little house,
Not too tall nor too wide;
I'm glad the hovering butterflies
Feel free to come inside.

Our little house is a friendly house,
It is not shy or vain;
It gossips with the talking trees,
And makes friends with the rain.

And quick leaves cast a shimmer of green
Against the whited walls,
And in the phlox, the courteous bees
Are paying duty calls.

—*Christopher Morley*

The Horseshoe

Wonder where this horseshoe went.
Up and down, up and down,
Up and past the monument,
Maybe into town.

Wait a minute. "Horseshoe,
How far have you been?"
Says it's been to Salem
And halfway to Lynn.

Wonder who was in the team.
Wonder what they saw.
Wonder if they passed a bridge—
Bridge with a draw.

Says it went from one bridge
Straight upon another.
Says it took a little girl
Driving with her mother.

—Edna St. Vincent Millay

Lonesome Train

The train that wails across the hills
Gathers in its cry
All the lonesomeness of dark,
The bigness of the sky.
Something deep inside me thrills
To hear a train go by.

—Dorothy Hall

Silver Ships

There are trails that a lad may follow
  When the years of his boyhood slip,
But I shall soar like a swallow
  On the wings of a silver ship,

Guiding my bird of metal,
  One with her throbbing frame,
Floating down like a petal,
  Roaring up like a flame;

Winding the wind that scatters
  Smoke from the chimney's lip,
Tearing the clouds to tatters
  With the wings of my silver ship;

Grazing the broad blue sky light
  Up where the falcons fare,
Riding the realms of twilight,
  Brushed by a comet's hair;

Snug in my coat of leather,
  Watching the skyline swing,
Shedding the world like a feather
  From the tip of a tilted wing.

There are trails that a lad may travel
  When the years of his boyhood wane,
But I'll let a rainbow ravel
  Through the wings of my silver plane.

—Mildred Plew Meigs

Old Quin Queeribus

Old Quin Queeribus—
He loved his garden so,
He wouldn't have a rake around,
A shovel or a hoe.

For each potato's eyes he bought
Fine spectacles of gold,
And mufflers for the corn, to keep
Its ears from getting cold.

On every head of lettuce green—
What do you think of that?—
And every head of cabbage, too,
He tied a garden hat.

Old Quin Queeribus—
He loved his garden so,
He couldn't eat his growing things,
He only let them grow!

—Nancy Byrd Turner

Tillie

Old Tillie Turveycombe
Sat to sew,
Just where a patch of fern did grow;
There, as she yawned,
And yawn wide did she,
Floated some seed
Down her gull-e-t;
And look you once,
And look you twice,
Poor old Tillie
Was gone in a trice.
But oh, when the wind
Do a-moaning come,
'Tis poor old Tillie
Sick for home;
And oh, when a voice
In the mist do sigh,
Old Tillie Turveycombe's
Floating by.

—*Walter de la Mare*

Autumn

The morns are meeker than they were,
The nuts are getting brown,
The berry's cheek is plumper,
The rose is out of town.

The maple wears a gayer scarf,
The field a scarlet gown.
Lest I should be old-fashioned,
I'll put a trinket on.

—Emily Dickinson

Snow

Oh the falling Snow!
Oh the falling Snow!
Where does it all come from?
Whither does it go?
Never never laughing,
Never never weeping,
Falling in its Sleep,
Forever ever sleeping—
From what Sleep of Heaven
Does it flow, and go
Into what Sleep of Earth,
The falling, falling Snow?

—Eleanor Farjeon

Stopping by Woods on a Snowy Evening

Whose woods these are I think I know.
His house is in the village though;
He will not see me stopping here
To watch his woods fill up with snow.

My little horse must think it queer
To stop without a farmhouse near
Between the woods and frozen lake
The darkest evening of the year.

He gives his harness bells a shake
To ask if there is some mistake.
The only other sound's the sweep
Of easy wind and downy flake.

The woods are lovely, dark and deep.
But I have promises to keep,
And miles to go before I sleep,
And miles to go before I sleep.

—Robert Frost

Ducks' Ditty

All along the backwater,
Through the rushes tall,
Ducks are a-dabbling,
Up tails all!

Ducks' tails, drakes' tails,
Yellow feet a-quiver,
Yellow bills all out of sight
Busy in the river!

Slushy green undergrowth
Where the roach swim—
Here we keep our larder
Cool and full and dim.

Everyone for what he likes!
We like to be
Heads down, tails up,
Dabbling free!

High in the blue above
Swifts whirl and call—
We are down a-dabbling
Up tails all!

—*Kenneth Grahame*

Swift Things Are Beautiful

Swift things are beautiful:
Swallows and deer,
And lightning that falls
Bright-veined and clear,
Rivers and meteors,
Wind in the wheat,
The strong-withered horse,
The runner's sure feet.
—*Elizabeth Coatsworth*

Dogs and Weather

I'd like a different dog
For every kind of weather—
A narrow greyhound for a fog,
A wolfhound strange and white
With a tail like a silver feather
To run with in the night,
When snow is still and winter stars are bright.

In the fall I'd like to see
In answer to my whistle,
A golden spaniel look at me.
But best of all for rain
A terrier, hairy as a thistle,
To trot with fine disdain
Beside me down the soaked, sweet-smelling lane.

—*Winifred Welles*

April Rain

It isn't raining rain for me,
It's raining daffodils;
In every dimpled drop I see
Wild flowers on the hills.

The clouds of gray engulf the day
And overwhelm the town;
It is not raining rain to me,
It's raining roses down.

It is not raining rain to me
But fields of clover bloom,
Where any buccaneering bee
Can find a bed and room.

A health unto the happy,
A fig for him who frets!
It is not raining rain to me,
It's raining violets.

—Robert Loveman

The Day Before April

The day before April
  Alone, alone,
I walked in the woods
  And sat on a stone.
I sat on a broad stone
  And sang to the birds.
The tune was God's making
  But I made the words.

—Mary Carolyn Davies

Comparison

Apple blossoms look like snow,
They're different, though.
Snow falls softly, but it brings
Noisy things:
Sleighs and bells, forts and fights,
Cozy nights.
But apple blossoms when they go,
White and slow,
Quiet all the orchard space,
Till the place
Hushed with falling sweetness seems
Filled with dreams.

—John Farrar

The Mist and All

I like the fall,
The mist and all.
I like the night owl's
Lonely call—
And wailing sound
Of wind around.

I like the gray
November day,
And bare, dead boughs
That coldly sway
Against my pane.
I like the rain.

I like to sit
And laugh at it—
And tend
My cozy fire a bit.
I like the fall—
The mist and all—

—Dixie Willson

November Night

Listen . . .
With faint dry sound,
Like steps of passing ghosts,
The leaves, frost-crisp'd,
  break from the trees
And fall.

—Adelaide Crapsey

The Cat and the Broom

The broom looks tattered and tired today,
The raggedest stick of a broom;
It couldn't reach up for a cobweb grey
Or sweep out the smallest room.

And Trusty Tompkins, our little black cat,
With fur like the finest silk,
Is curled up tight in a ball on the mat
Too sleepy to drink his milk.

But the bad old broom looks rakish and sly,
As if it had been on a spree;
And Puss from a narrow satin eye
Looks wickedly out at me.

Ho, ho! I know what the rascal pair
In the midnight hours were at;
It wasn't mousing or sweeping the stair
That made them look like that.

I know by the old broom's battered plight
And Tompkins' look of sin
They were both of them out with a witch last night,
And they've only just got in.

—A. A. Kenny

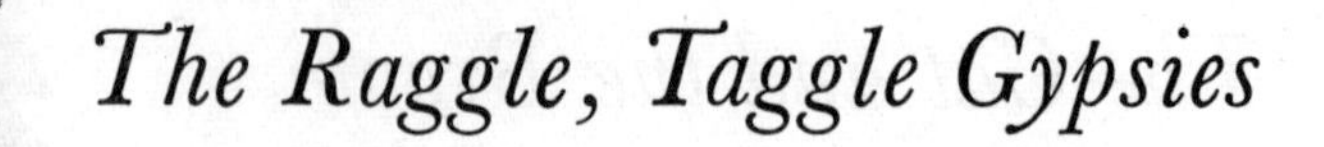

The Raggle, Taggle Gypsies

There were three gypsies a-come to my door,
  And downstairs ran this lady, O.
One sang high and another sang low,
  And the other sang "Bonnie, Bonnie Biskay, O."

Then she pulled off her silken gown,
  And put on hose of leather, O.
With the ragged, ragged rags about her door
  She's off with the Raggle, Taggle Gypsies, O.

'Twas late last night when my lord came home,
  Inquiring for his lady, O.
The servants said on every hand,
  "She's gone with the Raggle, Taggle Gypsies, O."

"Oh, saddle for me my milk-white steed,
  Oh, saddle for me my pony, O.
That I may ride and seek my bride
  Who's gone with the Raggle, Taggle Gypsies, O."

Oh, he rode high and he rode low,
He rode through woods and copses, O.
Until he came to an open field,
And there he espied his lady, O.

"What makes you leave your house and lands?
What makes you leave your money, O?
What makes you leave your new-wedded lord
To go with the Raggle, Taggle Gypsies, O?"

"What care I for my house and lands?
What care I for my money, O,
What care I for my new-wedded lord?
I'm off with the Raggle, Taggle Gypsies, O."

"Last night you slept on a goose-feather bed,
With the sheet turned down so bravely, O.
Tonight you will sleep in the cold, open field,
Along with the Raggle, Taggle Gypsies, O."

"What care I for your goose-feather bed,
With the sheet turned down so bravely, O?
For tonight I shall sleep in a cold, open field,
Along with the Raggle, Taggle Gypsies, O."

—Old Folk Song

The Cowboy's Life

The bawl of a steer,
To a cowboy's ear,
Is music of sweetest strain;
And the yelping notes
Of the gay coyotes
To him are a glad refrain.

For a kingly crown
In the noisy town
His saddle he wouldn't change;
No life so free
As the life we see
Way out on the Yaso range.

The rapid beat
Of his broncho's feet
On the sod as he speeds along,
Keeps living time
To the ringing rhyme
Of his rollicking cowboy song.

The winds may howl
And the thunder growl
Or the breezes may safely moan;—
A cowboy's life
Is a royal life,
His saddle his kingly throne.

—James Barton Adams

Whoopee Ti Yi Yo

As I was a-walking one morning for pleasure,
I spied a cowpuncher all riding alone;
His hat was throwed back
and his spurs was a-jinglin'
As he approached me a-singin' this song:

Whoopee ti yi yo, git along, little dogies;
It's your misfortune and none of my own.
Whoopee ti yi yo, git along, little dogies,
For you know Wyoming will be your new home.

Early in spring we round up the dogies,
Mark and brand and bob off their tails;
Round up our horses, load up the chuck wagon,
Then throw the dogies upon the old trail.

It's whooping and yelling
and driving the dogies;
Oh, how I wish you would go on!
It's whooping and punching
and go on, little dogies,
For you know Wyoming will be your new home.

—*Unknown*

Faith, I Wish I Were a Leprechaun

Faith, I wish I were a leprechaun
Beneath a hawthorn tree,
A-cobblin' of wee, magic boots,
A-eatin' luscious, lovely fruits;
Oh, fiddle-dum, oh, fiddle-dee,
I wish I were a leprechaun
Beneath a hawthorn tree!

Faith, I wish I were a leprechaun
Beneath a hawthorn tree,
A-throwin' snuff into the eyes
Of young and old and dull and wise;
Oh, fiddle-dum, oh, fiddle-dee,
I wish I were a leprechaun
Beneath a hawthorn tree!

Faith, I wish I were a leprechaun
Beneath a hawthorn tree,
With no more irksome thing to do
Than sew a small, bewitchin' shoe;
Oh, fiddle-dum, oh, fiddle-dee,
I wish I were a leprechaun
Beneath a hawthorn tree!

—Margaret Ritter

Real People

These boys and girls
were just as real as you—
Like you, they used to dream
and eat and play;
Were mostly good,
but full of mischief too—
Perhaps you'll grow up
in a book some day!

—Dorothy Hall

Dick Whittington and His Cat

A Story of Old England

More than 500 years ago, there really was a Dick Whittington, who really did become Lord Mayor of London. Young people have always liked to believe that Dick's cat was real, too.

Once upon a time in England lived a boy called Dick Whittington. His father and mother died when he was young. All he had to eat and to wear was what the other poor folk in the village could spare him. And that was not very much.

One day, Dick watched a wagon drive down the village street. The eight horses all had bells on their heads. "That fine wagon must be going to London!" thought Dick. "Oh, if I could only go there, too!" Like all the country folk of his day, the poor boy was sure that London was a wonderful place, where the streets were paved with gold.

The wagoner was walking beside his horses, his whip in his hand. "Please, sir," said Dick timidly, "may I go with you to London town?" And when the kind wagoner learned that Dick had no parents to care, he was willing.

At last they got to London. Dick was in such a hurry to

see the gold-paved streets that off he ran without even saying goodbye. He ran and he ran and he ran. But alas! the streets were just as muddy and dirty as in his own village at home.

Poor Dick nearly starved in London. There was no work to be had. At last, when he had not eaten for three days, he lay down on a doorstep, weak and ill. Here he was spied by the cook, an ugly, bad-tempered old woman.

"For shame, you lazy beggar!" she scolded. "Be off or I'll give you a bath of hot dishwater!" Just then, the owner of the house himself appeared. He was Mr. Fitzwarren, a rich merchant.

At the sight of the ragged boy lying on his doorstep, Mr. Fitzwarren shook his head. Poor children were expected to work almost from the time they could toddle. Still, the merchant spoke kindly. "Why are you not at work, my boy?"

"Because I can get no work," Dick answered faintly. "And I am ready to die of hunger."

Mr. Fitzwarren had Dick brought in and fed and given an attic to sleep in. He was to clean the pans and run errands for the cook.

Dick would have been content if it hadn't been for the cook's bad temper. She worked him from dawn to dark, and often beat him. Besides, the merchant's house was old and overrun with mice. In his attic at night, Dick could hardly sleep for the scuffling and the squeaking. Finally, he decided to buy a cat.

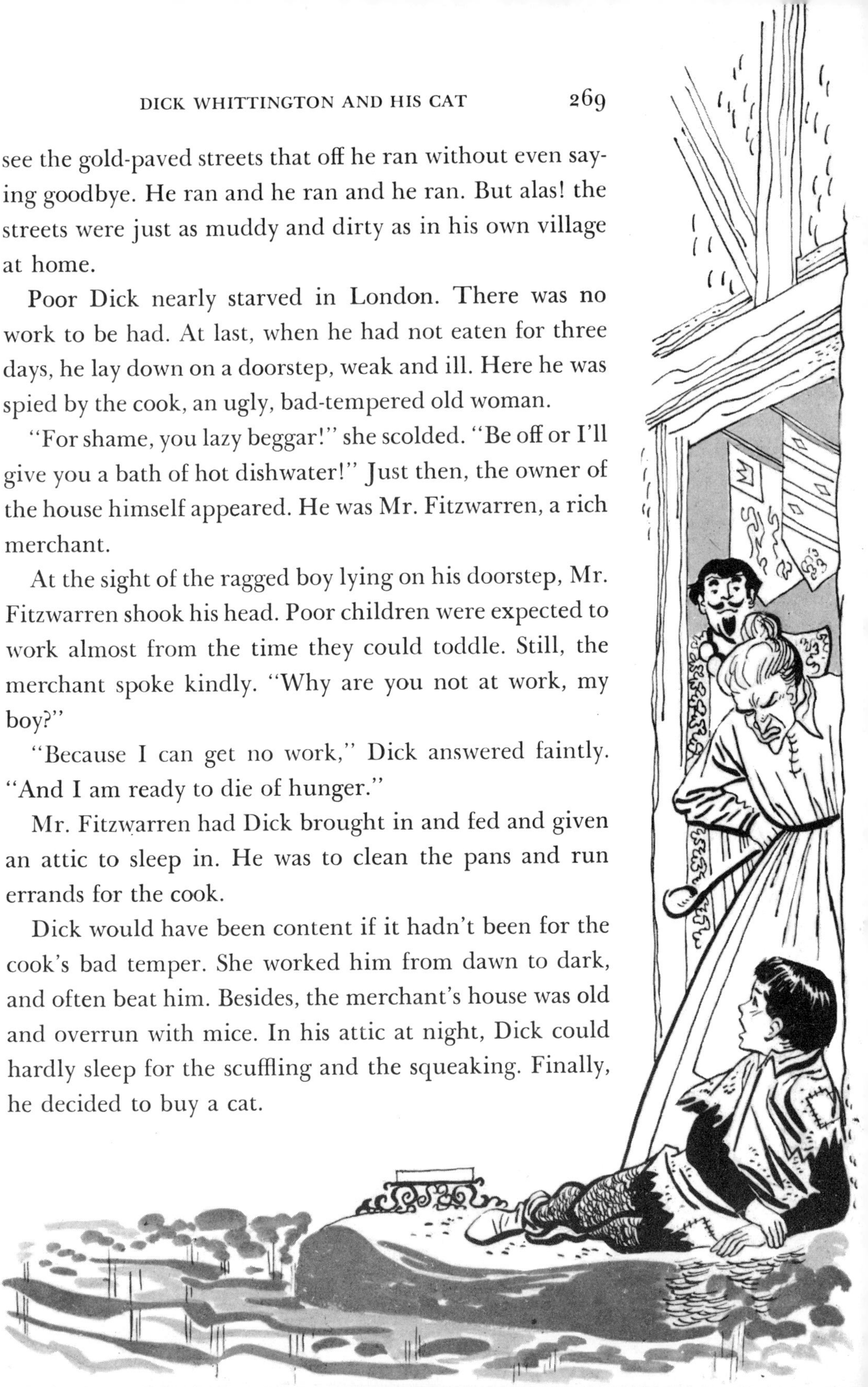

With the only penny he had in the world, Dick went out into the streets. There he saw a little girl with a fine large cat in her arms.

"Little girl, will you sell me your cat for a penny?"

"Yes, I will," said the little girl. "And she is a good mouser, too."

So Dick took Mrs. Puss to his attic. From that day on, there was peace and quiet with the mice.

Some time later, Mr. Fitzwarren had a ship ready to set sail to foreign ports. And, as was his custom, he called all his servants together. Each one brought some money, or goods to send out for trade.

Only Dick did not appear. Miss Alice, Mr. Fitzwarren's daughter, guessed what the trouble was. She sent for the boy, saying, "Father, I will lay down some money for Dick, out of my own purse."

"No, daughter, that you may not do. The rule is, you know, that each must send something of his own."

Then Dick spoke up. "All I have in the world is a cat, which I bought for a penny from a little girl."

"Fetch your cat, then, my lad, and let her go."

So Dick fetched Mrs. Puss and gave her to the captain, while the others grinned. But Miss Alice saw that Dick hated to part with his cat. Secretly, she gave him some money to buy another.

After that, Miss Alice did many kind little things for Dick. It made the old cook so cross and jealous that she treated Dick worse than ever. At last, he thought he could not stand it any longer. So early one morning, the poor boy tied his few ragged clothes up into a bundle and crept softly out of the house.

He trudged as far as Halloway. There he sat down on a stone—to this day called Whittington's stone. As he sat there, the bells of Bow Church began to ring. And plain as plain, they said to Dick:

Turn again, Whittington,
Thrice Lord Mayor of London.

"Lord Mayor of London!" said Dick to himself. "To be Lord Mayor of London, and ride in a fine coach! Why, what is the cuffing and scolding of a poor old woman, if I am to be Lord Mayor of London at last?"

So, taking up his bundle, Dick returned. He was lucky enough to get into the house and start his work before the old cook came downstairs.

A Cat That Looked at a King

In the meantime, Mr. Fitzwarren's ship, the *Unicorn,* was driven by storms to the Barbary Coast of Africa, where English ships seldom came. The people there were Moors. They came down to the ship in throngs, to stare at the English sailors.

The captain sent samples of his cargo to the Moorish king, and in return was invited to visit the king and queen at the palace. There, he was received most politely, and food was brought. But hardly were the dishes on the table when a whole army of rats and mice rushed in, and made short work of the meal.

The captain was astonished. "Is this not—er, well, unpleasant—to His Majesty?" he asked cautiously.

"Oh, yes," the servants said. "The king would give half his treasure to be rid of these terrible pests."

Then the captain remembered Whittington's cat. "Your Majesty," he said, "on board my ship is a marvelous creature. It could soon deliver you from these rats."

The king jumped up and cracked his heels together for joy. "Bring the creature at once," he ordered. "If it can do what you say, I will load your ship with gold and jewels."

So the captain went off to the ship while the cooks prepared another meal. He got back with Mrs. Puss just as the rats and mice rushed out for the second time.

Mrs. Puss did not need to be told what to do. Jumping out of the captain's arms, she pounced right and left on her enemies. In a few minutes, those that were not dead had run squeaking to their holes. The king and queen were speechless with delight.

"Here, pussy, pussy!" the captain called. Mrs. Puss came up and rubbed around his feet, and the captain, taking her up, presented her to the queen.

At first, the queen was a little afraid. But when the captain stroked the cat and said, "Pussy, pussy," the queen also put out her hand and said, "Putty, putty!" And Mrs. Puss jumped into the queen's lap, purring, and settled down for a nap.

When the king learned that Mrs. Puss's kittens would keep not only his palace but the whole country free from rats, he bought the ship's cargo at a handsome price. But he gave ten times as much for Mrs. Puss as for all the rest.

One morning, Mr. Fitzwarren had gone early to his counting-house. He had had no word of the *Unicorn,* and was beginning to feel uneasy. Just then there was a knock at the door. "Who knocks?" he called.

"Your captain," came the answer. "I bring good news of the *Unicorn* and all her cargo."

When Mr. Fitzwarren heard the whole wonderful story, he could only exclaim over and over again. At last, he sent for all the household.

Again, Dick would have excused himself. But Mr. Fitzwarren insisted, and even had Dick sit down in a chair. At first, the poor boy thought everybody was making fun of him.

"Indeed, Mr. Whittington, we are not making fun of you," Mr. Fitzwarren said. "The captain has sold your cat to the King of Barbary for more than my whole fortune." And he had the captain and his men open the treasure, to show Dick it was really true.

Dick wanted to share his riches with Mr. Fitzwarren and Miss Alice. But they would not accept any. He had to content himself with giving presents to the captain and the crew, and even to the old cook.

Then Dick had to send for a tailor, and dress like a gentleman. And when his face was washed and he was dressed in fine clothes, Miss Alice's liking for Dick turned into love. So they were married, and the Lord Mayor of London himself came to their wedding.

Dick was Sheriff of London and three times Lord Mayor, as the Bow Bells had foretold. He was also made a knight by the king. And for many years, the stone figure of Sir Richard Whittington, with his cat in his arms, could be seen over the doorway to one of the public buildings put up while he was Mayor.

Andy Stands Guard

Stanley Young

When Andrew Jackson was twelve years old, the American Revolution was coming in earnest to the Carolina frontier. Andy's father was dead, and his brother Hugh was fighting with the American army. No news of Hugh had come for a long time. So Andy's mother set out to look for him, with Andy's Uncle Crawford. Andy was left with his aunt, to guard the house.

Aunt Crawford and Andy watched them wind their way down the rough corduroy road. Then they turned to go into the house.

"Your mother's a brave woman," Aunt Crawford said, wiping her eyes on her apron.

Andy nodded. Secretly, he didn't see why his mother had to go looking for Hugh. Hugh was a soldier, a man now. He could look out for himself.

"Come now," Aunt Crawford said. "We've the dishes to do."

A frown broke over Andy's face. "Uncle said I was to guard the house."

"You can guard from the kitchen," Aunt Crawford said, smiling.

Andy took up his gun and reluctantly followed her. He dried the dishes faithfully, but down to the last pewter cup his eyes and mind were out of the window. He had set his gun up in one of the cabin rifle holes, ready for action. Every cabin, as well as every blockhouse, had these square openings about every five feet around the entire building. Andy kept darting from one hole to the other as if he expected a raid any minute. His jumping made his aunt nervous.

"You'll have me jumping next," she said. "Go on outside."

Andy grabbed up his rifle and tore for the door. There was a tall pine just outside. With his gun fastened to his belt with leather thongs, Andy shinnied up the pine, hugging the tree with his knees until his hands caught the first branch. He pulled himself up and climbed to the highest branch. Shading his eyes, he looked out over

the landscape. Far below was Twelve Mile Creek, filled with logs pushing their slow way down the valley to the Catawba. Up the valley, right, he could see the smoke curling from Long Potter's house.

Andy looked away to the left. As far as he could see, the landscape lay peaceful in the gray morning light. But when he looked nearer he saw something that almost made him fall out of the tree. Not a hundred yards away, in the edge of the forest, he saw a man dodging from right to left and back again. The man was evidently pursuing something but Andy could not see what it was. The man wore buckskins like everyone else. But his face, at this distance, could not be recognized.

Behind the man, only a few steps now, Andy could see the copper-brown, half-naked figure of an Indian brave. The Indian was following the settler, step by step, and gaining on him. Andy saw the Indian raise his tomahawk high above his head. Almost instinctively, almost before he had time to be afraid, Andy pulled his rifle tight to his shoulder and fired.

The woods rang with the sound. Andy looked and saw that the Indian had disappeared and the white man was turning his head from side to side in surprise trying to locate the direction of the shot. Andy slid to the ground. He stopped long enough to ram fresh shot and powder into his gun. Then he hurried toward the spot where he had seen the Indian. Aunt Crawford came out of the house and called to him, but he ran on.

The Schoolmaster

It took Andy no more than a minute to reach the spot. When he saw the white man's long black hair and his hawkish nose he recognized him at once. Old Horn-Rim, the schoolmaster. Andy ran up to him, shouting.

"Why, Master Jackson!" the schoolmaster exclaimed. "Did you fire that shot just now?"

"I did, sir," Andy said.

"Well now, that's a pity. I was pursuing one of the various diurnal lepidopterous insects that so abound in this region—"

"And an Indian was after you," Andy said shortly. "I shot at him from that tree. He was about to tomahawk you."

The schoolmaster's eyes widened. Andy left him and ran over to the tree close by where he saw the bark scarred. His shot had hit the tree behind which the Indian had hidden.

"Here," Andy said. "Here are his footprints, right enough."

"Well," the schoolmaster said. "Well, I thought the Indians were peaceable around here."

"There's a war on," Andy said. "The Redcoats get them stirred up."

There was a pause. The schoolmaster smiled down at the excited boy.

"Andy, I suppose if there's one person around here whose life you shouldn't be too particular about, it's the schoolmaster's."

Andy looked embarrassed, not knowing what to say. Old Horn-Rim was all right but he wasn't very exciting, as a rule.

"What did you say you were chasing?" Andy asked, anxious to change the subject. His eyes peered into the shadows of the forest.

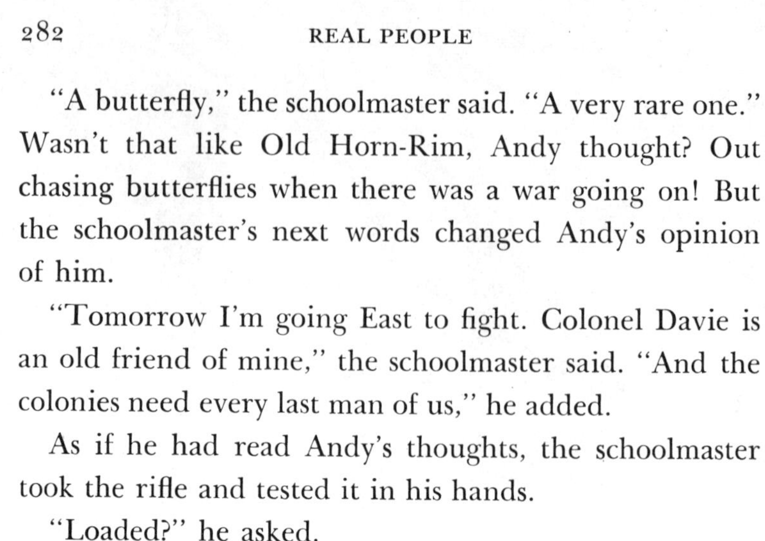

"A butterfly," the schoolmaster said. "A very rare one." Wasn't that like Old Horn-Rim, Andy thought? Out chasing butterflies when there was a war going on! But the schoolmaster's next words changed Andy's opinion of him.

"Tomorrow I'm going East to fight. Colonel Davie is an old friend of mine," the schoolmaster said. "And the colonies need every last man of us," he added.

As if he had read Andy's thoughts, the schoolmaster took the rifle and tested it in his hands.

"Loaded?" he asked.

Andy nodded. The schoolmaster raised the gun to his shoulder.

"See that bare limb over there? That dead one on the poplar?" he asked.

Andy nodded again. Surely the schoolmaster wasn't going to try to hit that! It was too far.

When the schoolmaster fired Andy saw the branch on the poplar fall to the ground. He was speechless. The schoolmaster handed the gun back to Andy.

"Let's walk over to your house," he said. "I want to tell your aunt that her brave nephew saved my life."

Andy walked along with him in silence, thinking. Old Horn-Rim, what a shot! Never again would he judge anyone by his outward appearance. And never again would he make fun of the schoolmaster, or hide hoptoads in the three-legged desk. Andy decided that perhaps his mother was right in wanting him to be a schoolmaster. Or maybe

he would be a lawyer, as Old Horn-Rim had so often suggested.

"If you'd been where I was you'd have hit that Indian, certain," Andy said.

"I wouldn't have tried to hit him. I'd have frightened him away, as you did, Andy," the schoolmaster replied.

Andy looked puzzled.

"The Indian is fighting for his land the same way we're fighting the British. No wonder they hate us, lad," the schoolmaster went on. "All the decent settlers—your father, your uncle, and most of them around here—bought their lands from the Indians. A lot of others just grabbed theirs, at the point of a rifle."

As the schoolmaster talked on, Andy forgot to be sorry over missing the Indian. He was glad now that he had only hit the tree. Maybe the Indians were like white men, some of them all right and some not.

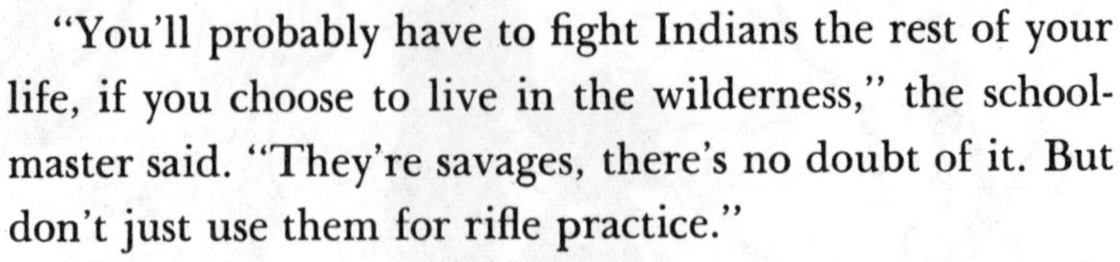

"You'll probably have to fight Indians the rest of your life, if you choose to live in the wilderness," the schoolmaster said. "They're savages, there's no doubt of it. But don't just use them for rifle practice."

Aunt Crawford was halfway to the forest when Andy and the schoolmaster came out. Her eyes were questioning and fearful well before she spoke.

Andy told her, simply, what had happened and the schoolmaster offered to stay at the cabin until Mr. Crawford came home.

Andy protested against this. He assured his aunt that one man around the place was quite enough.

The schoolmaster smiled. "The Scotch-Irish are a stubborn lot," he said. "The salt of the earth, though. How do I know? I'm one myself."

And then shaking Andy's hand and thanking him again, elaborately and at length in three-syllable words, he started down the path toward Twelve Mile Creek. Andy looked after him and saw with amazement that the schoolmaster had begun to dodge back and forth, on and off the path, just as he had been doing when the Indian was after him.

"All that for a diurnal lepidopterous insect," Andy said.

Aunt Crawford stared at him with her eyes popping.

"What! Were you swearing, Andrew?" she asked severely.

"No'm," he said. "I was merely discussin' butterflies."

Aunt Crawford shrugged her shoulders and decided that the Indian affair had momentarily robbed her nephew of his wits. She turned and went into the house. Andy, his eyes on the forest, stood in silent watch by the door wondering what he would do if a Redcoat suddenly appeared over the hill.

Peregrine White and Virginia Dare

Virginia Dare was the first baby of English parentage to be born in this country—in 1587, in the "lost" colony of Roanoke, Virginia. Peregrine White was the first child born in the Pilgrim colony in Massachusetts in 1620.

Peregrine White
And Virginia Dare
Were the first real Americans
Anywhere.

Others might find it
Strange to come
Over the ocean
To make a home,

England and memory
Left behind—
But Virginia and Peregrine
Didn't mind.

One of them born
On Roanoke
And the other cradled
In Pilgrim oak.

Rogues might bicker
And good men pray.
Did they pay attention?
No, not they.

Men might grumble
And women weep
But Virginia and Peregrine
Went to sleep.

They had their dinner
And napped and then
When they woke up
It was dinner again.

They didn't worry,
They didn't wish,
They didn't farm
And they didn't fish.

There was lots of work
But they didn't do it.
They were pioneers
But they never knew it.

Wolves in the forest
And Indian drums!
Virginia and Peregrine
Sucked their thumbs.

They were only babies.
They didn't care.
Peregrine White
And Virginia Dare.

—*Rosemary and Stephen Vincent Benét*

Lift Off

Gene Gurney

On February 20, 1962, American newspaper headlines told the story everyone had been waiting for:

GLENN ORBITS EARTH
THREE TIMES SAFELY.

After 1,160 days of hard, painstaking effort, the men of Project Mercury had achieved their goal.

There had been some discouraging setbacks during those 1,160 days, but none were more disturbing than the ones that occurred right at the end. The flight that finally proved to be so successful on February 20th had been postponed no less than ten times!

After the astrochimp Enos completed his two orbits of the earth on November 29, 1961, manned flight around the earth was next on the Project Mercury schedule. Before Enos, an unmanned capsule and the Atlas booster had performed well. There was nothing more that could be learned until a man was placed in orbit.

The man chosen to make the all-important trip was—Lieutenant Colonel John H. Glenn, Jr., at forty the oldest of the seven astronauts. His alternate, the astronaut who would go if Glenn should become ill, was Lieutenant Commander Malcolm Scott Carpenter. The date was first set for some time before the end of the year. It was hoped that, like the Soviet Union, the United States would be able to orbit a man in 1961.

The length of time spent in preparation between the Mercury launchings had averaged about six weeks. After Enos' flight, workers at Cape Canaveral thought that by working extra hours they could be ready in less time. But there was too much to do and too much at stake to take chances on hasty work. The date was finally set for January 16, 1962. And even that proved to be too soon.

During the pre-flight check, a defect was found in the capsule's air-conditioning system; it meant a week's delay. The repairs couldn't be completed in a week—another delay. Then there was trouble with the emergency oxygen supply to the capsule's cabin and the astronaut's pressure suit. The date of the launching had to be set back again—to January 27th.

This time the preliminary checks showed that both the Atlas and the capsule were ready to go. Astronaut Glenn, who had been training daily for the flight, was also ready. It looked as if January 27th might be the big day.

The astronaut was up at two in the morning. At 5:15 A.M. he climbed into the space capsule. The moon was shining and everything looked good for the launching.

At 9:10 A.M. the flight was called off. Several minor technical difficulties had held up the countdown. While technicians worked to correct them, an unexpected cloud cover rolled in over Cape Canaveral. It was thick and it showed no signs of lifting. Project Mercury officials would not be able to follow the Atlas as it lifted off the pad. The safety of the astronaut depended on optical as well as electronic tracking.

"Well, there'll be another day," said the weary Colonel Glenn as he left the launching pad after four hours in the capsule.

As it turned out, there were to be several more days. Fuel had leaked into an insulated bulkhead of the Atlas missile. The insulation had to be replaced. And then the weather caused more delays. Like Astronauts Shepard and Grissom before him, Glenn would land in the Atlantic, and weather is usually bad in the mid-Atlantic during February. A series of storms moved across the area. The waiting recovery ships pitched and rolled in strong winds and waves twenty feet high. A capsule landing in such seas was likely to be lost.

The storms continued to move in. Cape Canaveral and the whole country continued to wait. The Atlas booster and the capsule stood on Pad 14 ready to go.

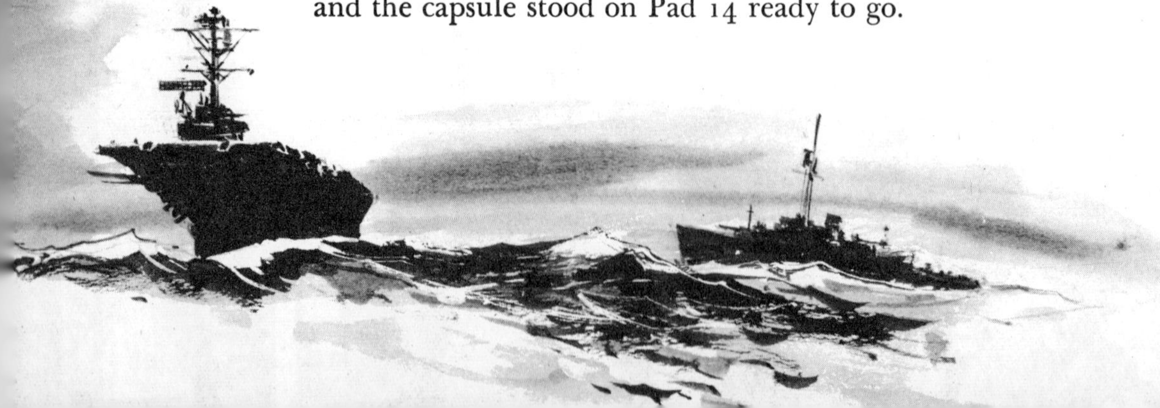

Astronaut Glenn went over his flight procedures again and again. Project Mercury was close to achieving its goal. Everything depended on the weather.

During the days of waiting, there were some who said Project Mercury was being too cautious; the officials were too insistent that everything be super-safe. "All progress involves some risk," they said. "Lindbergh would never have crossed the Atlantic if he had been flying for Project Mercury."

But Mercury officials refused to take any chances. Their job was to send a man into space and into orbit, and then bring him safely back to earth. They wanted to learn if a man could carry out useful activities while traveling in space. No activity could be useful if the man didn't come back safely.

There was another reason why Project Mercury was proceeding cautiously. None of its activities were being kept secret. The whole world could watch, and was watching, what happened at Cape Canaveral. The Soviet Union had already sent two men into orbit around the earth. Now it was the turn of the United States. Failure would mean a serious loss of prestige.

The sky was covered with clouds when John Glenn was awakened at 2:20 on the morning of February 20, 1962. Although the weather didn't look encouraging, out at the launch area the final countdown had begun at 11:30 P.M. Breakfast was at 2:45 A.M.—orange juice, scrambled eggs, steak, and toast. The same menu had been prepared for astronauts Shepard and Grissom, and for Glenn himself, on January 27th.

The physical examination, which started at 3:00 A.M., lasted an hour. In spite of the weary days of waiting, the astronaut was in excellent shape. And so were the Atlas and the capsule. The countdown was proceeding without a hitch.

At 4:00 A.M. the count was stopped at T minus 120 minutes. This was a planned hold to give the technicians some extra time if they needed it. So far everything was right on schedule. By 4:30 Astronaut Glenn was getting into his twenty-pound space suit. Pressure tests to make sure the suit would hold oxygen were next.

At 5:00 A.M. he was ready to leave Hangar S for the launching area. It was still cloudy. Astronaut Carpenter and the flight surgeon rode to Pad 14 with Glenn. Pad 14 was ablaze with lights. After the astronauts arrived, the hold was extended for 45 minutes. Trouble had been discovered in the guidance system of the Atlas booster.

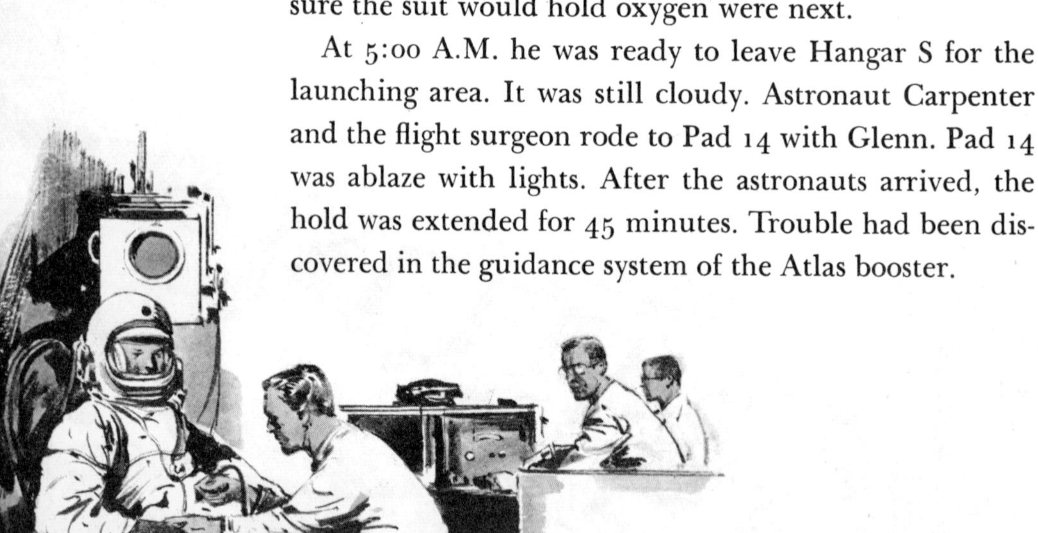

At 6:00 A.M. Glenn left the van that had brought him from Hangar S. Crewmen working in the launching area could see him smile behind his space visor as he walked briskly to the elevator. There had been some breaks in the clouds, but they had closed in again. Above the capsule, which had been named Friendship 7, the sky was black and forbidding.

The countdown was resumed at 6:26—T minus 120. The astronaut was in the capsule and the hatch was closed, but he couldn't be sealed in. There was a broken bolt on the hatch cover. The bolt had to be replaced. It was now 7:25—T minus 60 and holding. The sky was still covered with clouds.

And so it went with the hands of the clock getting ever closer to 9:00. There was growing concern about the time. Unless Friendship 7 could be launched before 9:30 or 9:45, its orbits would have to be reduced to two or even to one. For a safe recovery, there had to be an ample margin of daylight left in the Atlantic landing area.

At 9:30 A.M. the count had reached T minus 15 minutes. Both the astronaut in the capsule and the Mercury officials were reporting all systems, "Go." The clouds that had hung over the Cape were gone. A beautiful sun was shining, and a feeling of hope had replaced the earlier gloom.

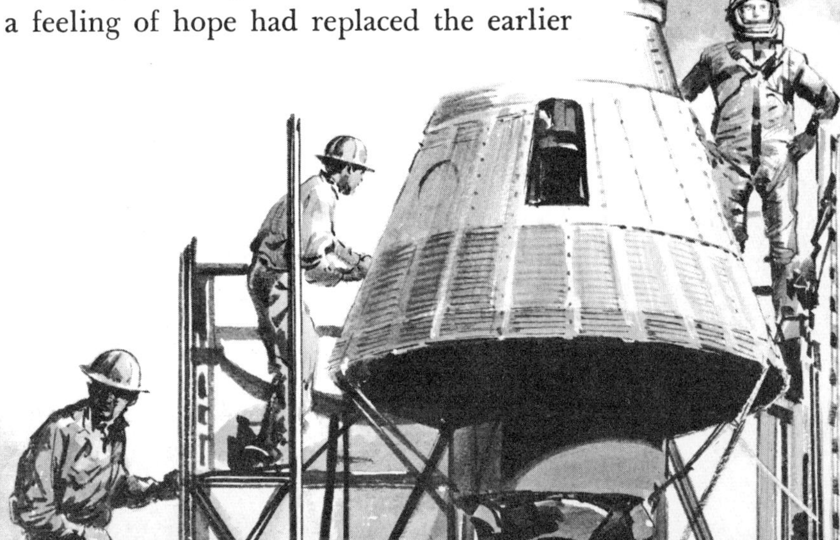

After just one more short delay, the count was resumed for the last time at 9:42. When the clock moved past 9:46, the count was in seconds: 9..., 8..., 7..., 6..., 5..., 4..., 3..., 2..., 1..., 0!

Fire and smoke appeared under the tail of the Atlas. The 130-ton rocket rose slowly from the launching pad trailing a bright, white-yellow flame. With a roar it went streaking skyward followed by a thin, white vapor trail. Within seconds it was gone.

From his capsule perched on top of the speeding Atlas, Astronaut Glenn reported: "Lift off, the clock is operating, we're under way."

Friendship 7 was moving toward its orbital altitude. As he rocketed through the area where there was still enough atmosphere to buffet the capsule, the astronaut told the Control Center: "Some vibration area coming up here now."

But he was having no trouble. All his instruments were working and he was reporting their readings to the Control Center in a calm, steady voice. The man who was receiving his messages was Alan Shepard, the astronaut whose ride in the capsule Freedom 7 had made him the United States' first spaceman.

From the moment of launching the men in the Control Center had been greatly concerned with the flight path of the Atlas. Any change from the planned direction would send the capsule into an orbit over areas where it could not be tracked and where it would be difficult to recover after landing. Likewise, the capsule's speed had to be just right. If it didn't reach a speed close to 17,500 miles an hour at the proper point, it wouldn't go into orbit at all and would have to be brought down at once. Too much speed, on the other hand, would result in an unplanned orbit that might expose the astronaut to dangerous radiation. And when the capsule came down, it might be out of reach of the recovery forces.

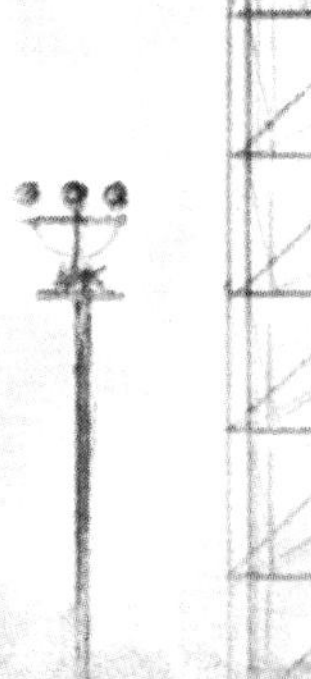

The two booster engines of the Atlas had exhausted their fuel two minutes after the launching, leaving the 60,000-pound thrust sustainer engine to lift the capsule into orbit. After five minutes of flight it, too, burned out, and Friendship 7 went into orbit at 17,545 miles an hour.

Computers at the Goddard Space Flight Center at Greenbelt, Maryland, had been electronically following the Atlas since it was one-half of one inch off the launching pad. Within 2½ seconds after the capsule went into orbit, information on its speed, elevation, and direction had been sent to Goddard, run through the computers there, and the results sent to the Cape. It was a good orbit!

From the Mercury Control Center, Alan Shepard relayed the happy news to Glenn in Friendship 7. "You have a go. At least seven orbits."

That meant that the orbit attained by Friendship 7 was good enough to carry it seven times around the earth. The plan, however, called for it to come down after three trips.

Upon going into orbit, Friendship 7 had turned around so that its blunt end was forward. This enabled Glenn to look back toward Cape Canaveral. Like Gagarin, Titov, Shepard, and Grissom—all of whom had traveled in space before him—the astronaut was greatly impressed with what he saw below him. There was a big cloud pattern stretching all the way to Florida. "Oh, that view is tremendous!" he exclaimed.

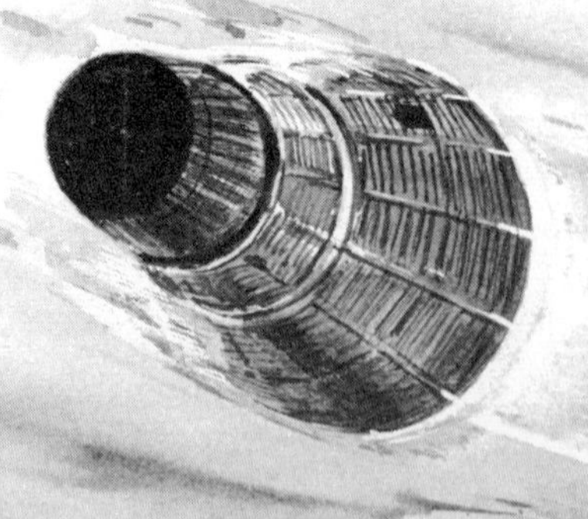

The President's Whiskers

Hertha Pauli

This story is a true one. Back in 1860, when Abraham Lincoln was running for President, a little girl named Grace Bedell wrote him a letter. In the letter, she said she thought he'd look a lot better with whiskers. Lincoln answered her letter, but Grace couldn't tell whether he planned to grow the whiskers.

Then Lincoln was elected. Grace was going to have a chance to see him!

The unforgettable date was February 16, 1861. On February 16, a special train would stop a few miles from Westfield—the train that was carrying Mr. Lincoln to the White House.

Grace hardly slept the night before. It was pitch dark when she wriggled into the sky-blue percale with the polkadots—her Sunday dress. She held the oil lamp up to the small mirror. Did she look like a real lady? No, the bonnet was missing. It had velvet ribbons and two pink flowers on top. In a moment, a perfect little lady smiled out of the mirror, and the flowers nodded approval.

The lady was satisfied. She put the lamp back on the table and leaned on the window sill, waiting impatiently for dawn to break.

Other windows began to light up in the village. Grace heard voices in the house, and the clatter of pots and pans. She got her warm cape and took a last look out of the window. A few high clouds were sailing slowly southward. It would be a beautiful day.

Downstairs, Mother was washing the dishes. Grace danced through the room. "Mother, does my skirt hang right?"

"Stand still a moment. Now turn, slowly. Yes, it's straight all around."

Grace's face fell suddenly. "There'll be so many people he won't even see me," she pouted.

"You're lucky to see him, dear," Mother said.

It was not yet sunup when the Bedells set out in the spring wagon. The older boys had gone ahead, but the rest of them sat under the tasseled top: Father holding the reins, Mother, Grace, Sam, even Kitty. The baby came along, too, asleep in Mother's arms, because Father insisted. "When she grows up," he said, "she'll want to tell she saw him, and she may not get another chance."

Grace could not sit still. "Look—" she pointed, jumping up and down triumphantly—"there are the Rices, but Bricktop is going to school today—"

If Grace was not quiet, Father said over his shoulder, *she* would be going to school today.

"Will you hold the baby awhile, dear?" Mother asked. Grace held the baby. She held it so quietly it did not even wake up.

Horses and vehicles crowded Main and North Portage streets. For days, Westfield had been in a dither; today it would be deserted. Shops were shut. On the post office door hung a big sign: "Closed for Business on February 16."

"Heavens, look at that crowd," said Mother. "Do drive carefully, Father."

The horse-and-buggy parade moved out of the village and westward. Harnesses glistened in the rising sun. Now and then, a farmer's wagon fell in from a side road, or a couple of men on horseback. There were more people on the road than for the fair.

They entered North East, crossing the tracks in the

center of the village. Another turn, and there was the depot, decked in red-white-and-blue bunting, with "Hail to the Chief" spelled out in big letters on a streamer across the tracks.

Mr. Bedell tied the horses to the hitchrail and put blankets on them so they would not freeze. The family headed for the depot, only to find a line of soldiers around it and no one permitted to pass except people with ribbons in their buttonholes. The Bedells had to stand in the crowd. Mother said they were lucky the ground was frozen or their dresses would be ruined.

Then—"They're coming!" Grace screamed.

Wagons came clattering up the road. Men jumped off and lined up as for a drill on the green. The fifes and drums played. There were the three older Bedell boys, and in front of them, barking commands just as if he were in the classroom, was Mr. Wedge! Grace felt actually proud of the assistant principal. Then came the carriages, led by Mr. Rice's. Mr. Rice drove his chestnuts himself, with a tall, gleaming stovepipe hat of black silk on his head. All the carriages were full of silk hats and beribboned buttonholes. Father explained that these marks distinguished the reception committee for Mr. Lincoln.

The crowd was still growing. People kept pushing in front until Grace hardly saw the depot any more. Even the flag on the roof disappeared from time to time behind the feathered hat of a large lady.

Baby Sue started to cry, and Mother went back to the wagon with her and Kitty and Sam. Only Father stayed with Grace. They were far back in the crowd now.

"Will he come now?" she asked.

Mr. Bedell drew out his watch. "If the paper had the schedule right, the train is due in an hour."

It was the longest hour in Grace's life.

A gull shrieked. Or—? There was a sudden hush. The shriek came again. It was no gull. It was a steam whistle.

"Here she comes!" And everybody started pushing and craning necks. Grace held onto Father's hand. And yet she was swept forward and sideways and back. People began to

yell, to cheer. Grace saw small clouds of black smoke rise into the blue sky, closer and closer. She stretched as high on her toes as she could and saw the top of a huge black funnel pass slowly behind many heads, hissing and puffing smoke, and then the flat roof of a car, and another, and a third with the Stars and Stripes fluttering over the rear platform.

The hat in front shifted a little. Grace had a glimpse of the platform. The noise was deafening.

When a Dream Comes True

One of the stovepipe hats had risen above the rest. A very tall, very black hat, quietly sticking out of a lot of fidgety black hats—this was all Grace could see, until the lady in front got so excited that her feathered headgear slipped to one side. Then she saw more. The calm hat was not half so shiny as the restless ones. It looked dusty and a bit wrinkled, pushed back on a head of black hair. Cries of "Speech! Speech!" rose. All around, there suddenly was dead silence.

"Ladies and gentlemen," someone said, "I have no speech to make and no time to speak in."

You could have heard a pin drop. And yet, the easy drawl rang as familiar as folks talking at any street corner. You almost thought you had heard the voice before.

"I appear before you that I may see you," it said, "and that you may see me."

Grace felt ice-cold. It was he. His voice. He was up there on the platform. She stretched so that it hurt, but all she saw was the wrinkled stovepipe hat.

"And I'm willing to admit that, so far as the ladies are concerned, I have the best of the bargain."

Some ladies tittered.

"Though I wish it to be understood that I don't make the same acknowledgment concerning the men."

Laughter rippled, swelled, burst through the crowd. Grace laughed and clapped her hands. In back of her, an old farmer slapped his thighs and cackled, "That's telling 'em, Abe." In front of her, the lady with the slipping feathers shrieked, "Hooray for President Lincoln!"

Father caught Grace up and set her on his shoulder.

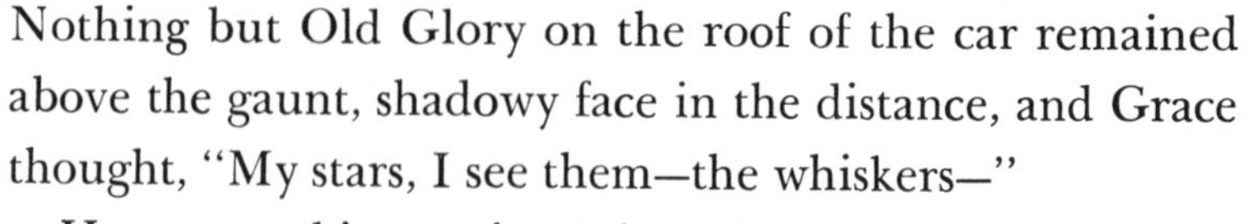

Nothing but Old Glory on the roof of the car remained above the gaunt, shadowy face in the distance, and Grace thought, "My stars, I see them—the whiskers—"

He was speaking again. "I have but one question, standing here beneath the flag of our country: Will you stand by me as I stand by the flag?"

Why was the crowd so still? For an instant, Grace could see the whole figure, immensely tall, in deep black from his boots to the hat that made him look endless.

Someone shouted: "We sure will, Abe!"

The crowd took it up. Hands and hats and women's handkerchiefs rose into the air amid thundering echoes: "Yes—yes—we sure will, Abe!"

Slowly the shouting died. "I don't care for them great orators," Grace heard the farmer behind her. "I want to hear jist a plain, common feller like the rest of us, that I kin foller an' know where he's driving. Abe Lincoln fills the bill."

Grace felt herself sliding down. She was on the ground, hemmed in like a fish in a barrel. Surely it was all over, and the silent crowd was waiting only for the train to start.

Once more, she heard the voice that made you feel you had heard it all your life. "I have a little correspondent in this place," he said.

How simple it sounded! But Grace knew it could not be. She was dreaming again, as a moment back, when she thought she had seen the whiskers.

"This little lady," the voice went on, "saw from the first what great improvement might be made in my appearance—"

It was a lovely dream. You had to keep your eyes shut tight; if you looked, it would be time to get up and go to school.

"—and if she is present, I would like to speak to her."

Grace opened her eyes wide. She was not in bed. She was in a crowd at the North East depot, unable to move, to see, to make a sound.

"Tell us the name," people shouted. "The name!"

And Mr. Lincoln replied distinctly: "Her name is Grace Bedell."

It was Father who took her hand and led her forward.

She went without knowing how, without noticing that a path was opened for them. There were steps ahead, and Father gave her a boost up to the platform in sight of a thousand people, up to a pair of big, black-booted feet. Somewhere above, she heard a slow chuckle.

"She wrote me that she thought I'd look better if I wore whiskers—"

He stooped. Grace felt strong hands under her arms. Suddenly, as if she had no weight at all, she was raised high in the air, kissed on both cheeks, and gently set down again. And her cheeks burned not only from bliss but from a scratching. Up there, sprouting darkly all around the

rugged face and covering cheeks and jaw, so that only the upper lip remained free, were the whiskers.

"You see, I let them grow for you, Grace," said Mr. Lincoln.

Grace's eyes traveled up along the black overcoat, all the way up to the whiskers and the wrinkled black hat. She could do nothing but look at the tall, gaunt, plain, familiar great man. She would have liked to stand and look forever and ever.

He took her hand. She heard him say that he hoped to see his little friend again some time; she understood that this moment had to end. He helped her down the steps and she went obediently, like a good girl, back to her proud father.

Grace's brothers, too, were suddenly there, and Mother, and Mr. Wedge, and the sour-faced Mr. Rice, and the postmaster, and Kitty, and a lot of yelling strangers. Grace saw them and did not see them. She heard cheers, yells, a shrill whistle, a rumbling and puffing and screeching. But her mind heard only three words, repeated over and over: "My little friend—my little friend . . ."

Abraham Lincoln

Remember he was poor and country-bred;
His face was lined; he walked with awkward gait.
Smart people laughed at him sometimes and said,
"How can so very plain a man be great?"

Remember he was humble, used to toil.
Strong arms he had to build a shack, a fence,
Long legs to tramp the woods, to plow the soil,
A head chuck full of backwoods common sense.

Remember all he ever had he earned.
He walked in time through stately White House doors;
But all he knew of men and life he learned
In little backwoods cabins, country stores.

Remember that his eyes could light with fun;
That wisdom, courage, set his name apart;
But when the rest is duly said and done,
Remember that men loved him for his heart.

—*Mildred Plew Meigs*

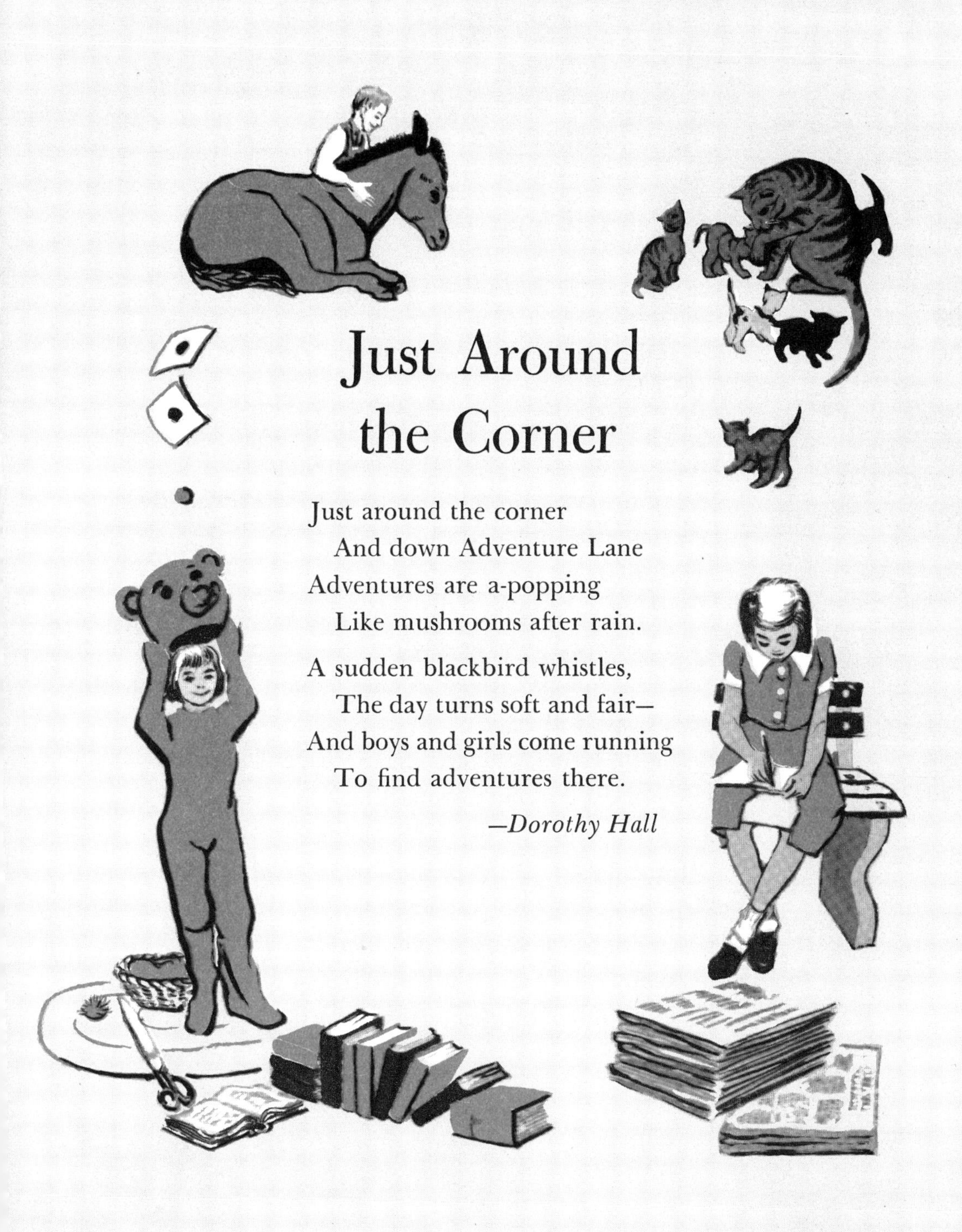

Just Around the Corner

Just around the corner
And down Adventure Lane
Adventures are a-popping
Like mushrooms after rain.

A sudden blackbird whistles,
The day turns soft and fair—
And boys and girls come running
To find adventures there.

—Dorothy Hall

Citronella Weather

Mildred Lawrence

"Hush, Malinda!" said Mother. "Daddy's writing an editorial."

Malinda hushed. When Daddy was writing an editorial, he absolutely, positively, must not be disturbed. But she did wish, when everybody else in the Rebel family had their name on the masthead of the *Argus,* that she could have hers there, too.

"Randolph Rebel, Editor and Publisher," it began. (That, of course, was Daddy.)

"Mrs. Randolph Rebel, Society Editor." (And that, of course, was Mother.)

"Junius Rebel, Advertising Manager." (Junius, Malinda's oldest brother, wrote things that said, "On Sale! This Week Only! Boots and Galoshes!")

"Jeremy Rebel, Custodian." (Jeremy, Malinda's second oldest brother, swept out the office and helped run the press when Big Eph didn't get there.)

"David Rebel, Circulation Manager." (David, Malinda's third-oldest brother, delivered all the papers every week.)

Only Malinda wasn't anybody at all. It made her feel very lonesome, like the orphan children that Mother sent the barrel of old clothes to every year.

"Please, please Daddy," begged Malinda, "can't I do something, too?"

"You're not old enough, Baby," said Daddy vaguely. But Malinda kept practicing writing news items and taking them out into the back room where Mr. Wooliver was setting type. Malinda liked talking to Mr. Wooliver. He was never too busy to pay attention. Besides, by sniffing around where Mr. Wooliver was, she could tell what the weather was that day.

If it was cold, Mr. Wooliver had a roll of cotton soaked in camphor behind each ear—"to ward off colds," he said. If it was warm, the cotton was soaked in citronella to keep the mosquitoes away.

"I never catch colds and I never get mosquito bites," said Mr. Wooliver, wiping enough ink off his hands so that he could pick up Malinda's news items.

" 'Annabelle Douglas's cat, Mee-Yow, has six baby kittens,' " he read. " 'One of them has six toes on its front feet.' Well, now, that's very good, young miss. Going to be a writer like your daddy, I see."

And so Malinda ran happily back to her favorite bench in the park and wrote down some more news.

"Clarinda Smith and Robby Holcomb found a hornets' nest down by the river last week," she wrote. "The hornets were not glad to see them. They got stung eight times."

She nibbled her pencil and looked down at the river far below. Nearly everybody in Riverdale lived down on the river bank. But the stores, and the churches, and the city hall, and the library were all at the top of the hill, a long climb even for Malinda.

"Lucius Wixby fell into the river Tuesday," wrote Malinda, "and spoiled his new suit that his mother bought at the bargain sale last week."

She ran back to the *Argus* to see if just this once Daddy would print some of her news items. But she had forgotten that this was the day when the rest of the family were going to the Press Club meeting at Highlands, across the river and sixty miles away. Malinda was to stay home with Great-aunt Essie.

Daddy rattled out a last-minute news item, Mother finished reading the last galley proof, and Junius made a correction on the general store's advertisement so that it would say that coats, not goats, were on sale at $14.95. Daddy took his news item out to Mr. Wooliver, who was

wearing camphor that day, even though it was very spring-like outside.

"Leave a place on the front page for the Press Club report," said Daddy. "I'll write it when I get home. You're the boss while I'm gone."

Mr. Wooliver winked at Malinda. "In that case, I'll ask the young miss to help me today," he said. "I'll have my hands full, seeing tomorrow's press day."

"Anything you like," said Daddy. "Good-by, Baby."

Malinda did wish that Daddy wouldn't call her Baby, but Mr. Wooliver seemed not to hear.

"Now, young miss," he said, settling the little rolls of camphor-cotton more securely behind his ears, "I have a feeling in my bones that it's going to rain. I favor your hurrying home for your boots and raincoat."

"Yes, sir," said Malinda.

"Oh, yes, and tell your Great-aunt Essie that you won't be home until after supper. The day before press day is a pretty busy day, but I think we can manage—that is, with the two of us."

"It's pouring down rain," said Malinda when she came back, puffing from the climb up the hill. "You were right. Camphor was just right for today."

"I very seldom miss," said Mr. Wooliver. "Let me see, now! Would you like to take these handbills over to the auctioneer? He's in a hurry for them."

Malinda scampered off. It was raining harder than ever now. The low place on the corner where the rain collected during every storm already looked like a small lake.

"Now you may put some of these leads between each line on this front-page story," said Mr. Wooliver, when she returned. "The leads, you know, are what make the fresh air between the rows of type."

Why, even the boys weren't allowed to touch Mr. Wooliver's type!

"You're so nice," said Malinda. "I'm having the best time!"

"I have to have help," said Mr. Wooliver gruffly. "Can't get this paper out all by myself. Now, then, will you answer the telephone?"

It was somebody from out in the country wanting to know if Malinda knew anything about a flood.

"No," said Malinda politely, "we don't. But it's raining quite hard."

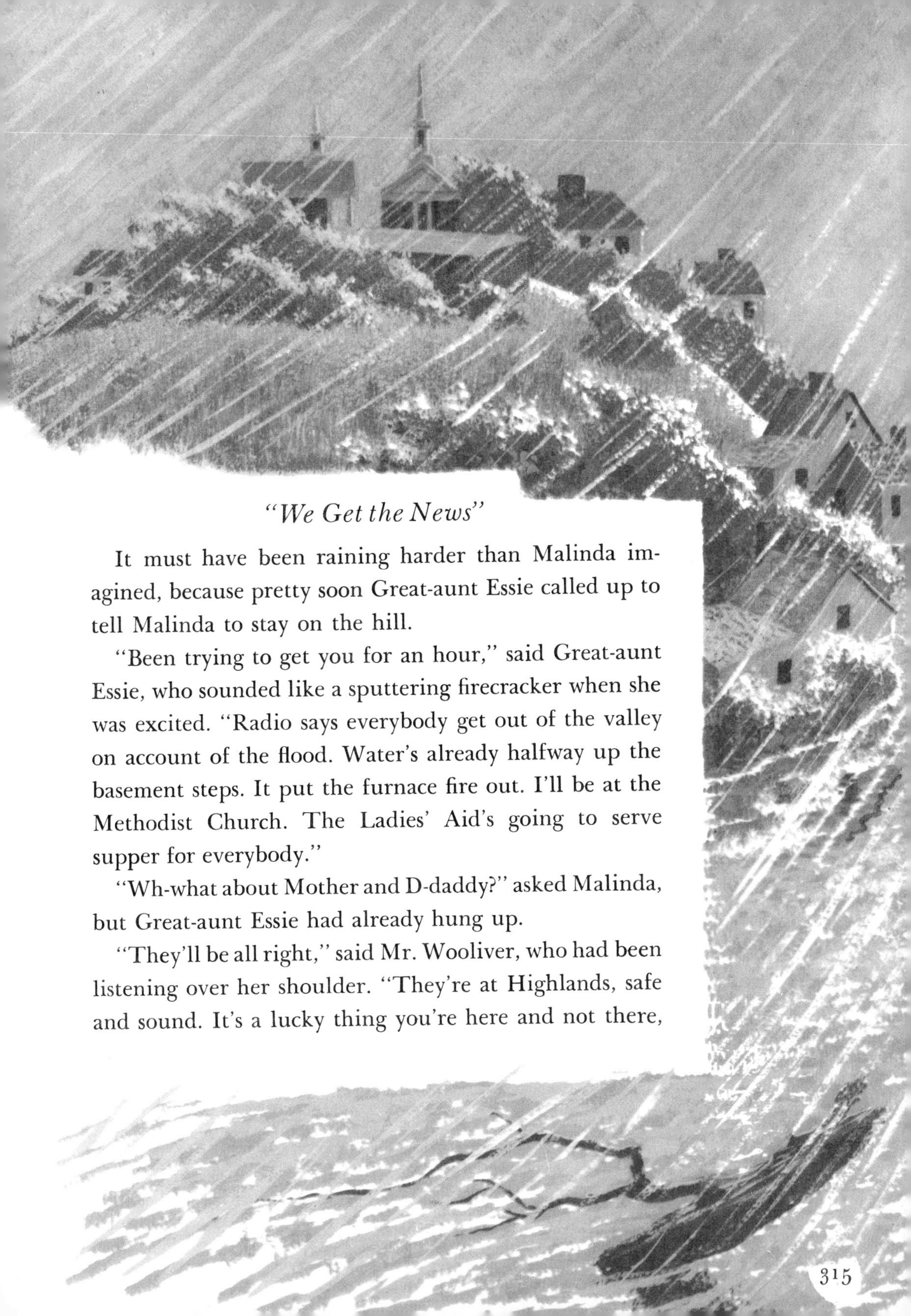

"We Get the News"

It must have been raining harder than Malinda imagined, because pretty soon Great-aunt Essie called up to tell Malinda to stay on the hill.

"Been trying to get you for an hour," said Great-aunt Essie, who sounded like a sputtering firecracker when she was excited. "Radio says everybody get out of the valley on account of the flood. Water's already halfway up the basement steps. It put the furnace fire out. I'll be at the Methodist Church. The Ladies' Aid's going to serve supper for everybody."

"Wh-what about Mother and D-daddy?" asked Malinda, but Great-aunt Essie had already hung up.

"They'll be all right," said Mr. Wooliver, who had been listening over her shoulder. "They're at Highlands, safe and sound. It's a lucky thing you're here and not there,

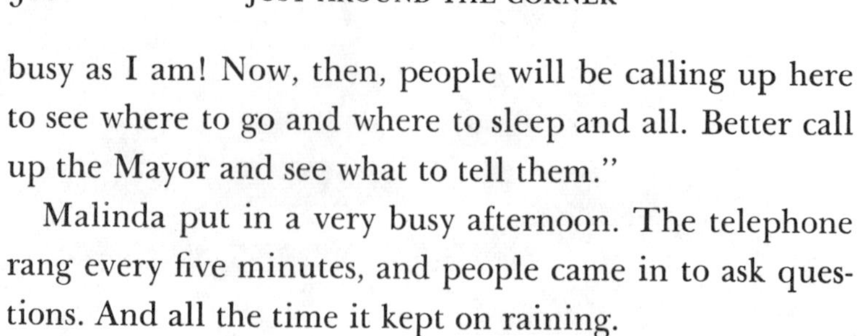

busy as I am! Now, then, people will be calling up here to see where to go and where to sleep and all. Better call up the Mayor and see what to tell them."

Malinda put in a very busy afternoon. The telephone rang every five minutes, and people came in to ask questions. And all the time it kept on raining.

"Radio says the road from Highlands is closed," Mr. Wooliver reported. "Looks as though we'll have to get this paper out by ourselves." Both Malinda and Mr. Wooliver knew very well that the *Argus* couldn't miss its publication day, flood or no flood.

"Lucky thing they wrote everything before they left, for writing is not my line," said Mr. Wooliver, counting page forms. "One, two, three, four, five, six, seven—oh, bless my stars! There's that big gap in the front page."

Malinda looked at the streamer at the top of Page One. *"Riverdale Argus,"* it said. "We Get the News."

"I think we should telephone Daddy," Malinda decided. "It says we get the news, and the flood is news, and Daddy won't like it if it's not in the paper."

"Long-distance telephone lines are out," said Mr. Wooliver gloomily.

There was a long pause while Malinda thought very hard. "Daddy won't let me write for the paper," she said, "on account of being too young."

There was another long pause. "But I guess I'll have to," she decided, "since I'm the only one in the family that's home."

"Quite right, too, young miss," said Mr. Wooliver. "And you'd better start now."

Malinda nibbled her pencil and tried to remember all the things that she had heard about the flood and also all the things that Daddy had told the boys about how to write stories for the *Argus*.

"Put the most important things first," Daddy always said, "in case you might not have room for the rest."

"Everybody in Riverdale is up on the Hill," wrote Malinda, "on account of the big flood. People are eating at the Methodist Church and sleeping in the city hall and the library. It looks very queer, but it is not so wet as it is at home.

"Mrs. Eustace said her clothes basket was floating around in her basement like a boat. Annabelle Douglas's cat, Mee-Yow, led her six kittens up the Hill to the fire house. Spotty, the fire department dog, does not like so many cats there.

"The Mayor says he thinks that people can go home in another day. Mrs. Ransome said she hoped so, because she wanted to take down her wash, which was hanging in the basement. It is under water now, but Mrs. Ransome says for once her wash got plenty of rinsing in fresh rain water."

Before Malinda knew it, it was time to go to the Methodist Church for supper.

"You sleep on the couch in Daddy's office," Malinda told Great-aunt Essie. "I can sleep on his desk."

"I know a better place than that," said Mr. Wooliver. "Sleep on the press. More room to turn over."

As she fell asleep, Malinda could hear Mr. Wooliver setting the type for her story about the flood. And then she didn't remember a thing until Mr. Wooliver was shaking her to wake her up.

"Big Eph's here, young miss," he said, "and we can't print the paper with little girls asleep on the press. Rain's settled down to a drizzle, and the water's starting to go down. You go to the church and get your breakfast, and then scoot along to school."

When Malinda came back from school in the afternoon, Daddy and Mother and Junius and Jeremy and David were all there. There was a neat stack of new papers on the counter. Malinda gave everybody a big hug.

"Did you have a good time?" she asked. "I slept on the press. And I helped Mr. Wooliver. And I—"

Suddenly she caught sight of the paper and the big headline which said, "Flood Routs Riverdale Residents." Right at the beginning of her story were the words, "By Malinda Rebel."

Malinda gasped. Why, even the boys had never had a by-line! She did hope that Daddy wouldn't be cross with Mr. Wooliver. "Daddy," she said, "did we do right? We couldn't get you and—"

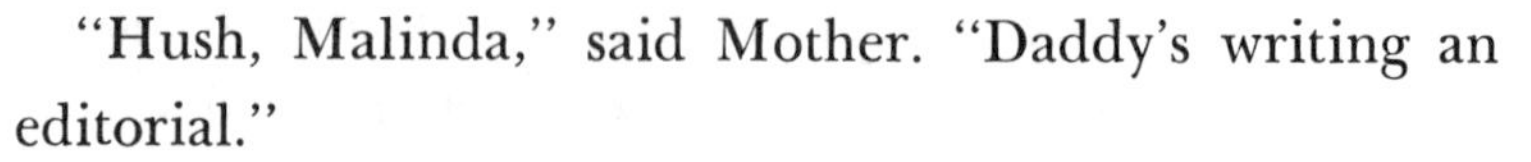

"Hush, Malinda," said Mother. "Daddy's writing an editorial."

"You come and sit beside me while I write it," said Daddy. "It's about you."

Malinda leaned her chin against Daddy's shoulder. Beside Daddy's typewriter lay a proof of the masthead. A new name had been added: "Malinda Rebel, Reporter."

"Oh, Daddy!" said Malinda.

But Daddy's typewriter was going clickety-clack.

"A Chip Off the Old Block," wrote Daddy. Then, "I'm a proud man today, and for once I am going to brag about one of my children. My daughter, Malinda—"

"Oh, Daddy!" said Malinda again.

Why, even the boys had never had an editorial written about them! Mother and Junius and Jeremy and David all stood around and watched Daddy while he wrote. Even Mr. Wooliver came in and peered over his glasses. In spite of the drizzle outside, Malinda knew that it was going to be a lovely day, because Mr. Wooliver smelled like an extra-large bottle of citronella.

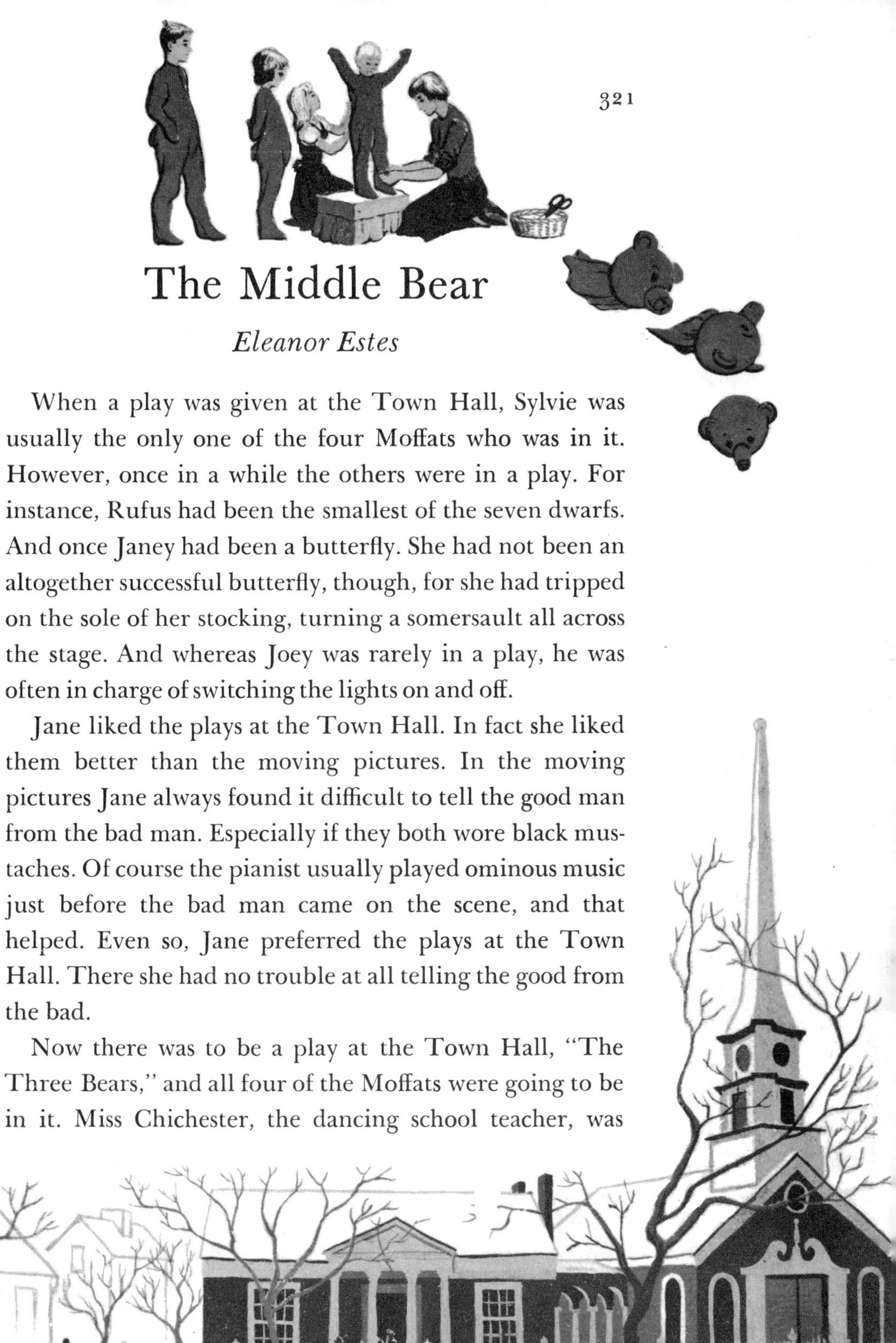

The Middle Bear

Eleanor Estes

When a play was given at the Town Hall, Sylvie was usually the only one of the four Moffats who was in it. However, once in a while the others were in a play. For instance, Rufus had been the smallest of the seven dwarfs. And once Janey had been a butterfly. She had not been an altogether successful butterfly, though, for she had tripped on the sole of her stocking, turning a somersault all across the stage. And whereas Joey was rarely in a play, he was often in charge of switching the lights on and off.

Jane liked the plays at the Town Hall. In fact she liked them better than the moving pictures. In the moving pictures Jane always found it difficult to tell the good man from the bad man. Especially if they both wore black mustaches. Of course the pianist usually played ominous music just before the bad man came on the scene, and that helped. Even so, Jane preferred the plays at the Town Hall. There she had no trouble at all telling the good from the bad.

Now there was to be a play at the Town Hall, "The Three Bears," and all four of the Moffats were going to be in it. Miss Chichester, the dancing school teacher, was putting it on. But the money for the tickets was not going into her pocket or into the Moffats' pocket, even though they were all in the play. The money was to help pay for the new parish house. The old one had burned down last May and now a new one was being built. "The Three Bears" was to help raise the money to finish it. A benefit performance, it was called.

In this benefit performance, Sylvie was to play the part of Goldilocks. Joey was to be the big bear, Rufus the little bear, and Janey the middle bear. Jane had not asked to be the middle bear. It just naturally came out that way. The middle Moffat was going to be the middle bear.

As a rule, Joey did not enjoy the idea of acting in a play any more than he liked going to dancing school. However, he felt this play would be different. He felt it would be like having a disguise on, to be inside of a bear costume. And Jane felt the same way. She thought the people in the audience would not recognize her as the butterfly who turned a somersault across the stage, because she would be comfortably hidden inside her brown bear costume. As for Rufus, he hoped that Sylvie, the Goldilocks of this game, would not sit down too hard on that nice little chair of his and really break it to bits. It was such a good chair, and he wished he had it at home.

Mama was making all the costumes, even the bear heads. A big one for Joey, a little one for Rufus, and a middle-sized one for Jane. Of course, she wasn't making them out of bear fur; she was using brown outing flannel.

Now Jane was trying on her middle bear costume. She stepped into the body of the costume and then Mama put the head on her.

"Make the holes for the eyes big enough," Jane begged. "So I'll see where I'm going and won't turn somersaults."

"Well," said Mama, "if I cut the eyes any larger, you will look like a deep sea diver instead of a bear."

"Oh, well . . ." said Jane hastily. "A bear's got to look like a bear. Never mind making them bigger, then."

Besides being in the play, each of the Moffats also had ten tickets to sell. And since Rufus really was too little to go from house to house and street to street selling tickets, the other three Moffats had even more to dispose of. Forty tickets!

At first Jane wondered if a girl should sell tickets to a play she was going to be in. Was that being conceited? Well, since the money was for the new parish house and not for the Moffats, she finally decided it was all right to sell the tickets. Besides, she thought, who would recognize her as the girl who sold tickets once she was inside her bear costume?

Sylvie sold most of her tickets like lightning to the ladies in the choir. But Joey's and Janey's tickets became grimier and grimier, they had such trouble disposing of them. Nancy Stokes said she would help even though she went to a different parish house. She and Joey and Jane went quietly and politely up on people's verandas and rang the bell.

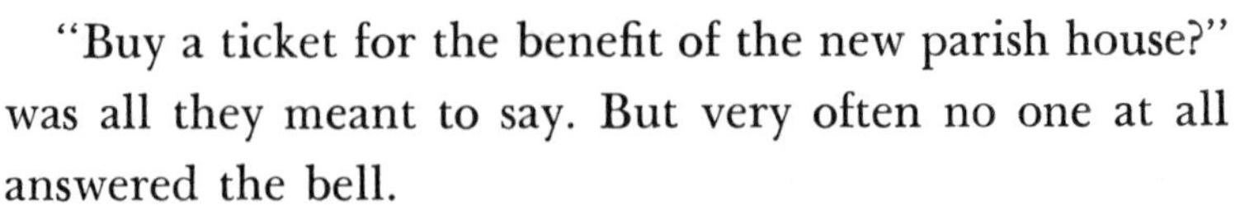

"Buy a ticket for the benefit of the new parish house?" was all they meant to say. But very often no one at all answered the bell.

"They can't all be away," said Nancy. "Do you think they hide behind the curtains when they see us coming?"

"Oh no," said Jane. "You see it'd be different if the money was for us. But it isn't. It's a benefit. Why should they hide?"

One lady said she was very sorry but she was making mincemeat. "See?" she said, holding up her hands. They were all covered with mincemeat. So she could not buy a ticket. Not possibly, and she closed the door in their faces.

"She could wash her hands," said Nancy angrily. The children called this lady "mincemeat," ever after. Of course, she never knew it.

Yes, the tickets were very hard to sell. But little by little the pile did dwindle. If only everybody were like Mrs. Stokes, they would go very fast. She bought four tickets! Jane was embarrassed.

"Tell your mother she doesn't have to buy all those tickets just 'cause all of us are in the play," she instructed Nancy.

But all the Stokes insisted they really wanted to go. And even if none of the Moffats were in it, they would still want to go, for the play would help to build a new parish house. What nice people! thought Jane. Here they were, a family who went to the white church, buying tickets to help build a parish house for Janey's church. She hoped she would be a good middle bear, so they would be proud they knew her.

At last, it was the night of the play. The four Moffats knew their lines perfectly. This was not surprising, considering they all lived in the same house and could practice their lines any time they wanted to. And, besides this, they had had two rehearsals, one in regular clothes and one in their bear costumes.

When Jane reached the Town Hall, she was surprised to find there were many features on the program besides "The Three Bears." The Gillespie twins were going to give a piano duet. "By the Brook," it was called. A boy was going to play the violin. Someone else was going to toe dance. And Miss Beale was going to sing a song. A big program. And the Moffats, all of them except Mama, were going to watch this whole performance from behind the scenes. They could not sit in the audience with the regular people with their bear costumes on, for that would give the whole show away.

Jane fastened her eye to a hole in the curtain. Mama had not yet come. Of course Mama would have to sit out front there with the regular people, even though she had made the costumes. The only people who had arrived so far were Clara Pringle and Brud. They were sitting in the front row and Jane wondered how they had gotten in because the front door that all the regular people were supposed to use wasn't even open yet.

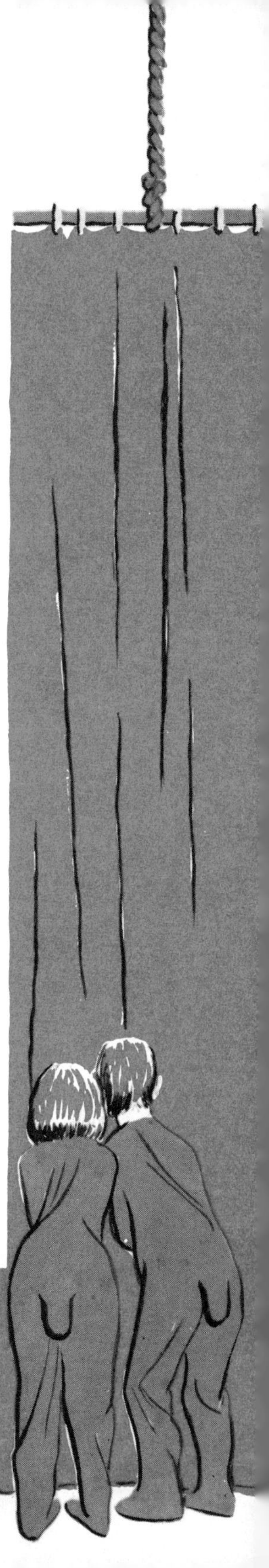

When Jane wasn't peering through a hole in the curtain, Joey or Rufus was. Each one hoped he would be the first to see Mama when she came in. Or now and then, they tried to squeeze through the opening at the side of the asbestos curtain. But the gnarled little janitor shook his head at them. So they stayed inside.

Sylvie was busy putting make-up on herself and on the dancers' faces. Jane watched them enviously. The only trouble with wearing a bear costume, she thought, was that she couldn't have her face painted. Well, she quickly consoled herself, she certainly would not have stage fright inside her bear head. Whereas she might if there were just paint on her face. "Somebody has been sitting in my chair," she rehearsed her lines. She stepped into her bear costume. But before putting on her head, she helped Rufus into *his* bear uniform. He didn't call it a costume. A uniform. A bear uniform. Jane set his head on his shoulders, found his two eyes for him so he could see out, and the little bear was ready.

Joey had no difficulty stepping into his costume and in finding his own two eyes. Now the big bear and the little bear were ready. Jane looked around for her head, to put it on. Where was it?

"Where's my head?" she asked. "My bear head."

Nobody paid any attention to her. Miss Chichester was running back and forth and all around, giving an order here and an order there. Once, as she rushed by, causing a great breeze, Jane yelled to make herself heard, "How can we act 'The Three Bears' unless I find my middle bear head?"

"Not just now. I'm too busy," was all Miss Chichester said.

Everybody was too busy to help Jane find her head. Sylvie was busy helping the toe dancer dress. Joey was busy running around doing this and doing that for Miss Chichester. And the little old janitor was busy tightening ropes and making sure the lights were working. Rufus could not be torn from a hole in the curtain. He was looking for Mama.

Jane sighed. Everybody is busy, she thought. She rummaged around in a big box of costumes. Maybe her bear head had been stuck into it. She found a dragon head and tried it on. How would that be? She looked in the mirror. The effect was interesting. But, no, she could not wear this, for a bear cannot be a dragon.

A Headless Bear

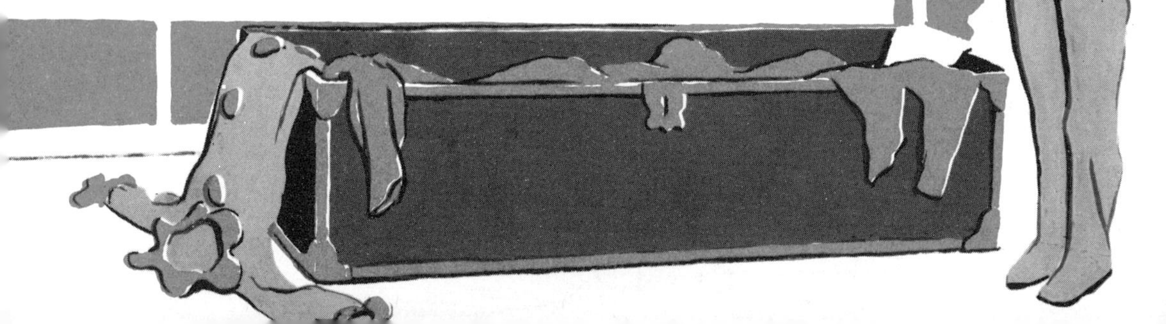

Goodness, thought Jane. The curtain will go up, and the middle bear won't be a whole bear. This was worse than tripping over her stocking the time she was a butterfly. Maybe Joey and Rufus somehow or another had two heads on. They didn't, though, just their own. Phew, it was warm inside these bear costumes. Jane stood beside Rufus and looked through another small hole in the curtain. Oh! The big door was open! People were beginning to arrive. And what kind of a bear would she

be without a head? Maybe she wouldn't be allowed to be a bear at all. But there certainly could not be three bears without a middle one.

"Don't worry," said Rufus, not moving an inch from his spot. "Lend you mine for half the play . . ."

"Thanks," said Jane. "But we all have to have our heads on all through the whole thing."

The Stokes were coming in! Jane felt worried. The only person who might be able to fix a new bear head for her in a hurry was Mama. Oh, if she had only made a couple of spare heads. But Mama wasn't coming yet. Jane resolved to go and meet her. She put on her tam and her chinchilla coat over her bear costume. Then she ran down the three narrow steps into the Hall. She crouched low in her coat in order not to give away the fact that she was clad in a bear costume. Nobody on this side of the curtain was supposed to know what people on her side of the curtain had on until the curtain rolled up. Surprise. That's what was important in a play.

Mr. Buckle was coming in now, walking towards the front row. Jane stooped low, with her knees bent beneath her. In front her coat nearly reached the ground. From the way she looked from the front, few would guess that she was the middle bear. Of course, her feet showed. They were encased in the brown costume. But she might be a brownie or even a squirrel.

"Hello, Mr. Buckle," said Jane. "I'm in a hurry . . ."

"Where are you going, middle Moffat?" he asked. "Aren't you the prima donna?"

"No, just the middle bear."

"Well, that's fine. The middle Moffat is the middle bear."

"Yes. Or I was until I lost my head."

"Oh, my," said Mr. Buckle. "This, then, is not your head?" he asked, pointing to her tam.

"Yes, but not my bear head. I don't mean bare head. Bear head! B-e-a-r. That kind of head."

"Mystifying. Very mystifying," said Mr. Buckle, settling himself slowly in a seat in the front row.

"You'll see later," said Jane, running down the aisle.

She ran all the way home. But the house was dark. Mama had already left. And she must have gone around the other way, or Jane would have passed her. Jane raced back to the Town Hall. There! Now! The lights were dim. The entertainment had begun. Jane tried to open the side door. Chief Mulligan was guarding this entrance. He did not want to let her in at first. He thought she was just a person. But when she showed him her costume, he opened the door just wide enough for her. The bear costume was as good as a password.

The toe dancer was doing the split. Jane tiptoed up the three steps and went backstage, wondering what would happen now. The show always goes on. There was some comfort in that thought. Somehow, someone would fix her head. Or possibly, while she was gone, her middle bear

head had been found. She hoped she would not have to act with her head bare.

Miss Chichester snatched her.

"Oh, there you are, Jane! Hop into your costume, dear."

"I'm in it," said Jane. "But I can't find my middle bear head."

"Heavens!" said Miss Chichester, grasping her own head. "What else will go wrong?"

Jane looked at her in surprise. What else *had* gone wrong? Had others lost worse than their heads?

"Where's the janitor?" Miss Chichester asked. "Maybe he let his grandchildren borrow it."

Jane knew he hadn't, but she couldn't tell Miss Chichester, for she had already flown off. And then Janey had an idea.

"I know what," she said to Joey. "Pin me together." And she pulled the neck part of her costume up over her head. Joey pinned it with two safety pins, and he cut two holes for her eyes. This costume was not comfortable now. Pulling it up and pinning it this way lifted Jane's arms so she had trouble making them hang down the way she thought a bear's should. However, at any rate, she now had a bear head of sorts.

"Do I look like a bear?" she asked Rufus.

"You look like a brown ghost," Rufus replied.

"Don't you worry," said Sylvie, coming up. "You look like a very nice little animal."

"But I'm supposed to be a bear, not a nice little animal," said Jane.

"Well," said Sylvie, "people will know you are supposed to be a bear because Rufus and Joey both have their bear heads on."

So Jane resigned herself to not being a perfect bear. She tried to comfort herself with the thought that she would still be in disguise. She hoped her acting would be so good it would counterbalance her bad head. "Somebody has been eating my porridge," she practiced.

Miss Chichester appeared. "The janitor said 'No,' " she said. She thoughtfully surveyed Jane a moment. "Hm-m-m, a makeshift," she observed. "Well, it's better than nothing," she agreed with Jane. But she decided to switch the order of the program around in order to give everybody one last chance to find the middle bear's head. She sent Miss Beale out onto the stage. Everybody hoped that while Miss Beale was singing, "In an Old-fashioned Garden," the head would appear. But it didn't.

"Keep a little in the background," said Miss Chichester to Jane. "Perhaps people will not notice."

"If I can only see where the background is," thought Jane. For she found it even harder to keep her eyes close to the holes cut in her costume than it had been to the real ones in her regular bear head.

Now the heavy curtain rolled up. It didn't stick halfway up as it sometimes did, and Sylvie, Goldilocks, in a blue pinafore and socks, ran out onto the stage amidst

loud applause. The play had begun! Sylvie had a great deal of acting to do all by herself before the three bears came home. But she wasn't scared. She was used to being on the stage alone.

The Show Must Go On

Jane's heart pounded as she and Joey and Rufus waited for their cue to come home. If only she didn't trip and turn a somersault!—for she really could not see very well. Somehow she managed to see out of only one eye at a time. These eyeholes must have been cut crooked. One hole kept getting hooked on her nose.

"Now!" Miss Chichester whispered. "Cue! Out with you three bears."

Joe, Jane, and Rufus, the three bears, lumbered out onto the stage. They were never supposed to just walk, always lumber and lope.

The applause was tremendous. It startled the three bears. The Town Hall was packed. Somebody must have sold a lot of tickets.

"There's Mama," said Rufus. He said it out loud.

He wasn't supposed to say anything out loud except about his porridge, his chair, and his bed. But anyway he said, "There's Mama." Jane could not see Mama. Lumbering out onto the stage had dislocated her costume, so that now she could not see at all. Fortunately, the footlights shone through the brown flannel of her costume so she could keep away from the edge of the stage.

The Moffats all knew their lines so well they did not forget them once. The only trouble was they did not have much chance to say them because the applause was so great every time they opened their mouths. At last, however, they reached the act about the three beds. An extra platform had been set up on the stage to look like the upstairs of a three bears' house. The three bears lumbered slowly up the steps.

Suddenly, shouts arose all over the Hall:

"Her head! Her head! The middle bear's head!"

"Sh-sh-sh," said others. "See what's going to happen."

As Jane could not see very well, she had no idea what these shouts referred to. She had the same head on now that she had had on all during this play so far. Why then all these shouts? Or had she really stayed in the background the way Miss Chichester had asked her to, and the audience had only just discovered the makeshift?

"Oh," whispered Joey to Jane. "I see it. It's your real bear head and it's on the top of my bed post."

"O-o-o-h!" said Jane. "Get it down."

"How can I?" said Joe. "With all these people watching me?"

"Try and get it when you punch your bed," urged Jane.

Joey was examining his big bear's bed now. "Hm-m-m," he said fiercely. "Somebody has been lying on my bed . . ." But he couldn't reach the middle bear's head. He did try. But he couldn't quite reach it, and there was more laughter from the audience.

Jane pulled her costume about until she could see through the eyehole. Ah, there was her head! On the post of the big bear's bed. No wonder people were laughing. What a place for the middle bear's head. Here she was, without it. And there it was, without her. Jane resolved to get it. Somehow or other she would rescue her head before this play was completely over. Now was her chance. It was her turn to talk about her bed. Instead, Jane said:

"Somebody has been trying on my head, and there it is!"

Jane hopped up on Joey's bed. She grabbed her middle bear head.

"Yes," she repeated. "Somebody has been trying on my head," but as she added, "and here it is!" the safety pins that held her makeshift head together popped open. The audience burst into roars of laughter as Janey's own real head emerged. Only for a second, though. For she clapped her middle bear head right on as fast as she could, and hopped off the bed. Goodness, she thought, I showed my real face and I didn't have any paint on it.

Unfortunately, Jane still could not see, for she had stuck her bear head on backwards. But the audience loved it. They clapped and they stamped. Bravo! Bravo! Bravo, middle bear! Big boys at the back of the hall put their fingers in their mouths and whistled. And it was a long time before Jane could say:

"Somebody has been sleeping in my bed," and the play could go on. At last, Rufus discovered Goldilocks in his

little bed, and she leaped out of the window. That was the end of the play and the curtain rolled down.

When the bowing began, Miss Chichester tried to send Jane in backwards, thinking the back of her was the front of her. Fortunately, Rufus held Jane by one paw, and Joey held the other. So she didn't get lost. And the three bears lumbered dizzily on and off many times, sometimes with Sylvie, and sometimes alone. And somebody yelled for "The mysterious middle bear!" It must have been the oldest inhabitant.

Miss Chichester turned Jane's head around for this bow, and at last Jane really did look like a perfect middle bear. Furthermore, she could see out. There was Mama, laughing so hard the tears were rolling down her cheeks. And there was Nancy Stokes with all the Stokes, and Olga was there. And there was Mr. Buckle, beaming up at the stage. Jane bowed and lumbered off the stage. She felt good now. Acting was fun, she thought, especially if you could be disguised in a bear uniform. And this time she had not turned a somersault across the stage as she had the time she was a butterfly. True, she had lost her head. But she had found it. And the show had gone on, the way people always say shows do.

Moreover, the Moffats had nice warm bear pajamas to sleep in for the rest of the winter. Of course, they didn't go to bed with the bear heads on. But the rest of the costumes were nice and warm.

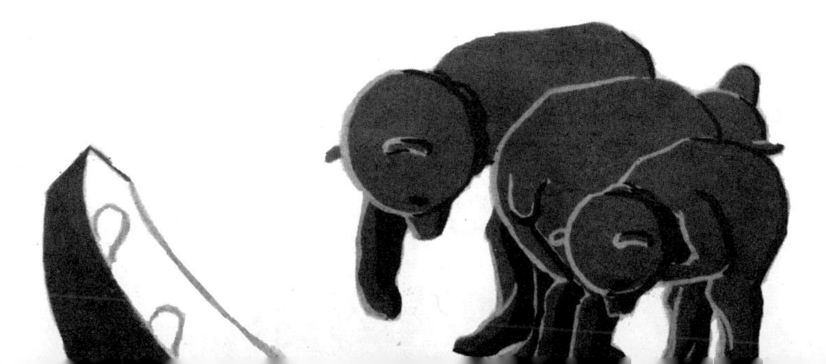

Yukon Trail

by Willis Lindquist

Under the lowering Alaskan sky young Steve Woodford stepped from the train at the snow-covered outpost of Nenana. He looked anxiously around for his Uncle Jim, the famous "Flying Doctor" of the Yukon of whom he had boasted so much at the orphanage.

For years he had dreamed of going to the Yukon. Now he was on his way and he was happy. He was going to have a real home and belong to a family. He hoped Uncle Jim and Aunt Bess would like him.

The young Indian who came up grinning couldn't have been over sixteen. "You're Steve?" he asked in perfect English. "Well, I'm Sam Ketchum. I've got a letter for you. There's been a lot of sickness up in the Yukon, and your uncle couldn't fly down for you."

Steve's heart sank as he took the letter. It was short. Uncle Jim wrote about how busy he was and that he might not be able to fly down for two or three weeks.

"Sam Ketchum is a young Indian guide who works for me," the letter went on. "I've told him to make you comfortable at the hotel. In a day or two he will be starting back for the Yukon with my new dog team. You could go with him if you wish, but I would not advise you to do so. It is a 350-mile mush through wilderness and tundra, and it would be a hardship for a boy accustomed to the soft life of civilization."

Steve read the letter several times at the hotel. It disturbed him that his uncle should think he was soft.

When he joined Sam for a dinner of venison roast he said, "I wanted to come up here last year, Sam. But Uncle Jim wouldn't let me. He wrote that I was too young. He said that the Yukon was a man's country and it was no place for a boy. So he made me wait a year. And now he thinks I'm soft. I'm going to show him, Sam. I'm going with you and the dog team."

Sam laughed. "It won't be easy," he warned. "But you have to learn about dogs sometime if you're going to be of any help to your uncle. We'll start at dawn."

It frightened Steve to think of the trip when he went to bed. He had never seen the big sled dogs. Some were part wolf and said to be dangerous.

It was still dark when the hotel man came with a set of fur breeches and a hooded parka, fur boots, and a fur sleeping bag.

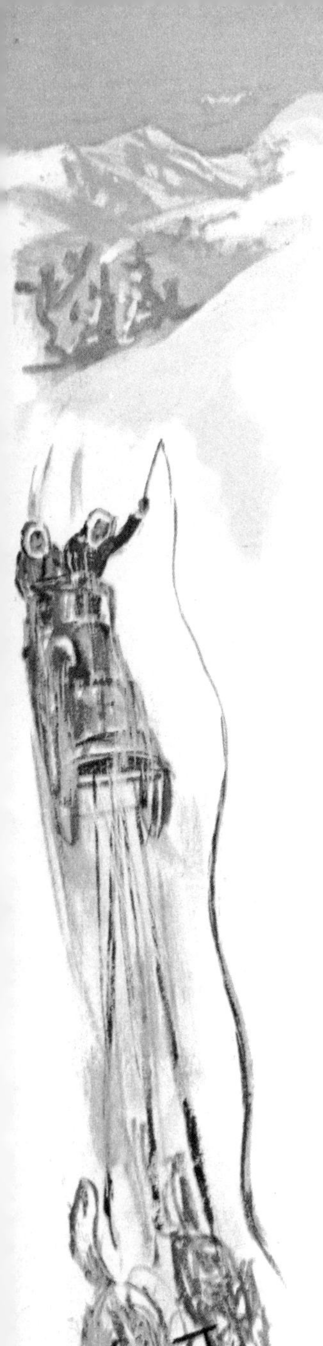

Sam was waiting for him at the sled, with eleven mighty huskies at their harnesses, anxious to be off.

"Better meet some of your dogs," Sam said. "This first one, your leader, is Mutt. He's been to the Yukon before, and he knows the trail."

The tawny big brute lowered its head and watched Steve with suspicion. Steve fought down his fear and leaned over to pet the dog. Its fangs bared in a snarl.

"Not too close," Sam warned. "Mutt doesn't know you yet. And you better stay clear of Kooga—this big Malemute. He's a real troublemaker."

"Why is the sled tied to a tree?" Steve asked.

"Because otherwise they'd be off like a flash and we couldn't stop them," Sam explained. He pointed to an iron rod suspended above the ground at the rear of the sled. It looked like a narrow rake. "That's your brake. You step on it and the prongs dig into the snow and stop the sled."

They packed, and Steve got on top of the sled.

"Hold on!" Sam warned as he untied the rope from the tree.

The dogs were off, eleven big brutes harnessed in pairs except for Mutt who took the lead. They raced over the snow in full gallop. The sled bounced and flew, and it took all of Steve's strength to hold on.

Standing on the runners in back, Sam gave a hearty laugh. "Dogs are always wild to get started. They'll soon slow down."

They did. For hours they went, skirting great slopes of spruce and Norway pine, and on and on into the still white wilderness.

At midday they stopped for a few minutes' rest and a bite to eat.

"Now you drive," suggested Sam. "I'll run behind for a while to get warm. But whatever you do, don't fall off the sled. You'll not be able to stop the dogs, and you'll lose them and the sled and all your food. It's not a good way to die."

Steve leaped on the runners. "Get going!" he shouted. Mutt turned his head back and looked at him, but nothing happened.

"Holler *mush,*" Sam suggested. "When you want to go right, holler *gee,* and for left, *up*. And swing the sled around corners so it doesn't tip."

Steve nodded. *"Mush!"* he screamed. It worked. He stood proudly on the runners. He was driving a dog team!

There was real work to it, he soon discovered. Keeping the sled upright at curves was tricky, and he had to be careful to avoid the stumps and rocks that might smash the sled. On the down slopes he stood on the brake to keep from running over the dogs.

But suddenly it happened. He made the mistake of looking back too long at Sam who was jogging half a mile behind them. He hit a slope, and his feet slipped from the runners. But he held on, dragging as the sled gathered speed downhill until it pushed the dogs forward into a wild, scrambled heap. Then the sled tipped.

It started one of the wildest dog fights Steve had ever seen. Each seemed to be blaming the others for what had happened, and they snarled and slashed with white-fanged fury.

"Stop them! Stop them!" yelled Sam.

Steve stood frozen with fear. He didn't move. He didn't dare venture close.

Sam came up at full speed, screaming at the dogs. He pried them loose one by one with a snowshoe, and straightened their harnesses which had become badly tangled. Then he mopped the sweat from his face.

"You'll have to learn how to do that quick," he gasped. "If you don't you'll lose a dog or two before you know it."

For five days they went on, and then Sam began to have chills and fever. "I was in the hospital for a week before you came," he explained. "Maybe I left too soon. It's coming back."

By noon he was groaning with pain and could not leave the sled. "There's a settlement over on Carlson Creek," he whispered. "You'd better get me there fast."

Steve reached the hollow among the bluffs in three

hours, and only the women and children were there to meet them. The men were out on a week-long hunt.

"This one needs a doctor," said an old woman.

Steve went cold with dread, but he knew what had to be done. "Sam says my lead dog knows the trail well. I'll go get the doctor."

Sam mumbled in protest. "You'll stay here," he gasped. "Your uncle flies to this settlement every so often for a check."

"It might be weeks," said the old woman, "there is much sickness."

"I'll go," said Steve. He had no choice. Soon he found himself alone on the trail with a fierce pack of Malemutes and Eskimo huskies, and he felt panic rising within him. He began to wonder if he could handle the team.

He began talking to the dogs, calling them by name as Sam had told him to do. He stopped for the night under a sheltering cliff near a staggering thicket of birches. Now the moment he dreaded most had come. He had to handle the big dogs.

Steve tried not to show his fear. The big leader dog watched with yellow eyes as he approached, its ears flattened to the massive head. As Steve reached down to unfasten the harness the wolf dog snarled.

"Easy, Mutt!" Swiftly, Steve unharnessed the dog and led it to the nearest birch tree and tied it up. He came away weak but bursting with happiness he had never known. *He could do it!* The other dogs, even the big Malemute Kooga, were easy after that.

One day followed another with perfect weather. The dogs were beginning to know him, some even licked his hand. But Mutt, the leader, remained sullen.

Then he saw the plane in the sky one morning. It circled above him, his uncle waved, and Steve, forming big letters in the snow, told him to go to Sam at Carlson's Settlement.

A howling Arctic blizzard started that night and kept him in his sleeping bag for two days. The third morning dawned clear, and he looked out on a white world.

As they mushed north that afternoon he became careless. He did not see the low branch until it struck him with a stunning blow in the face. He was falling. "Don't lose your sled or you die!" Sam's words came roaring back to his ears.

With all his strength he tried to hold on. But it was no use. His fingers slipped and he lunged headlong into the snow. He floundered. He tried to rise to his feet, but the earth seemed to tilt on end, and he couldn't tell which side was up.

The dogs and the sled were speeding away. He could see them vaguely. In a few moments they would be gone. There was nothing he could do to stop them. His food, his sleeping bag, even his snowshoes were on the sled. A man couldn't live very long on the lonely white tundra without them.

In that reeling instant of terror he seemed doomed. His mind cleared a little, and instinctively he cried out at the top of his lungs.

"Gee! Gee! Gee, Mutt."

He held his breath. For a terrible instant nothing happened. But suddenly the big lead dog swung to the right. He waited until the whole team had turned. Then he screamed again. "Gee! Gee, Mutt!" Once more the lead dog turned.

They were coming back now. Steve got to his feet and stumbled to meet them, waving his arms. He tripped over a snowdrift and sprawled before the onrushing team. That was all he could remember for a long time.

When he opened his eyes finally it seemed that a miracle had happened. Mutt, towering over him, was licking his face.

He threw his arms around the big dog, buried his face in the heavy fur, and let the tears come. Even a man could cry in Alaska, if there was no one to see his tears.

From that day on his uncle paid daily visits to watch his progress and to drop sandwiches and food from Aunt Bess. In the first of these packages he found a note.

"I have seen Sam," wrote his uncle. "He's doing fine,

thanks to you. If you keep up your good speed you should reach home in three days. We'll be waiting."

Steve felt a deep inner excitement. Home! In three days! He could drive a dog team now, and he felt sure that he could be of real use to his uncle. They would not find him soft and useless. They would like him.

Near sunset, three days later, as he came down the slope into the small settlement of Unison in the Yukon, his uncle and half the village came out to meet him. They were cheering and waving and smiling. His tall uncle wore a large smile, and threw an arm over his shoulder.

"Good boy, Steve," he said warmly. To the people of the village he said, raising his voice. "I'm mighty proud to introduce you to my nephew Steve. He mushed all the way from Nenana in fifteen days, and that's a record for any of us to shoot at."

Later when Aunt Bess and Uncle Jim and Steve were alone Uncle Jim said, "I want to confess, Steve, that I've been worried about having you here. I wanted you to be happy, but I knew that a soft white boy from civilization would soon be looked upon by these people with contempt."

He smiled and took Steve firmly by the shoulders. "But I see now I was wrong. I need not have worried. You did what had to be done. You've got the makings of a real Yukon man."

Steve turned away quickly to hide the mist of happiness that had come into his eyes.

Winner Take a Mule

E. H. Lansing

Eleven-year-old Jeb Tillson and mean Sam Cotter had a dispute about a mule. It might have meant blood, but Jeb's Uncle Raff proposed a shooting match instead, winner to take the mule. Uncle Raff and Sam were both known in the mountains as crack shots. Mr. Olmstead agreed to judge the contest.

"You men are to shoot at the two targets on the fence," shouted Mr. Olmstead so everyone could hear. "Ten shots each, turn and turn about. Raff take the target to the right. Sam the one to the left. The man who gets the most shots nearest his bull's-eye wins."

Every head turned toward the two targets on the fence. Each one was a square of white paper with a red circle in its center. Jeb thought the red circles looked very small. He stood close to the mule and held tight to the halter rope. He watched Uncle Raff as he stepped forward to take the first shot. Jeb heard the report of the gun, but he couldn't see whether the shot had hit. Then it was Sam's turn.

Jeb counted the shots. Three for Uncle Raff, three for Sam. Mr. Olmstead wasn't to look at the targets until each man had ten shots.

Jeb's hands were stiff from holding the mule's rope. His eyes ached from trying to see the red circles. The shots rang in his ears like the crash of thunder. He lost count of them.

At last Mr. Olmstead raised his hand. "Ten each," he called. "That's all."

A rustle of talk ran through the crowd as Mr. Olmstead went toward the targets. Jeb closed his eyes and leaned against the mule. But he couldn't keep them closed. He had to know that Uncle Raff had won.

Mr. Olmstead looked from one target to the other. He studied each one so long the crowd grew impatient. Cries of "Who won?" came from every side.

Mr. Olmstead turned to the crowd. "Every one of those shots hit the red circles," he shouted. "The contest's a draw."

A great shout came from the people. Both Uncle Raff and Sam looked very pleased with themselves. But Jeb did not shout. The question of who was to have the mule was still unsettled.

Mr. Olmstead raised his hand for silence. He held up a shining half dollar. "I'll toss this in the air twice. Raff gets first shot at it. Sam second. The one who hits nearest the center wins."

Uncle Raff and Sam nodded agreement. They watched Mr. Olmstead as he stood by the fence with the coin in his hand. Uncle Raff limped forward down the slope of the meadow to take his stand for his shot.

Then Jeb caught his breath with a sharp sound. Uncle Raff had slipped and fallen. He landed with a thud on his shooting arm. When he sat up, his arm hung at his side. Jeb dropped the rope and raced to kneel down by Uncle Raff.

"Wrenched bad," said Uncle Raff. His face was tight with pain.

"I win," said Sam in a loud voice. "I win 'cause he can't shoot no more and I kin."

Uncle Raff did not answer Sam in words. He looked at Jeb and handed him his gun. Jeb knew what he must do. He got to his feet with the gun in his hands.

"I ain't shooting against no boy!" Sam's harsh voice made Jeb jump.

"Don't mind him, Jeb," said Uncle Raff in his easy way. "You got a right to shoot. You're a Tillson."

"I won already!" bellowed Sam.

Mr. Olmstead opened his mouth to speak, but someone got ahead of him. A shrill voice came from the crowd.

"Don't you pay him no never mind, Jeb Tillson! You kin shoot as good as him any day in the mornin'."

Jeb suddenly felt better. Granny hadn't been able to keep away from the shooting match after all. Now she pushed her way forward through the crowd. Her sharp face was bright with anger.

A loud murmur of approval came from the listening people. Everyone agreed with Granny that Jeb had a right to shoot in Uncle Raff's place.

Mr. Olmstead nodded at Jeb. "Go ahead," he said.

But Sam Cotter was not going to let the crowd have everything its own way. "Iffen I'm to shoot agin a mere boy I claim the right to shoot first," he said fiercely. "I got some say-so in this shootin' match."

Mr. Olmstead shrugged his shoulders. "I guess Jeb doesn't mind who goes first. Do you, Jeb?"

Jeb shook his head. "I don't mind." He was glad to let Sam shoot first. It would give him time to steady his nerve.

Mr. Olmstead held the coin in his hand, waiting for Sam to give him the signal. Sam lifted his gun to his shoulder, then nodded at Mr. Olmstead. The coin flew high into the air, a bright flash of silver in the sunshine. Jeb watched the coin, waiting for the sound of Sam's shot. But no sound came.

Sam was holding his gun in both hands, staring angrily at the trigger. "Jammed," muttered Sam, "jammed tighter'n sausage meat."

Uncle Raff chuckled. "Mebbe Jeb wins. He kin shoot and you can't."

Sam glared at Uncle Raff. His own words were coming back to him and he could think of nothing to say.

Then Jeb moved forward with Uncle Raff's gun in his hands. He did not think what he was doing. But deep in

his heart, he wanted to win the mule fairly. He held out Uncle Raff's gun toward Sam.

"Use this gun," said Jeb quietly.

For a long minute, Sam looked at Jeb without moving. Then the hard lines of his jaw softened. "Thanks, boy," said Sam. His voice was as quiet as Jeb's had been. He took the gun and stepped into shooting position.

Once again Sam nodded at Mr. Olmstead. Once again the coin rose in a whirling flash toward the sky. This time, Sam's shot rang out loud and clear. The coin jerked and fell to the ground.

Jeb watched Mr. Olmstead walk toward the place where the coin had fallen. Mr. Olmstead picked up the coin and studied it carefully. Then he held it up to the people. "Nicked off the edge," he cried.

The watching crowd murmured its applause. No one liked Sam well enough to cheer him loudly. But everyone was polite enough to acknowledge a good shot.

Sam did not look at Jeb as he handed back the gun. Jeb clutched the smooth barrel with both hands and walked to the shooting stand. He did not think or feel anything. For a moment his eyes blurred, and he had a horrible fear that he would not even see the coin, much less hit it.

Then he heard a sharp familiar voice. "Stand up to hit, Jeb. Act like you was glad-proud to be a Tillson."

Granny's brisk words were like a dash of cold water in

Jeb's face. His muscles stiffened and he could think clearly. He turned and grinned at Granny.

Then he lifted the gun and looked at Mr. Olmstead. He saw the tiny coin in Mr. Olmstead's hands. When he gave the signal, it would fly into the air.

Jeb's hands shook. He lowered his gun and looked toward the mule. The mule was watching Jeb. One long ear flapped forward in a friendly greeting.

"Go it, Jeb!" Ben Larkin's high excited voice sounded very loud to Jeb.

Then another voice spoke. "What you waitin' fer, Jeb?" Uncle Raff's calm, sure words steadied the boy.

He took a firm grip on the rifle. He lifted it to his shoulder and nodded at Mr. Olmstead. The sun caught at the silver coin. Jeb saw its brightness right at the end of the gun barrel. His finger pressed the trigger. Then Jeb shut his eyes.

He didn't open them until he heard a shout from the people. Then he saw Mr. Olmstead holding the coin high.

"Right plunk in the middle!" shouted Mr. Olmstead.

The crowd surged forward and pushed around Jeb. People thumped him on the back. Ben jumped up and down like a jack-in-the-box, yelling with joy. Granny's thin face was stiff with pride.

Jeb scarcely felt the thumps on his back. He didn't hear what anyone said. He just stood still and knew the mule was his for keeps.

Ahoy, There!

"Ahoy" is how the ships at sea
And sailors call a greeting;
It is a vast and cheerful word
That sets my heart to beating.

I see the waves go up and down
And feel the sea winds blow:
Ahoy, there, mates ahoy—and let
Landlubbers say, "Hello"!

—Dorothy Hall

With Fife and Drum

Dessa Fultz

Children of lighthouse keepers are used to emergencies. They have to be practical and quick-witted. But no one had expected that two girls left alone for the day would have to deal with an enemy warship. The story of Rebecca and Abigail Bates has been handed down in family records.

A cool breeze carried the pleasant tang of salt water through the lighthouse window on that morning of September first, 1814. But fourteen-year-old Rebecca Bates was too busy to heed the fine weather. She gave the reflector of the whale-oil lamp in the lighthouse tower a last rub. Then she folded the polishing cloth and handed it to her twelve-year-old sister, Abigail.

"There!" said Rebecca. "That's about as clean as clean can be."

"Yes, indeed," said Abigail, agreeing with her sister.

The girls were the daughters of the lighthouse keeper at Scituate [sĭt′ū̇·ăt], Massachusetts. That morning after breakfast, Mr. and Mrs. Bates had gone off in the family buggy. Their errand, five or six miles inland, would keep them away till evening.

Behind them they had left enough chores to keep Rebecca and Abigail busy for many hours. First, the girls had tidied the white cottage back of the lighthouse. Then they had climbed the steep stairway to the top of the tower and filled and cleaned the lamp.

The lighthouse was at the end of the low, sandy spit that formed one side of Scituate Harbor. From many windows of the tower, the entire harbor could be seen. Rocking gently on its blue waters were boats of various kinds, including two schooners loaded with flour.

The lighthouse windows also looked out on the village of Scituate. In front of it lay rolling sand dunes, and behind it, the quiet forest.

Abigail glanced from the window. The tide was so low that some of the fishing boats were stuck in the mud flats. Suddenly her eyes grew round with fright. "Rebecca! Look!" she cried to her elder sister.

Rebecca was accustomed to Abigail's panics, but this time there was real cause for terror. The older girl's hand flew to her mouth. Then she turned and murmured to Abigail, "It's a British warship!"

They stared at the stately ship that was heading under full sail toward the entrance to the bay.

"The British soldiers will burn the fishing boats," Abigail cried, "and the schooners of flour and Uncle's new sloop."

"They'll probably burn the village, too," said Rebecca. "But they'll have to wait for high tide before they can come close enough to shore to do real harm."

Abigail's tears flowed on. "But high tide is only five hours away. I'm scared. Aren't you, Rebecca?"

The older girl shook her head. "I certainly don't like to think of houses and boats burning. But there must be something we can do about it! We just have to think!"

Strangers in the Harbor

Abigail wiped her eyes, but it was hard to put fear out of her mind. Then suddenly the girls saw people running. Some were going to the cliff to watch. Others were getting into rowboats.

"They've seen the warship!" exclaimed Rebecca. "They're all trying to save the tackle and nets on their fishing boats."

At last Abigail had an idea. "Let's get father's spyglass and see what is happening on the British ship." She ran off, and soon the two were taking turns peering through the glass.

Part of the time they watched the decks of the warship. Part of the time they watched the village, where groups of

people could be seen on the cliff and in the streets. Everyone seemed to be talking excitedly.

Minutes passed. Slowly, very slowly, the tide was rising. When an hour had passed, the small boats that had been grounded were tugging at their moorings. Now the people were no longer gathered in the streets. Most of the men had gone into the old fishhouse. Those who were left were loading household goods onto carts.

Rebecca knew what this meant. "The men who have guns are going to use the fishhouse for a fort," she said. "The others are going to find safety in the woods."

More minutes and then hours passed. At last the tide was high, and the warship came sailing toward the mouth of Scituate Harbor. Just outside the bay she dropped anchor.

"They're going to bring soldiers ashore," said Abigail.

Five large rowboats were lowered. They were manned by sailors and filled with soldiers wearing red coats. Oars dipped and rose in unison. Guns glittered in the sunshine. The rowboats passed the lighthouse and entered the bay.

Suddenly anger darkened Rebecca's face. She handed the spyglass to Abigail. "Look at that first boatload of soldiers," she stormed. "They are setting fire to a fishing boat."

In spite of the rapidly spreading flames, not a sound came from the fishhouse where the men with guns were hiding.

"Why don't our people shoot?" cried Abigail. "Why are they waiting?"

"Perhaps they'll shoot when the soldiers come nearer," said Rebecca. "Remember that they don't have much ammunition. They can't waste it."

"Can't they make some kind of noise?" asked Abigail. "They could beat the drum, couldn't they?"

"They haven't got it," Rebecca explained. "Father brought it home last night. It's in the kitchen with his fife." Then she stopped, and turned her brightening face to her sister.

"I have an idea," Rebecca announced. "You and I can play that fife and drum!"

Abigail looked puzzled. "Really, Rebecca," she said. "This isn't a very good time for music."

"Don't you see?" Rebecca persisted. "It will make the British think an army is coming to defend the town. We'll sound like an army marching down the point to head them off."

At first Abigail looked startled. Then her expression changed, and she began to laugh.

An Army of Two

The two girls raced down the steps and into the cottage. Opening a chest in the kitchen, Rebecca took out a drum and drumsticks and handed them to Abigail. "You can be the drummer."

Then she took a fife from the closet. "I'll play this. The only tune I know is 'Yankee Doodle,' but it will do."

"We'll sound like an army," said Abigail. "Just the two of us!"

Taking the fife and drum, the girls sneaked out the back way and kept hidden by bushes and sand dunes till they reached the outside beach. Then Rebecca put the fife to her lips. Abigail held her drumsticks in position. As she beat out the time, Rebecca joined her.

Up and down, up and down, they marched, drumming and fifing.

Luckily, the warship was anchored south of the lighthouse, and the beach, on the north side of the spit, curved to the west. The tiny army made up of two girls was hidden from the men on the ship and from those in the rowboats. But the salt breeze carried the roll of the drum

and the shrill squeak of the fife far out over the water. It carried the sound to the village, too, and soon Rebecca and Abigail heard cheering from the old fishhouse.

"Oh, my!" said Abigail. "We've made the men in the fishhouse think that help is coming from Boston or Plymouth. How disappointed they will be."

"Never mind that," said Rebecca. "If we're fooling them, we're fooling the Redcoats, too."

Again the drumsticks beat out a march, and the notes of "Yankee Doodle" whirled through the air.

Suddenly there came the sharp crack of gunfire.

For the first time, Rebecca began to look worried. "The soldiers aren't fooled after all," she said. "They're firing on the men in the village."

"I'm going to find out," cried Abigail, whose bravery now seemed endless. She dropped the drum and climbed up the dune. She had barely reached a place from which she could see, when she shouted, "Good! Good!"

"Good?" asked Rebecca. "What's good?"

"It's our men!" Abigail announced. "They're firing on the Redcoats. They must have grown bold when they thought help was coming."

Rebecca scrambled up to join her. Some of the British boats were turning and heading back to the warship. And some of the Scituate men were getting into their own boats to chase the British.

Suddenly the girls began to laugh. "The tables have turned," said Rebecca. "Let's get back to work. Now that we've made everyone think we're an army, we've got to keep them thinking so a little longer. Come on."

Two girls with aching muscles marched up and down the beach, fifing and drumming.

Then all sounds of firing ceased. Anxiously the girls peered over a sand dune. Some of the boats in the harbor were still burning, but not a Redcoat was in sight.

"They must have gone back to their ship, every last one of them," said Abigail. She turned her gaze seaward. "Look!" she cried. "The ship is moving. It's going away."

"We fooled them," exclaimed Rebecca, dropping down on the beach to rest. "They've left without firing a shot."

The words were hardly out of her mouth before a cannon on shipboard sent a round shot toward the lighthouse. A fountain of white water spurted from the sea just beyond the sandy spit.

"They didn't hit anything," said Rebecca. "And I expect they feel pretty foolish. After all the trouble they took to come here, they didn't do a thing except set a few fishing boats on fire."

Abigail laughed. "I'm sure they would feel worse if they knew that what kept them from burning all the boats and the town, too, were . . ."

"Two girls and a fife and a drum," finished Rebecca.

The Greatest River in the World

Catherine O. Peare

When Sam Clemens was a boy, he was lucky to live on the Mississippi River. In fact, from the language of the river boatmen he took the name "Mark Twain," under which he wrote many books. Along the banks of the river, during Sam's boyhood, there was always something happening. Sam himself was one of the busiest boys in his home town. He was a good swimmer, full of schemes for hunting treasure or exploring caves. He daydreamed of being a steamboatman some day. As he grew older, he tried one job after another. For a while he worked as a printer. When he was not working, he liked to read and to travel.

One day Sam happened to dip into a book about South America, and his eyes grew wider as he learned about the Amazon River in Brazil. Another great river, that was a thousand miles wide at its mouth!

"I am going to South America to explore the Amazon!" he announced.

All he had to do was find a ship in New Orleans or New York that was going to South America. New Orleans seemed like a better idea than New York, so he boarded a steamer, the *Paul Jones,* and started south.

Sam Clemens hadn't forgotten his dream of being a steamboatman. He stood at the rail a while, watching the river grow wider and deeper. Then he left the rail and wandered all the way up to the pilothouse, which was flanked by two giant smokestacks. He stood at the door of the circular room, looking at the big wheel and the man whose hand rested on it.

"How would you like a young man to learn the river?" he asked politely.

"I wouldn't like it," the pilot growled at him. "Cub pilots are more trouble than they're worth."

Sam stood his ground. He had just decided that he was tired of being a printer. He wanted to be a river pilot.

"Do you know the Bowen boys?" he asked.

It turned out that the man did know the Bowen boys. In fact, he had taught Will Bowen to be a pilot. After that the pilot grew more friendly. For the next two weeks, while the *Paul Jones* journeyed down the river to New Orleans, Sam hung around the pilothouse and talked with the pilot.

The man standing at the big wheel had been on the Mississippi for many years. He had experienced great adventures. He had narrowly escaped death at the hands of bad men who traveled the Mississippi. His steamship had almost exploded more than once. Or so he said, and so Sam believed. Sam hadn't yet learned that rivermen were full of tall yarns.

Sam hated to say good-by at New Orleans. But he was headed for the Amazon in South America, or so he thought. He was due for a disappointment. There weren't any ships going to the Amazon. There weren't going to be any for at least ten years. Sam rushed back to his pilot friend.

"Please take me on as a cub pilot," he begged.

"No!"

Sam didn't give up. He went back every day for three days. At last the pilot agreed to teach Sam Clemens to be a river pilot.

"It will cost you five hundred dollars," he said. Sam had only ten dollars.

"River pilots earn good pay," said Sam hopefully. "As soon as I'm a river pilot I'll pay you back."

It was agreed, and Sam Clemens started on one of the greatest adventures he was ever to have—his life on the Mississippi.

"The boat backed out from New Orleans at four in the afternoon, and it was 'our watch' until eight. Mr. Bixby, my chief, 'straightened her up,' plowed her along past the sterns of the other boats that lay at the Levee, and then said, 'Here, take her; shave those steamships as close as you'd peel an apple.' "

Sam, the Cub Pilot

For the first time in his life, Sam took hold of the wheel and felt the steamboat move to his command. The wheel was made of hard, heavy wood with sixteen spokes. It would have been taller than a man if it hadn't turned partly below the level of the floor. It was fully nine feet across. When the current was swift, the pilot had to place his foot, as well as his hands, on one of the spokes in order to keep the wheel steady.

Of course, Sam was afraid of going too close to the other boats, and he left far too much space. The pilot scolded him with a long torrent of words, and Sam's training had begun.

The Mississippi had to be memorized mile by mile. Every landmark along both shores meant something. Every town, every bend in the river, every island, every clump of trees—all the way from New Orleans to St. Louis.

"Memorize the shape of the Mississippi, too," he was told, "because when you're steering a boat in the pitch dark, you won't be able to see any landmarks."

Sam thought it would take him the rest of his life to memorize the shape of the Mississippi.

And that wasn't all. The river was always changing. A boat could come through a spot one time and find deep

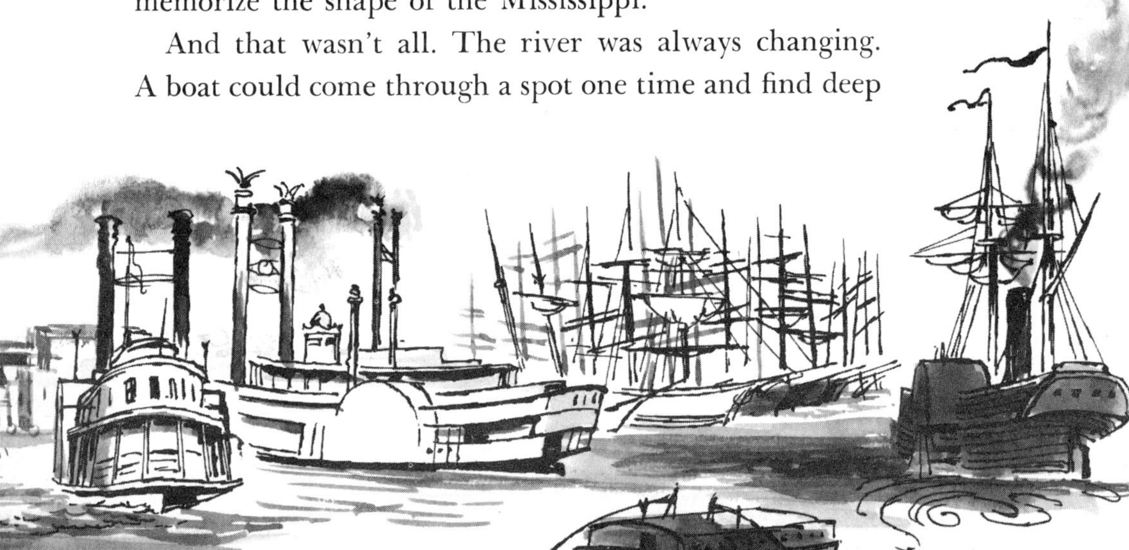

water. On the next trip it would find a dangerous sand bar. A pilot had to watch the changing color of the water to know the depth. He had to listen to the leadsmen shouting their measurements as they let down the line to find the bottom of the river.

"M-a-r-k three! M-a-r-k three! Quarter-less-three! Half twain! Quarter twain! M-a-r-k twain!"

These shouted measurements told the pilot that he was entering shallower water. The pilot pulled his bell ropes and gave correct bell signals to the men in the engine room for more speed or less. If the pilot made a mistake, he could wreck the boat, lose expensive cargo, perhaps even kill his passengers and crew.

Sam decided that there was nobody in the world so important as a river pilot.

There were rainy, misty days on the river when everything seemed to change shape. And there were foggy nights when the pilot could see nothing at all. He still had to steer his boat.

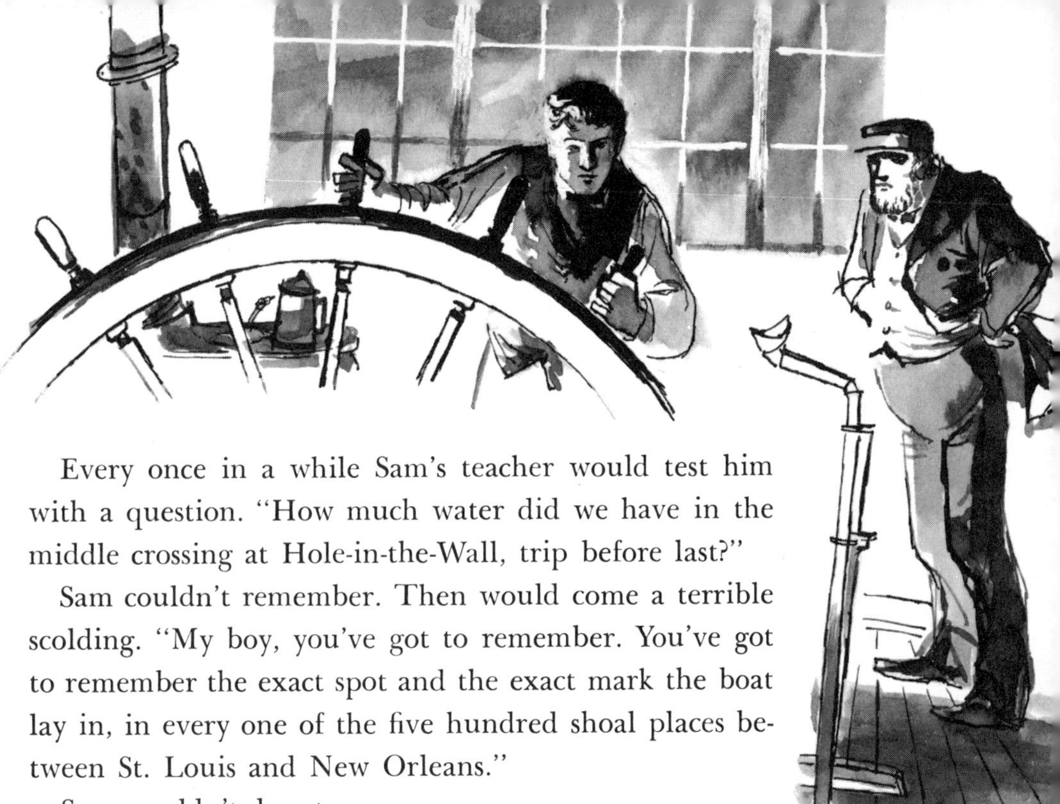

Every once in a while Sam's teacher would test him with a question. "How much water did we have in the middle crossing at Hole-in-the-Wall, trip before last?"

Sam couldn't remember. Then would come a terrible scolding. "My boy, you've got to remember. You've got to remember the exact spot and the exact mark the boat lay in, in every one of the five hundred shoal places between St. Louis and New Orleans."

Sam wouldn't dare to answer.

"When I say I'll learn a man the river, I mean it," said the pilot gruffly. "You can depend on it, I'll learn him or kill him."

Sam Wins His License

Sam did learn the Mississippi, all the river's curves and bends, all the changes of the seasons, too. In the spring the water was much deeper than at the end of the summer. The melting snows farther north did that. He learned the river going north, and he learned the river going south.

Sam Clemens learned the river so well that he became an expert. He studied with more than one pilot. He

worked on a freight boat and then on a passenger boat, the *Pennsylvania*. Sam was getting closer and closer to his pilot's license.

He received his pilot's license in the fall when he was only twenty-three years old. It had taken him a year and a half of hard work and study. At last he was a riverboatman. He could vie with the best of them, and he could tell yarns as tall as any of them! Sometimes Sam Clemens' yarns were a little taller. He still read in his spare time and even wrote down some of the river tales that he heard.

He used to like to tell the yarn about the time he rescued an old man from a burning building. The man was hanging out of a window four flights up, calling for help. "The ladders weren't long enough. Nobody had enough presence of mind—nobody but me. I came to the rescue. I yelled for a rope. When it came I threw the old man the end of it. He caught it and I told him to tie it around his waist. He did so, and I pulled him down."

Every once in a while a yarn that certainly sounded as though Sam Clemens had made it up was published in a local newspaper. He signed his short stories and humorous articles "Mark Twain," the river term which means "safe water."

Sam Clemens was a pilot on the Mississippi River for three years. He had just about forgotten that he wanted to go to South America and explore the Amazon River. The Amazon? Who cared a fig about the Amazon? The Mississippi was the greatest river in the world!

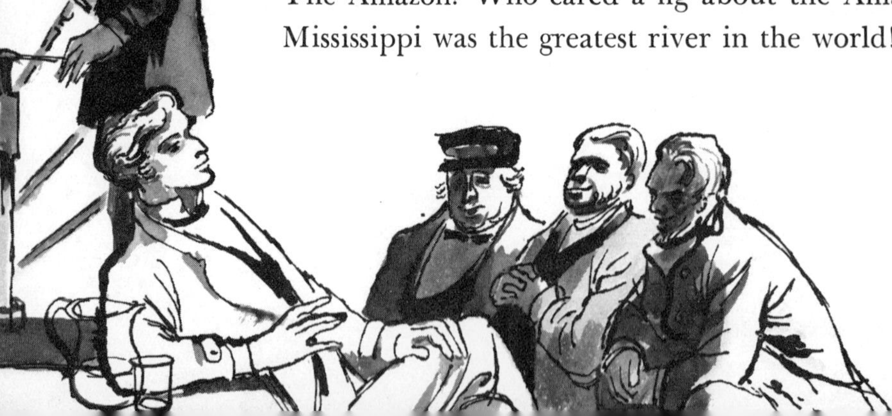

The Ferryboat on the Beach

Nora B. Stirling

At two thirty in the afternoon of September 21, 1938, fifteen-year-old Shirley Disbury and Eileen O'Connor gaily boarded the ferryboat *Governor Carr* plying between Newport, Rhode Island, and tiny Conanicut Island in Narragansett Bay. Twice every school day they made this same half-hour trip. But the trip today was going to be very different from any other they had ever taken. For, all unknowing, they were in a race for their lives with nature's most violent and destructive monster.

Four days before, somewhere in the Caribbean, a mass of cool dry air had rushed toward another mass of hot moist air, sending it whirling upward in a wild spiraling motion. The whirling grew faster and faster, sucking more and more air in with it and at the same time moving in a northerly direction.

The winds on the edge of the spiral were a mere thirty or forty miles an hour, but closer in they hit two hundred, while at dead center was a spot of utter calm. In this hurricane's eye the air pressure was so low, the waves swelled up into it in a mountain of water that traveled with the whirlwind as it roared north to the United States.

This was the terrible hurricane of 1938, the worst disaster ever to strike New England.

In 1938, the Weather Bureau was not equipped to give out storm warnings as it is today. Eileen and Shirley, along with Captain Harry Fillmore and the eighty other schoolboys and schoolgirls, supposed that the high winds and waves were just another good blow, exciting but nothing to get alarmed about. Indeed, the two girls were planning to stay aboard for another round trip amid the flying spray, but by the time the ferry had tied up at the Jamestown pier, Captain Fillmore was looking serious.

"All out," he shouted with a queer note in his voice.

The hurricane was now almost upon them. As Shirley struggled homeward, she was blown flat against the store fronts along the way. At Eileen's house the combined strength of her mother and brother and sister could barely hold the door on its hinges while she squeezed through.

"The ship would be safer back at Newport." The Captain yelled to his first mate, and as he gave orders to cast off, twelve men and two women hurried aboard. But it was too late for seeking safety; there was no safety in Newport or anywhere else.

The hurricane was now screaming seventy, eighty, ninety miles an hour, and the mountain of water at its core rose over barns, trees, and church tops. Houses were picked up and borne on the crest of it and dashed down again in splinters. Beaches were washed away, whole villages dissolved. The city of Providence drowned under thirteen feet of swirling water. Men and women swam through the streets—those who *could* swim—while cars and busses crowded with people disappeared from sight. Yachts were tossed about on the bay like empty matchboxes—and the clumsy *Governor Carr,* tugging loose the hawsers that tied her to the pier, rose on the flood and swept half a mile up the shore. There the crested wave, passing on, left her stranded on the lawn of the Wetherill's summer home.

By six o'clock the hurricane had roared on into Canada. It left behind a hundred million dollars' worth of damage and 312 Rhode Islanders dead. And still some people miraculously escaped. One small girl navigated a mattress like a raft for three hours, coming to a safe landing on a wooden fence. Four fishermen, taking refuge on the roof of a cottage, soared off on a flight over the country club and landed gently a couple of miles away.

The passengers and crew of the beached ferryboat called for help until someone heard, and when a tall ladder was propped against the side of the hull they climbed down onto the summer colonists' front lawn. The sandy soil was already dry, and they came through their exciting adventure without even wetting their feet.

It took months to clean up the mess. For the first few days Eileen and Shirley, like the other girls and boys, reveled in the excitement and enforced holidays, and then the following week school reopened in Newport. They were ferried to and fro in a government launch and got

from the attention a pleasantly important feeling. Nevertheless they were always loyal to the *Governor Carr,* whom they considered the queen of all ferryboats. They watched impatiently for her to get back into service.

After some months, when the most urgent clean up jobs were finished, someone said, "Now let's get that huge thing off the Wetherill's lawn," and professional ship salvors were called in. But this was not regular ship salvage. Removing a ferryboat from a front lawn, particularly a lawn that was more rocks than grass, called for very special know-how, and Shirley and Eileen got into the habit of walking along after school to see it being done. How long, they asked the workmen, before they would be riding the *Governor Carr* again?

The workmen were making no promises. No one knew whether the bump with which the boat had sat down had caused her internal damage. It would show up only after she was launched, and they would just have to wait and see.

Since she was lying on her port side, huge hydraulic jacks were employed to lift her to an even keel. Then, in holes dug underneath, a wooden cradle was built to support her in this upright position. At the same time, divers

offshore dug an inclined channel from the sea floor right up under the cradle, and in it laid a wooden rack. On this track and on the cradle they smeared a heavy coat of grease.

So here was the *Governor Carr,* poised like a bobsled at the top of the run. All she needed was a good starter. And that was to be supplied by a derrick anchored offshore holding a heavy cable whose other end was hooked to her stern. On December 7, 1938, all was ready for the launching.

The girls woke very early and got on their bicycles. By six thirty, five hundred people, mostly boys and girls, had gathered to see the queen of ferryboats on her big day. At six fifty Captain Ed Berry gave the signal to the men on the derrick. The winch started to turn. The cable tautened and groaned, and the derrick itself dragged on its anchor as the strain increased. Every eye was fixed on the cradle

and the track under it, and at six minutes to seven a man yelled, "She's moving!"

Now a shout went up, and boys whistled, and auto horns blared as the pull of gravity took up the winch's pull. In a few moments the great hulk, like a clumsy whale out of water, was sliding comfortably back into its native element and the *Governor Carr* was relaunched.

Later news was equally good. The ferryboat had survived her bump without internal injuries, and she returned shortly to the service of the boys and girls of Conanicut, who thought her the finest of her kind.

Glossary

This glossary, or small dictionary, contains the more unusual words from the stories in this book. Usually, only the meaning is given that fits the word the first time it is used. The "key" at the bottom of the pages helps to show how each word is pronounced. The regular dictionary should be used to learn meanings of other words you find difficult, or other meanings for the words given here.

A

a·ban'doned (ȧ·băn'dŭnd). Deserted, no longer lived in.

a·bound' (ȧ·bound'). To be numerous or plentiful.

ab'so·lute (ăb'sō̇·lūt). Complete, perfect.

ac·com'mo·dat'ing (ă·kŏm'ō̇·dāt'ĭng). Obliging, eager to please.

a·chieve'ment (ȧ·chēv'mĕnt). Accomplishment, performance of an act deserving praise.

ac·knowl'edg·ment (ăk·nŏl'ĕj·mĕnt). Act of admitting the truth about any matter.

ac·quire' (ă·kwīr'). To get or obtain, usually by one's own work.

a·loft' (ȧ·lôft'). In the air.

am·bi'tious (ăm·bĭsh'ŭs). Eager to win fame, power, or superiority.

an'ces'tor (ăn'sĕs'tẽr). Forefather, person who lived long ago and from whom one is descended.

a·nem'o·ne (ȧ·nĕm'ō̇·nē̇). Spring-flowering plant with white or bright-colored blossoms.

an'te·lope (ăn'tē̇·lōp). Graceful, swift-footed animal of the goat family.

ap'pa·ra'tus (ăp'ȧ·rā'tŭs). Instrument, equipment, machine.

ap·par'ent (ă·păr'ĕnt). Clear to the mind, easily understood.

ap·peal' (ȧ·pēl'). To beg for help.

ap·proach' (ă·prōch'). To come or go near.

as·bes'tos (ăs·bĕs'tŏs). Grayish, fireproof mineral used especially for shingles.

as·sure' (ă·shŏŏr'). To make one sure or certain of something.

at·tend' (ă·tĕnd'). To pay attention, listen.

auc'tion·eer' (ôk'shŭn·ēr'). Person who runs a sale of goods to whoever offers the highest prices.

auk (ôk). Diving sea bird of the Northern Hemisphere.

au·thor'i·ty (ô·thŏr'ĭ·tĭ). Power to rule or govern.

a·void' (ȧ·void'). To keep away from, shun.

awk'ward (ôk'wẽrd). Not skillful, clumsy.

B

bag (băg). To kill on a hunt.

ban'is·ters (băn'ĭs·tẽrz). The railings beside a staircase.

ban'quet (băng'kwĕt). Feast.

ban'ter (băn'tẽr). Good-natured joking.

bat'ter (băt'ẽr). To wear down through long, hard use.

bay (bā). Reddish-brown.

be·hold' (bē̇·hōld'). To see, gaze upon.

ben'e·fit (bĕn'ē̇·fĭt). Advantage.

be·ware' (bē̇·wâr'). To be cautious, careful, or on guard.

ā, āte; ȧ, furnȧce; ă, ăt; ă, ăppear; â, câre; ä, cär; ȧ, pȧss; ȧ, sofȧ; ē, bē; ē̇, bē̇gin; ĕ, lĕt; ĕ, silĕnt; ẽ, watẽr; ē, hēre; ī, hīde; ĭ, hĭd; ĭ, cabĭn; ō, hōpe;

bick'er (bĭk'ẽr). To quarrel.

bliss (blĭs). Great happiness.

blown (blōn). Out of breath, tired and panting.

bore (bōr). To weary or tire someone by dullness.

box (bŏks). Small section or compartment in a theater or sports arena. It contains several seats with a very good view of the stage or field.

bran'dish (brăn'dĭsh). To wave something threateningly.

bri'dle (brī'd'l). Straps around a horse's head by which the rider controls the animal.

brood (brōōd). Young birds having the same mother.

buc'ca·neer' (bŭk'ȧ·nēr'). Pirate.

bun'ting (bŭn'tĭng). Cloth printed in the colors of the flag and used for decorations on patriotic occasions.

bur'dock' (bûr'dŏk'). Coarse weed with burlike flower heads.

bur'row (bûr'ō). Hole in the ground dug by some kinds of animals for a home.

by'-line' (bī'·līn'). Line at the head of a newspaper article telling who wrote it.

C

cache (kăsh). To hide treasure.

cal'cu·late (kăl'kū·lāt). To measure by using either actual figures or careful thought and estimate.

ca'liph (kā'lĭf). Title formerly given to rulers of the Mohammedan countries of Asia.

cam'phor (kăm'fẽr). Sap of an Asiatic tree used for medicine.

can'ter (kăn'tẽr). Slow gallop.

ca·reer' (kȧ·rēr'). Course of one's life.

cask (kȧsk). Barrel.

cast (kȧst). To throw.

cav'ern (kăv'ẽrn). Large cave.

cen'tu·ry (sĕn'tū·rĭ). Period of 100 years.

chan'de·lier' (shăn'dĕ·lēr'). Branched, glittering light fixture hanging from the ceiling.

chest'nut (chĕs'nŭt). Orange-brown—used in describing a horse.

chil'blain' (chĭl'blān'). Itching sore caused by cold weather.

chin·chil'la (chĭn·chĭl'ȧ). Small South American animal. Its soft gray fur is used in expensive coats.

chis'el (chĭz''l). To chip with a sharp-edged tool.

cir'cu·la'tion (sûr'kū·lā'shŭn). Movement of blood through the body.

clump (klŭmp). Closely packed group.

clus'ter (klŭs'tẽr). Bunch.

clutch (klŭch). To grip or hold tightly.

coil (koil). To wind in a circle.

col·lapse' (kŏ·lăps'). To fall in a heap.

col·lect' (kŏ·lĕkt'). To gather in one place.

com·bine' (kŏm·bīn'). To unite, make into one.

com·mer'cial·ly (kŏ·mûr'shăl·lĭ). In business.

con'cha (kŏng'kȧ). Flat, round, metal trimming.

Con'es·to'ga wag'on (kŏn'ĕs·tō'gȧ wăg'ŭn). Covered wagon.

con'scious (kŏn'shŭs). Aware, able to notice.

con·sid'er·a·ble (kŏn·sĭd'ẽr·ȧ·b'l). Large.

ō, ōmit; ŏ, hŏp; ŏ, cŏntain; ô, ôr; ô, sôft; ōō, fōōd; ŏŏ, fŏŏt; oi, oil; ou, out; ū, ūse; ū, ūnite; ŭ, ŭs; ŭ, circŭs; û, fûr; tū, natūre; dū, verdūre; th, thin; th, than.

con·sole′ (kŏn·sōl′). To comfort.

con·sult′ (kŏn·sŭlt′). To seek someone's advice or opinion.

con·trap′tion (kŏn·trăp′shŭn). Gadget.

con′trast (kŏn′trăst). Very great difference.

con·ven′ient (kŏn·vēn′yĕnt). Easy and satisfactory.

copse (kŏps). Thicket.

coun′ter·bal′ance (koun′tẽr·băl′ăns). To offset, make up for.

cou′pling (kŭp′lĭng). Connector.

cove (kōv). Small bay.

coy (koi). Bashful or shy in an impish way.

crafts′man (kråfts′măn). Person who works at a skilled trade.

crane (krān). To stretch out one's neck as a crane does.

crave (krāv). To long for.

crea′ture (krē′tūr). Any kind of animal.

crim′son (krĭm′z′n). Blood-red.

crisp (krĭsp). Short and sharp, clear-cut.

cus·to′di·an (kŭs·tō′dĭ·ăn). Person who takes care of a building. Some of his duties are like those of a janitor.

cut′lass (kŭt′lȧs). Short, heavy sword with a curved blade.

D

dain′ty (dān′tĭ). Pretty, but also frail or weak.

dam′ask (dăm′ȧsk). Cloth used in covering chairs, sofas, etc.

daze (dāz). To confuse, bewilder.

de·lib′er·ate (dė·lĭb′ẽr·ĭt). Carefully planned.

del′i·cate (dĕl′ĭ·kĭt). Frail.

de·pend′a·ble (dė·pĕn′dȧ·b′l). Trustworthy, reliable.

di·late′ (dī·lāt′). To grow larger.

dis·cuss′ (dĭs·kŭs′). To talk about.

dis·dain′ (dĭs·dān′). Scorn.

dis′lo·cate (dĭs′lō·kāt). To disarrange, put out of order or out of place.

dis·tinc′tion (dĭs·tĭngk′shŭn). Honor, special recognition.

dis·tin′guish (dĭs·tĭng′gwĭsh). To set apart, make noticeable.

dis·tin′guished (dĭs·tĭng′gwĭsht). Famous.

dis·tract′ (dĭs·trăkt′). To confuse, perplex.

dis·trust′ (dĭs·trŭst′). Doubt, absence of faith.

doff (dŏf). To lift or take off, as a hat or coat.

dome (dōm). Roof shaped like half a ball.

dor′sal (dôr′săl). Back fin.

dou′ble [back] (dŭb′′l). To make a sharp turn and almost retrace one's steps as a way of throwing a pursuer off the track.

dour (dōōr). Stern, severe.

drake (drāk). Male duck.

drawl (drôl). Slow manner of speaking.

driz′zle (drĭz′′l). To rain in very small drops, to sprinkle.

dune (dūn). Mound or ridge of sand that is shaped and reshaped by the action of the wind.

E

ed′i·to′ri·al (ĕd′ĭ·tō′rĭ·ăl). Newspaper article giving the editor's or publisher's opinion.

ee′rie (ē′rĭ). Weird, causing fear.

ā, āte; ả, furnảce; ă, ăt; ă, ăppear; â, câre; ä, cär; ȧ, pȧss; ȧ, sofȧ; ē, bē; ė, bėgin; ĕ, lĕt; ĕ, silĕnt; ẽ, watẽr; ę, hęre; ī, hīde; ĭ, hĭd; ĭ, cabĭn; ō, hōpe;

ei'der down (ī'dẽr doun). Very soft feathers growing under the outer feathers of the eider or sea duck.

e·lab'o·rate (ė·lăb'ō·rĭt). Carefully planned in all details.

e·lec'tro·mag'net (ė·lĕk'trō·măg'nĕt). Piece of iron that becomes a strong magnet when current is passing through wire coiled around the iron.

e·merge' (ė·mûrj'). To come out into view.

en·gage' (ĕn·gāj'). To hire, employ.

en·gulf' (ĕn·gŭlf'). To swallow up.

en·thu'si·as'tic (ĕn·thū'zĭ·ăs'tĭk). Eager.

en'vi·ous (ĕn'vĭ·ŭs). Feeling discontent at someone else's good fortune.

ev'i·dent (ĕv'ĭ·dĕnt). Clearly seen and understood.

ex·cel' (ĕk·sĕl'). To do something better than other people do.

ex'e·cute (ĕk'sė·kūt). To perform, to do.

ex·per'i·ment (ĕks·pĕr'ĭ·mĕnt). To conduct trials in order to learn what will happen under certain conditions.

ex·pose' (ĕks·pōz'). To leave unprotected.

ex'quis·ite (ĕks'kwĭ·zĭt). Very beautiful.

F

fag'got (făg'ŭt). Bundle of sticks to be used as firewood.

fal'con (fôl'kŭn). Small, swift hawk.

fa·mil'iar (fȧ·mĭl'yẽr). Friendly.

fes'ti·val (fĕs'tĭ·văl). Time of feasting and joy.

fidg'et·y (fĭj'ĕ·tĭ). Moving restlessly.

fig'ure·head' (fĭg'ūr·hĕd'). Carved wooden head or statue formerly used to decorate the bow of a sailing vessel.

fil'i·al (fĭl'ĭ·ăl). Like a son.

fix'ture (fĭks'tūr). Permanent part of something, like a gas outlet.

flank (flăngk). To be at the side of.

flick (flĭk). To move something jerkily.

flick'er (flĭk'ẽr). To flap or flutter; to glow brightly and dimly by turns.

flush (flŭsh). To blush, turn red.

foal (fōl). Colt, young horse.

ford (fōrd). Place where one can wade across a river.

fra'grant (frā'grănt). Sweet-smelling.

frank (frăngk). Free in expressing one's opinions, outspoken, not reserved.

fran'tic (frăn'tĭk). Wild, deeply troubled.

frisk (frĭsk). To frolic, to leap about in joy.

frond (frŏnd). Leaf of a palm or a fern.

fur'nish (fûr'nĭsh). To equip, supply.

G

gal'lant (găl'ănt). Noble, stately.

gal'ley proof (găl'ĭ prōōf). Sheet of paper printed from type set in a tray but not arranged in page form.

gan'der (găn'dẽr). Male goose.

gar'ment (gär'mĕnt). Any article of clothing.

gaunt (gônt). Very thin or lean, as if from illness.

glimpse (glĭmps). Short, quick view.

glit'ter (glĭt'ẽr). To sparkle.

gloom (glōōm). Thick shade.

gnu (nōō). Large antelope or goatlike animal of Africa.

gor'geous (gôr'jŭs). Beautiful, magnificent.

gruff (grŭf). Harsh.

ō, ōmit; ŏ, hŏp; ŏ, cŏntain; ô, ôr; ô, sôft; ōō, fōōd; ŏŏ, fŏŏt; oi, oil; ou, out; ū, ūse; ū, ūnite; ŭ, ŭs; ŭ, circŭs; û, fûr; tū, natūre; dū, verdūre; th, thin; th, than.

grum′ble (grŭm′b'l). To show displeasure or complaint by making a low rumbling sound; to growl.

gul′let (gŭl′ĕt). Throat.

gust (gŭst). Sudden, strong blast, particularly of wind.

H

haugh′ty (hô′tĭ). Scornfully proud.

heath′er (hĕth′ẽr). British bush with lavender flowers.

heed (hēd). To take notice of, pay careful attention to.

her′ring (hĕr′ĭng). A kind of food fish, usually smoked or salted. Young herring are called sardines.

hes′i·tate (hĕz′ĭ·tāt). To pause while making up one's mind.

high′boy′ (hī′boi′). Narrow chest of drawers mounted on a wider base.

hi·lar′i·ty (hĭ·lăr′ĭ·tĭ). Noisy gaiety.

hind (hīnd). Female red deer.

hith′er (hĭth′ẽr). To this place, here.

hob′ble (hŏb″l). To limp.

home′stead·er (hōm′stĕd·ẽr). Person who lives on land bought from our national government.

horse′car′ (hôrs′kär′). Horse-drawn railroad car or streetcar.

hum′bug′ (hŭm′bŭg′). Trick.

I

ig′no·rance (ĭg′nō·răns). Lack of knowledge.

ig·nore′ (ĭg·nōr′). To pay no attention to.

i·gua′na (ĭ·gwä′nȧ). Large lizard of tropical America.

il·le′gal (ĭl·lē′găl). Not lawful.

im·mense′ (ĭ·mĕns′). Very great, vast.

im′pact (ĭm′păkt). Hard bump or blow.

im·pres′sion (ĭm·prĕsh′ŭn). Idea, opinion.

im′pulse (ĭm′pŭls). Sudden strong wish to take action in a certain way.

in′di·cate (ĭn′dĭ·kāt). To point out.

in·dig′nant (ĭn·dĭg′nănt). Angry.

in·fer′nal (ĭn·fûr′năl). Devilish.

in·gen′ious (ĭn·jēn′yŭs). Cleverly made.

in·quire′ (ĭn·kwīr′). To ask about.

in·sid′i·ous (ĭn·sĭd′ĭ·ŭs). Sly, deceitful.

in·sist′ (ĭn·sĭst′). To take a stand or a point of view and refuse to give it up.

in·stinc′tive (ĭn·stĭngk′tĭv). Natural, unthinking, impulsive.

in′su·la′tor (ĭn′sū·lā′tẽr). Material that prevents electricity or heat from passing through.

in·ten′tion (ĭn·tĕn′shŭn). Determination to do something, purpose.

in′ter·rupt′ (ĭn′tĕ·rŭpt′). To break in with words of one's own when someone else is speaking.

in′tro·duce′ (ĭn′trō·dūs′). To cause someone to meet other people.

in·vig′o·rate (ĭn·vĭg′ō·rāt). To refresh, enliven.

in·vis′i·ble (ĭn·vĭz′ĭ·b'l). Not able to be seen.

irk′some (ûrk′sŭm). Tiresome.

J

jan′gling (jăng′glĭng). Rough jingling noise.

K

kilt (kĭlt). Short, pleated skirt worn by men in Scotland.

ki·mo′no (kĭ·mō′nŭ). Loose robe worn by Japanese people.

knap′sack′ (năp′săk′). Canvas bag for

ā, āte; ȧ, furnȧce; ă, ăt; ă, ăppear; â, câre; ä, cär; ȧ, pȧss; ȧ, sofȧ; ē, bē; ē, bēgin; ĕ, lĕt; ĕ, silĕnt; ẽ, watẽr; ḙ, hḙre; ī, hīde; ĭ, hĭd; ĭ, cabĭn; ō, hōpe;

carrying clothing, etc., on one's back while traveling.

L

lag (lăg). To move slowly.

land′mark′ (lănd′märk′). Something easily recognized and useful as a guide.

land′scape (lănd′skāp). Total area of land that one can see at a glance.

lard′er (lär′dẽr). Storeroom for meats and other foods.

lathe (lāth). Machine for cutting and shaping wood or metal.

lay′out′ (lā′out′). Arrangement, plan.

leads′man (lĕdz′măn). Man on ship's crew who throws out a piece of lead on a string to find out how deep the water is.

leash (lēsh). Strap for controlling an animal when one is walking with him.

lev′ee (lĕv′ė). Landing platform, wharf.

li′cense (lī′sĕns). Paper giving one legal permission to do something, such as own a dog, drive a car, etc.

lim′ber (lĭm′bẽr). Bending easily.

lim′pid (lĭm′pĭd). Very clear.

lo′cal (lō′kăl). Belonging to a certain region or place.

lope (lōp). To bound along easily.

lore (lōr). Knowledge, learning.

lunge (lŭnj). To plunge, move forward in headlong fashion.

M

mag′is·trate (măj′ĭs·trāt). City official or officer.

ma·hog′a·ny (mȧ·hŏg′ȧ·nĭ). Valuable tropical wood, reddish-brown in color, used for furniture.

man′go (măng′gō). A tropical fruit.

man′sion (măn′shŭn). Large, expensive house.

mark (märk). Marker of leather or cloth on a measuring line.

marsh (märsh). Swamp.

mast′head′ (mast′hĕd′). Statement printed in every newspaper giving title of paper, name of owner and editor, advertising rates, etc.

meg′a·phone (mĕg′ȧ·fōn). Speaking trumpet; funnel-shaped device to make one's voice sound louder and carry farther.

men′tion (mĕn′shŭn). To name or refer to briefly.

mer′chant (mûr′chănt). Trader, storekeeper.

mer′maid′ (mûr′mād′). Imaginary inhabitant of the ocean, half woman and half fish.

me′te·or (mē′tė·ẽr). Shooting star.

mil′let (mĭl′ĕt). Kind of grain, cereal.

mis′sion·ar′y (mĭsh′ŭn·ĕr′ĭ). Person sent out by a church to teach religion, usually in a foreign land.

moat (mōt). Deep, wide ditch, usually full of water, around a castle.

mod′el (mŏd″l). Pattern or figure that is to be followed in making copies.

mod′est (mŏd′ĕst). Not boastful.

mon′grel (mŭng′grĕl). Animal, especially a dog, of mixed breed.

moor (mo͞or). Area of waste land.

moor′ings (mo͞or′ĭngz). Ropes, cables, or anchors by which a ship is fastened.

mould (mōld). Furry, often greenish, growth on anything damp or rotten.

ō̇, ō̇mit; ŏ, hŏp; ŏ̆, cŏ̆ntain; ô, ôr; ŏ̇, sŏ̇ft; o͞o, fo͞od; o͝o, fo͝ot; oi, oil; ou, out; ū, ūse; ụ̄, ụ̄nite; ŭ, ŭs; ŭ̆, circŭ̆s; û, fûr; tū, natūre; dū, verdūre; th, thin; th, than.

muf′fler (mŭf′lẽr). Scarf, usually of thick wool.

mu·se′um (mū̇·zē′ŭm). Building where one may see articles valuable from a historical point of view.

mys′ti·fy (mĭs′tĭ·fī). To puzzle.

N

nos′tril (nŏs′trĭl). One of the two holes in a nose.

nour′ish·ing (nûr′ĭsh·ĭng). Helping the growth of one's body, nutritious.

numb (nŭm). Without feeling.

O

oc·ca′sion (ŏ·kā′zhŭn). Time.

oc′to·pus (ŏk′tō̇·pŭs). Sea creature with eight arms.

o·ka′pi (ō̇·kä′pĭ). Rare African animal resembling the giraffe, but with a much shorter neck.

om′ni·bus (ŏm′nĭ·bŭs). Bus, public vehicle which carries many people.

or′a·tor (ŏr′ȧ·tẽr). Public speaker.

or′di·nar′y (ôr′dĭ·nĕr′ĭ). Usual, common, normal.

out′rage (out′rāj). To insult or offend very much.

out′skirts′ (out′skûrts′). Edges or outlying parts of a town or city.

o′ver·whelm′ (ō′vẽr·hwĕlm′). To cover over completely, submerge.

P

pal′try (pôl′trĭ). Worthless, trifling.

pan′el (păn′ĕl). Sliding section of a wall.

pan′ic (păn′ĭk). Uncontrollable fright, unreasoning fear.

par′ti·cle (pär′tĭ·k′l). Tiny piece.

peas′ant (pĕz′ănt). A poor farmer, especially a poor farmer in European countries.

peb′ble (pĕb″l). Small stone.

pen′al·ty (pĕn′ăl·tĭ). A fine.

per·cale′ (pẽr·kāl′). Closely woven cotton cloth, often printed on one side.

per′ma·nent (pûr′mȧ·nĕnt). Lasting, unchanging.

per·sist′ (pẽr·sĭst′). To keep on saying or doing something.

per·suade′ (pẽr·swād′). To talk someone into doing something.

pest (pĕst). Destructive, troublesome insect or animal.

pheas′ant (fĕz′ănt). Long-tailed, brilliantly colored game bird.

phlox (flŏks). A garden flower of various colors.

pi·az′za (pĭ·ăz′ȧ). Porch, veranda.

pick′et (pĭk′ĕt). To tie to a stake.

pi′geon·hole′ (pĭj′ŭn·hōl′). One of several sections in a desk in which letters and papers are kept.

pi′lot·house′ (pī′lŭt·hous′). Room on the upper deck of a ship for the steering gear and pilot.

pin′a·fore′ (pĭn′ȧ·fōr′). Girl's apron.

plas′ter (plȧs′tẽr). To coat or cover with a thin layer.

plight (plīt). Unpleasant state or condition.

plod′der (plŏd′ẽr). One who moves slowly but steadily.

plume (plōōm). Long feather, or anything which looks like one.

por′ter (pōr′tẽr). Person who carries heavy loads to earn his living.

pos′se (pŏs′ē̇). Group of men forming a search party.

ā, āte; ȧ̇, furnȧ̇ce; ă, ăt; ă, ăppear; â, câre; ä, cär; ȧ, pȧss; ȧ, sofȧ; ē, bē; ē̇, bē̇gin; ĕ, lĕt; ĕ, silĕnt; ẽ, watẽr; ę, hęre; ī, hīde; ĭ, hĭd; ĭ, cabĭn; ō, hōpe;

pre·cise′ (prē̇·sīs′). Exact.

pri′ma don′na (prē′mȧ dŏn′ȧ). Female star of a play.

pro·test′ (prō̇·tĕst′). To object, argue against.

prowl (proul). To move quietly about as if in search of something to eat or to steal.

Q

quail (kwāl). To lose courage; to tremble in fear.

quaint (kwānt). Strange but pleasing.

quer′u·lous (kwĕr′ū̇·lŭs). Complaining, fretful.

R

raft′er (ráf′tẽr). One of many slanting beams or timbers in a roof.

rak′ish (rāk′ĭsh). Sporty, spirited.

ram′shack′le (răm′shăk′′l). Tumbledown, rickety.

rash (răsh). Too hasty, not cautious.

reck′less (rĕk′lĕs). Careless, not cautious.

reef (rēf). Rocky or sandy ridge at or near the surface of the sea.

re·flec′tion (rē̇·flĕk′shŭn). Image seen in a mirror.

re·form′ (rē̇·fôrm′). To correct or improve one's behavior.

re·frain′ (rē̇·frān′). Repeated verse in a song or a poem.

re·late′ (rē̇·lāt′). To tell or to narrate.

re·lieve′ (rē̇·lēv′). To free from strain or worry.

re·proach′ (rē̇·prōch′). To find fault with, blame.

rep′u·ta′tion (rĕp′ū̇·tā′shŭn). Fame.

re·quest′ (rē̇·kwĕst′). Something asked for, or the act of asking for something.

re·solve′ (rē̇·zŏlv′). To decide or determine.

re·tired′ (rē̇·tīrd′). No longer working at one's chosen career—usually because of old age.

re·tir′ing (rē̇·tīr′ĭng). Shy.

re·tort′ (rē̇·tôrt′). To answer back, reply sharply.

rind (rīnd). Thick skin of fruit.

roach (rōch). A kind of fresh-water fish.

rogue (rōg). Rascal, good-for-nothing fellow.

rol′lick·ing (rŏl′ĭk·ĭng). Loud and gay, boisterous.

ro·sette′ (rō̇·zĕt′). Likeness of a rose, as made of ribbon or carved in wood.

rue (rōō). To regret very much.

ruff (rŭf). Fur which grows on the neck of an animal and looks like a collar.

rus′tle (rŭs′′l). To make a series of small sounds like swishing silk, leaves, etc.

S

scald (skôld). To burn with a hot liquid.

scam′per (skăm′pẽr). To run lightly and hurriedly.

sched′ule (skĕd′ūl). Timetable, list of events in the order in which they should happen.

schoon′er (skōōn′ẽr). Sailing ship with two or more masts one behind the other.

scroll (skrōl). Pretty design drawn on paper.

se·cure′ (sē̇·kūr′). Firm, safe.

se·date′ (sē̇·dāt′). Quiet, calm.

sel′dom (sĕl′dŭm). Not often, rarely.

ō̇, ō̇mit; ŏ, hŏp; ŏ, cŏntain; ô, ôr; ô, sôft; o͞o, fo͞od; o͝o, fo͝ot; oi, oil; ou, out; ū, ūse; ū̇, ū̇nite; ŭ, ŭs; ŭ, circŭs; û, fûr; tū, natūre; dū, verdūre; th, thin; th, than.

ser'geant (sär'jĕnt). An officer in a police force, usually next below a captain in rank.

se'ri·ous (sȩr'ĭ·ŭs). Important.

ser'pent (sûr'pĕnt). Large snake.

sheep'ish (shēp'ĭsh). Stupid or timid as a sheep.

shel'ter (shĕl'tẽr). To protect, give refuge to.

shoal (shōl). Shallow spot.

shuf'fle (shŭf''l). To move about in a clumsy way, dragging one's feet.

slight (slīt). Small.

sloop (slo͞op). Sailboat having one mast with several different kinds of sails rigged to it fore and aft.

smoke'stack' (smōk'stăk'). Chimney.

smoth'er (smŭth'ẽr). To be choked from lack of air.

so'ber·ly (sō'bẽr·lĭ). Seriously, without smiling.

sooth'ing (so͞oth'ĭng). Calming, comforting.

spit (spĭt). Narrow point of land running out into the water.

splen'dor (splĕn'dẽr). Brilliance, magnificence, glory.

sprout (sprout). To grow rapidly.

spruce (spro͞os). A kind of evergreen tree with a pointed top.

spry (sprī). Brisk, lively.

star'tle (stär't'l). To frighten suddenly but briefly.

stern (stûrn). Harsh.

sti'fle (stī'f'l). To smother, to cause to gasp for air.

stile (stīl). Steps going over a fence or a wall.

stir'rup (stĭr'ŭp). One of two supports for the feet of a horseback rider.

stow (stō). To pack.

strain (strān). To use to the utmost or as much as possible.

stub'born (stŭb'ẽrn). Determined, willful.

sug·ges'tion (sŭg·jĕs'chŭn). Idea presented in the hope that someone else will accept it and act accordingly.

su'per·sti'tious (sū'pẽr·stĭsh'ŭs). Believing in magic.

surge (sûrj). To move forward like a great wave.

sur·vey' (sẽr·vā'). To look at closely.

swath (swôth). Strip of grass, grain, etc., cut by a mowing machine.

sway (swā). To swing from side to side.

sway'-backed' (swā'băkt). Having a sagging back.

swift (swĭft). Bird which looks like a swallow but is related to the hummingbird.

T

tal'ent (tăl'ĕnt). Skill and ability.

tan'ta·lize (tăn'tȧ·līz). To tease.

tar'tan (tär'tăn). Woolen cloth with a Scotch plaid or crisscross pattern of various colors.

tem'po·rar'y (tĕm'pō·rĕr'ĭ). Lasting only a short time; not permanent.

tend'en·cy (tĕn'dĕn·sĭ). Natural liking for or leaning toward.

ten'sion (tĕn'shŭn). Straining, pulling.

ter'race (tĕr'ĭs). Flat stretch of ground higher than the surrounding land.

thigh (thī). Part of the leg which is above the knee.

thim'ble·ber'ry (thĭm'b'l·bĕr'ĭ). A kind of raspberry.

thor'ough (thûr'ō̇). Complete.

tilt (tĭlt). To tip; to lean to one side or the other.

tim'ber (tĭm'bẽr). Woods, forest, or material for construction.

tim'id (tĭm'ĭd). Fearful, not brave.

tinge (tĭnj). To color slightly, to tint.

ton'ic (tŏn'ĭk). Medicine.

tor'rent (tŏr'ĕnt). Rushing stream, heavy rain, downpour.

trans·mit'ter (trăns·mĭt'ẽr). Part of a telephone that collects sound waves and sends them out over a wire.

trin'ket (trĭng'kĕt). Inexpensive ring, pin, or other bit of jewelry.

trudge (trŭj). To walk steadily but wearily.

tur'ban (tûr'băn). Hat like a cap with a scarf wound about it.

U

un·do'ing (ŭn·do͞o'ĭng). Ruin, downfall.

u'ni·corn (ū'nĭ·kôrn). Imaginary animal resembling a horse with one horn.

u'ni·son (ū'nĭ·sŭn). Rhythmic agreement so as to move or behave as one.

up'wind' (ŭp'wĭnd'). Into or against the wind.

ut'most (ŭt'mōst). Greatest.

V

vague (vāg). Not clear, indefinite.

van'ish (văn'ĭsh). To disappear.

var'i·ous (vâr'ĭ·ŭs). Several, different.

ve'hi·cle (vē'ĭ·k'l). Wagon, carriage.

ven'er·a·ble (vĕn'ẽr·ȧ·b'l). Deserving honor and respect because of great age.

vex (vĕks). To annoy or irritate.

vi·bra'tion (vī·brā'shŭn). Rapid movement to and fro of sound waves.

vie (vī). To compete, enter a contest.

vol'un·teer' (vŏl'ŭn·tēr'). To offer freely.

W

wal'low (wŏl'ō). Place where animals roll in mud.

wane (wān). To grow smaller or fewer; to decrease.

ware'house' (wâr'hous'). Storehouse.

wheeze (hwēz). To breathe hard and with a sort of whistling sound.

whith'er (hwĭth'ẽr). To which place.

wran'gler (răng'glẽr). Cowboy.

ō̇, ō̇mit; ŏ, hŏp; ŏ, cŏntain; ô, ôr; ô, sôft; o͞o, fo͞od; o͝o, fo͝ot; oi, oil; ou, out; ū, ūse; ŭ, ŭnite; ŭ, ŭs; ŭ, circŭs; û, fûr; tū, natūre; dū, verdūre; th, thin; th, than.

Acknowledgments

For their courteous permission to use the following selections, we wish to express our gratitude and appreciation to the following authors, agents, publishers, and periodicals:

Abingdon-Cokesbury Press: "The Shindig" from COWBOY BOOTS by Shannon Garst, copyright 1946 by Doris Shannon Garst. — Brandt & Brandt: "Peregrine White and Virginia Dare" by Rosemary and Stephen Vincent Benét, from A BOOK OF AMERICANS, published by Rinehart & Company, Inc., copyright 1933 by Rosemary and Stephen Vincent Benét; "Jimmy Takes Vanishing Lessons" by Walter Brooks, copyright 1950 by Walter Brooks; and "The Horseshoe" by Edna St. Vincent Millay, from Part VII of "From a Very Little Sphinx" in SELECTED POEMS FOR YOUNG PEOPLE, published by Harper & Brothers, copyright 1923, 1951 by Edna St. Vincent Millay. —Coward-McCann, Inc.: "Digging for Treasure" from THE TREASURE SEEKERS by E.Nesbit, copyright by Coward-McCann.—Thomas Y. Crowell Company: "Winner Take a Mule" from SHOOT FOR A MULE by Elisabeth H. Lansing, copyright 1951 by E. H. Lansing.—Mary Carolyn Davies: "The Day Before April" from THE DRUMS IN OUR STREET.—Doubleday & Company, Inc.: "Papa Takes Over" from KILDEE HOUSE by Rutherford Montgomery, copyright 1949 by Rutherford Montgomery; "The President's Whiskers" from LINCOLN'S LITTLE CORRESPONDENT by Hertha Pauli, copyright 1951, 1952, by Hertha Pauli; and "Ferryboat on the Beach" by Nora B. Stirling from UP FROM THE SEA, copyright 1963 by Nora B. Stirling;—Mrs. Linka Friedman and Louis Loveman: "April Rain" from MY POETRY BOOK by Robert Loveman.—Harcourt, Brace and Company, Inc.: "The Middle Bear" from THE MIDDLE MOFFAT by Eleanor Estes, copyright 1942 by Harcourt, Brace and Company, Inc.—Harper & Row: "The Blizzard" from THE LONG WINTER by Laura Ingalls Wilder, copyright 1940 by Harper & Brothers. Harper & Row and Hamish Hamilton Ltd.: excerpts from CHARLOTTE'S WEB by E. B. White, copyright 1952 by E. B. White. —Henry Holt and Company, Inc.: "Tillie" from COLLECTED POEMS by Walter de la Mare, copyright 1920 by Henry Holt and Company, Inc., 1948 by Walter de la Mare; "Dust of Snow" and "Stopping by Woods on a Snowy Evening" from NEW HAMPSHIRE by Robert Frost, copyright 1923 by Henry Holt and Company, Inc., 1951 by Robert Frost.—Houghton Mifflin Company: "The Apple and the Arrow" by Mary and Conrad Buff, copyright 1951 by Houghton Mifflin Company; and "Texas Trains and Trails" from THE CHILDREN SING IN THE FAR WEST by Mary Austin.—Willis Lindquist: "Yukon Trail" first published in The American Junior Red Cross News.—J. B. Lippincott, Inc.: "Simba's First Lion" from LION BOY by Alden G. Stevens, copyright 1938 by J. B. Lippincott.—Little, Brown & Company: "Troubles With a Penguin" from MR. POPPER'S PENGUINS by Richard and Florence Atwater, copyright 1938 by Richard and Florence Atwater; "Old Quin Queeribus" from ZODIAC TOWN by Nancy Byrd Turner; and "Autumn" from POEMS BY EMILY DICKINSON, edited by Martha Dickinson and Alfred Leete Hampson, Little, Brown & Co., 1939. —David Lloyd: "Jiya Makes a Choice" from THE BIG WAVE by Pearl S. Buck, copyright 1947 by The Curtis Publishing Company, 1948 by Pearl S. Buck, published by The John Day Company. —Mrs. Ruby Terrill Lomax: "The Cowboy's Life" and "Whoopee Ti Yi Yo" from COWBOY SONGS, collected by John A. Lomax. — Longmans, Green & Co.: "Duff Strikes Back" from DUFF, THE STORY OF A BEAR by William Marshall Rush, copyright 1950 by William Marshall Rush.—The Macmillan Company: "Swift Things Are Beautiful" and "The Cat and the Bear" from AWAY GOES SALLY by Elizabeth Coatsworth, copyright 1943; "The Lion" from JOHNNY APPLESEED AND OTHER POEMS by Vachel Lindsay, copyright 1928; "Faith, I Wish I Were a Leprechaun" from MIRRORS by Margaret Ritter, copyright 1925; and "The Shark" from CALL IT COURAGE by Armstrong Sperry, copyright 1940.—Clifford H. Meigs: "The Pirate Don Durk of Dowdee," "Silver Ships" and "Abraham Lincoln," from *Child Life,* by Mildred Plew Meigs.—G. P. Putnam's Sons: "Master of All Masters" from ENGLISH FAIRY TALES by Joseph Jacobs, copyright 1902.—Random House, Inc.: "Lift Off" adapted from AMERICANS INTO ORBIT by Gene Gurney, copyright 1962 by Gene Gurney.—Rinehart & Company, Inc.: "Andy Stands Guard" from YOUNG HICKORY by Stanley Young, copyright 1940 by Stanley Young.—Charles Scribner's Sons: "Ducks' Ditty" from the WIND IN THE WILLOWS by Kenneth Grahame, copyright 1908, 1935 by Charles Scribner's Sons.—Story Parade, Inc., for the following stories, copyright in the years indicated by Story Parade, Inc.: "The Old Woman and the Tiger" by Mary Hemingway (1946); "Citronella Weather" by Mildred Lawrence (1949); "Whitey and Jinglebob" by Glen Rounds (1946).—The Viking Press, Inc.: "Little Georgie Sings a Song" from RABBIT HILL by Robert Lawson, copyright 1944 by Robert Lawson, adapted from the original texts by permission of The Viking Press, Inc.; and "Water Noises" from UNDER THE TREE by Elizabeth Madox Roberts, copyright 1922 by B. W. Huebsch, Inc.; 1950 by Ivor S. Roberts—James W. Shearer: "Dogs and Weather" from SKIPPING ALONG ALONE by Winifred Welles, copyright 1931 by The Macmillan Company.—Dixie Willson: "The Mist and All" from *Child Life.*—World Publishing Company, Inc.: "Dan Drake's First Patient" from BUCKSKIN SCOUT by Marion Renick and Margaret C. Tyler, copyright 1953 by World Publishing Company; and "I Arise" and "I Will Walk" from BEYOND THE HIGH HILLS, A BOOK OF ESKIMO POEMS, copyright 1961 by World Publishing Company. —Yale University Press: "Comparison" from SONGS FOR PARENTS by John Farrar, copyright 1921 by Yale University Press.

2 3 4 5 6 7 8 — 72 71 70 69 68 67 66